DEDICATION

This book is dedicated to all the citizens of the United States of America who have made this program of interplanetary exploration possible and who, along with all mankind, will benefit from the increased awareness of the universe and how the Earth and its peoples relate to it.

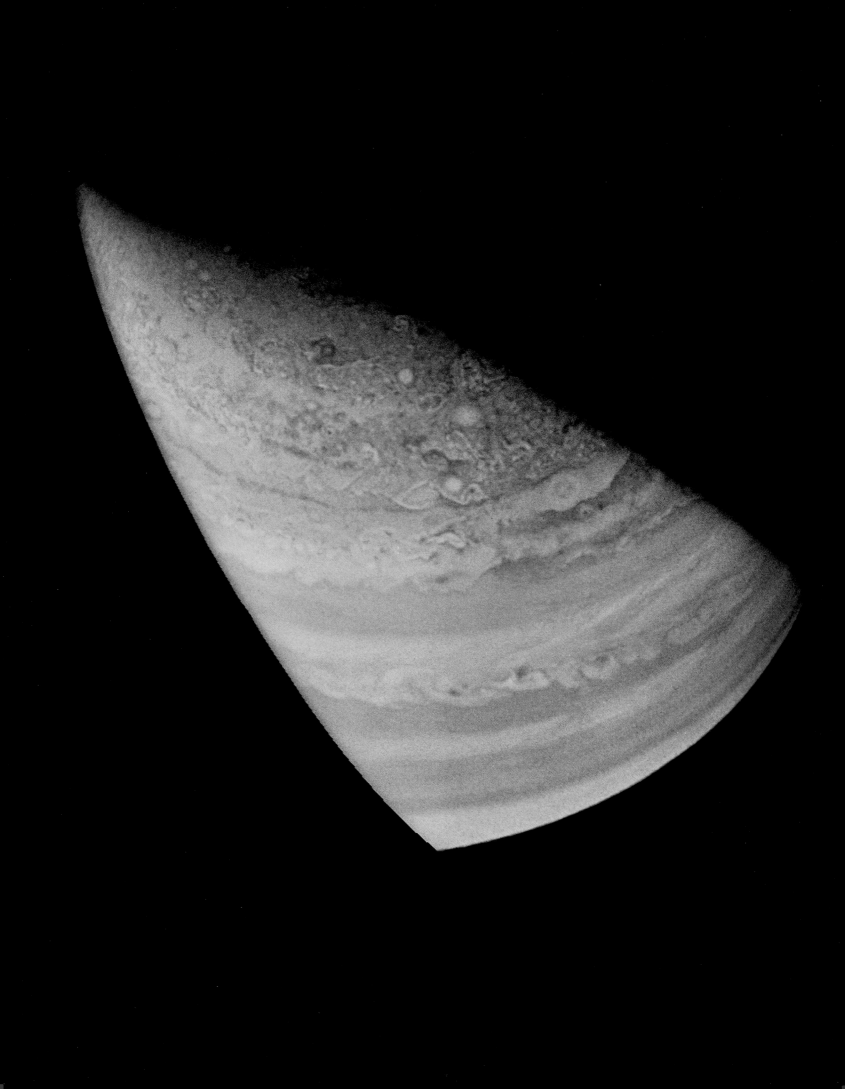

PIONEER
FIRST TO JUPITER, SATURN, AND BEYOND

NASA SP-446

RICHARD O. FIMMEL
Manager, Pioneer Missions
Ames Research Center

JAMES VAN ALLEN
Professor of Physics
University of Iowa

ERIC BURGESS
Science Writer

Prepared at Ames Research Center

Scientific and Technical Information Office **1980**
NATIONAL AERONAUTICS AND SPACE ADMINISTRATION
Washington, D.C.

☆ U.S. GOVERNMENT PRINTING OFFICE : 1980—O-328-155

For sale by the Superintendent of Documents
U.S. Government Printing Office, Washington, D.C. 20402

Contents

Foreword vi

Introduction viii

Authors' Preface x

1 — Pioneer to the Giant Planets 1

2 — The Pioneer Jupiter/Saturn Mission 25

3 — The Pioneer Spacecraft 43

4 — Pioneer Science at New Frontiers 51

5 — First into the Outer Solar System 69

6 — Results at the New Frontiers 111

7 — Images from Jupiter and Saturn 159

8 — First Encounter with the Giant 179

9 — Jupiter Revisited 201

10 — Saturn Encounter 223

Epilog — Beyond the Outer Giants 245

Appendix 1 — The Imaging Photopolarimeter 251

Appendix 2 — Technical Details of Planetary Images 253

Appendix 3 — Pioneer Team 265

Appendix 4 — Pioneer Award Recipients 273

Index 276

Foreword

Some ventures are appropriately named, and Pioneer is surely one of them. The people associated with this program really are pioneers of space exploration. Often it seems that pioneers, being out in front, do not receive the general recognition that historically they should deserve. Fortunately, this is not the case with these Pioneer explorations of Jupiter and Saturn. Many people are beginning to understand the tremendous revolutionary steps we are starting to take into the future as we make important discoveries about the planets of the outer Solar System, as we find out things that we had no glimmering of before these pioneering missions. I anticipate that years from now, when people look back on our time, they will single out the Pioneer program as one of special importance to space science and the broadening of our intellectual horizon.

We have now moved out beyond the familiar part of the Solar System to explore planetary objects so unusual that their very existence was something people might accept intellectually but not really in any immediate sense.

I like to compare this latter part of the 20th century with the 15th and 16th centuries, the time during which the oceans of Earth were first explored. The sailing ships first edged their way along the shores of Europe. Then they felt their way around Africa. Finally, they struck out across the open oceans and headed for lands so remote, countries so extraordinary, that the reports of the returning explorers were even more incredible than

the fictions they replaced. With Pioneer, we felt our way out through the asteroid belt and struck out into the uncharted oceans of the outer Solar System. The excitement of the first flybys of Jupiter and Saturn was a unique experience, enabling us to replace the speculative images of Jupiter and Saturn with actual physical reports. The Pioneers truly initiated a new stage of space exploration, blazing a trail for other spacecraft: the Voyagers, Galileo, other spacecraft yet unnamed, and some even unimagined.

Dr. Thomas A. Mutch
Associate Administrator for Space Science
NASA Headquarters

Introduction

The Pioneer spacecraft have ventured into previously unexplored space far beyond the orbit of Mars, and their missions have added greatly to mankind's knowledge of our Solar System. Throughout history, man has been driven by his innate sense of adventure and curiosity to explore new frontiers, to study what he has found, and to add to his understanding of his place in the cosmos. Author James Michener, in testimony before a Congressional subcommittee, provided an excellent description of this drive and its importance to our civilization:

"I do not for a moment believe that the spiritual well-being of our nation depends primarily upon a successful space program. I am sure that we could as a nation attain great spiritual reassurance from rebuilding our cities or distributing our farm produce better.

But I also believe that there are moments in history when challenges occur of such a compelling nature that to miss them is to miss the whole meaning of an epoch. Space is such a challenge.

We risk great peril if we kill off this spirit of adventure, for we cannot predict how and in what seemingly unrelated fields it will manifest itself. A nation which loses its forward thrust is in danger, and one of the most effective ways to retain that thrust is to keep exploring possibilities. The sense of exploration is intimately bound up with human resolve, and for a nation to believe that it is still committed to forward motion is to ensure its continuance.

. . . We should be most careful about retreating from the specific challenge of our age. We should be reluctant to turn our back upon the frontier of this epoch. Space is indifferent to what we do; it has no feeling, no design, no interest in whether we grapple with it or not. But we cannot be indifferent to space, because the grand slow march of our intelligence has brought us, in our generation, to a point from which we can explore and understand and utilize it. To turn back now would be to deny our history, our capabilities."

The Pioneers have been true explorers — the first to navigate the asteroid belts, the first to encounter Jupiter and its fierce radiation belts and Saturn and its rings, and they will be the first manmade objects to leave our Solar System. They have probed new frontiers and explored regions of the Solar System very different from those of the inner system near Earth. Originally, the Pioneer missions were intended to explore only Jupiter and the interplanetary space beyond Mars, but as the mission progressed an opportunity to reach Saturn also developed and the pathway was opened to another unexplored planet. To carry out their missions, the Pioneers have traveled enormous distances and have operated effectively for extended periods. In so doing, the engineering accomplishments of this mission have matched the scientific accomplishments. Pioneers 10 and 11 have been in space over 8 years and 7 years, respectively, and have traveled 4.6 billion kilometers and 4.1 billion kilometers, respectively. All of the spacecraft systems continue to operate reliably after the years in deep space and in spite of encounters with hostile radiation environments.

The mission has continued far beyond achieving its original objectives. The spacecraft continue to send data as they reach toward the boundaries of the Solar System. To undertake a mission of such length called for great and continued dedication on the part of scientists and engineers who had to devote a major portion of their professional careers to the mission. The Pioneers and the people who made them possible have clearly met the challenge of which Michener spoke.

C. A. Syvertson
Director
Ames Research Center

Authors' Preface

The success of Pioneer 11 in its encounter with Saturn and the continued mission of Pioneers 10 and 11 into the outer Solar System necessitated an updating of the earlier publications (SP-349, Pioneer Odyssey, Encounter with a Giant, and SP-349/396, Pioneer Odyssey). Results from further analyses of data from the encounters with Jupiter, interplanetary results, and results from Pioneer 11's encounter with Saturn are included. Because the bibliography associated with this mission has now become extremely large and continues to grow, it is published separately as NASA Technical Memorandum 81233, available from NASA Scientific and Technical Information Facility, P.O. Box 8757, Baltimore/Washington International Airport, Md. 21240.

In the preparation of this book, the authors gratefully acknowledge having drawn upon the work of many others too numerous to mention individually. Many scientists and project staff personnel were interviewed during research to assemble material for the book. Of particular importance was valuable assistance in the form of initial suggestions and later comments on all or parts of the drafts of the book by Robert R. Nunamaker, John W. Dyer, and John H. Wolfe. The reviews by principal investigators and members of their teams are also appreciated.

Personnel from Ames Research Center, the Pioneer Project Staff, the Technical Information Division, and the Phototechnology Branch were particularly helpful in providing information and research material and in producing the book.

The authors are also indebted to personnel of the Lunar and Planetary Laboratory and the Optical Sciences Center of the University of Arizona for astronomical information and photographs and for the production of images of Jupiter and Saturn reproduced in this book. Special thanks must be given to Edward Beshore, James J. Burke, Bruce DaCosta, Joseph S. Gotobed, Robert Kingston, Robin Strickland (computer processing), Charles Blenman, Jr., Lyn R. Doose, Charles KenKnight, and John W. Fountain (photographic processing).

Additional thanks must be given to William Swindell, University of Arizona, for use of material written for the earlier Pioneer publications and incorporated into this new publication.

Richard O. Fimmel
James A. Van Allen
Eric Burgess
August 1980

1
Pioneer to the Giant Planets

The space age began in 1957 when the first artificial satellite orbited Earth – 31 years after the flight of Robert H. Goddard's first liquid propellant rocket. Within only another 22 years, spacecraft of the National Aeronautics and Space Administration had explored all the planets of our Solar System that were known to mankind before the invention of the telescope.

On September 1, 1979, Pioneer 11 climaxed these 22 years of space exploration by reaching Saturn after journeying through space for 6-1/2 years over a distance of 3.2 billion kilometers. On its approach to Saturn, Pioneer found that the giant planet has a magnetic field and a complex magnetosphere buffeted by the solar wind. These discoveries added to earlier ones made by Pioneer about the magnetic field and magnetosphere of Jupiter.

Pioneer revealed unique and spectacular views of Saturn and its ring system. If an observer had been onboard the spacecraft as it swept by this mighty ringed planet, the view would have been spectacular. Behind the spacecraft, the Sun had shrunk to only about one-ninth the size it appears on Earth. Ahead, Saturn appeared as a rotating, flattened globe with banded patterns. The spacecraft approached the planet from above while the south side of the rings were illuminated by the Sun. This view of the magnificent ring system is one never seen from Earth. The usually bright rings appeared dark and the usually dark gaps between them were bright. This vantage point provided scientists with much new information about the structure of these rings — rings that had been regarded as unique until recently when much less spectacular rings were discovered around the planets Jupiter and Uranus.

At a speed approaching 114,000 km/hr, the spacecraft rushed toward Saturn. Over the several days before closest approach, the detailed structure of the rings gradually became clearer. One by one, the bright specks of Saturn's family of small satellites and the globe of the huge satellite Titan appeared.

As Pioneer moved closer to Saturn, the most critical period of the mission was at hand — when the spacecraft crossed the plane of the rings and hurtled beneath them for its closest approach to within 21,400 km of the cloudtops of Saturn. There was no way of knowing from Earth whether ring particles were present inside the bright visible rings. Even a relatively few particles could destroy the spacecraft.

The polar areas of Saturn were by this time visible and the belts of weather systems at lower latitudes were more distinct, although still much less clearly defined than the weather systems of Jupiter observed by Pioneer several years before. Evidence of jet streams in the upper atmosphere began also to appear. The shadow of the rings on the planet clearly showed the divisions in the ring system.

At just under 1 million kilometers from Saturn and 4 hr before closest approach, Pioneer discovered a faint narrow ring outside the bright A ring. About the same time, the spacecraft's imaging system revealed a new inner satellite of Saturn. Data from the charged particle experi-

ments showed unusual variations that indicated the presence of another previously unknown small satellite. During the next few hours, the planet and its rings expanded to fill the spacecraft's field of view as it hurtled toward the plane of the ring system. The mission controllers and monitors on Earth anxiously wondered whether the spacecraft would survive to complete its mission.

At 10:36 a.m., September 1, 1979, the spacecraft plunged through the ring plane. Not until 86 min later — the time for radio waves traveling at 300,000 km/sec to reach Earth from Saturn — did the message reach the controllers back on Earth that the spacecraft was undamaged. Pioneer was continuing its mission.

Back on the spacecraft, a magnificent view of the fully illuminated rings unfolded. The rings stretched overhead in great curved sheets as Pioneer rushed along beneath them. Pioneer moved so fast and was so close to the rings that images could not be obtained for transmission to Earth. Hurtling beneath the rings and over the cloudtops, the spacecraft recorded unique details of the alien environment near this giant planet. Then Pioneer plunged back through the ring plane, again without damage to the spacecraft. The encounter with Saturn was an unqualified success.

As Pioneer sped away from Saturn, the view was of a crescent-shaped planet crossed by dark rings and their shadow bands. Ahead was the large satellite Titan, which Pioneer would pass at a distance of almost 354,000 km on September 2. As it did so, the spacecraft obtained the first images of the largest satellite in our Solar System. With Titan shrinking into a starlike object behind it, and having explored the two giants, Jupiter and Saturn, for the first time, Pioneer still had not completed its mission. The spacecraft headed out of our Solar System toward the distant stars, seeking information about interplanetary space to the orbit of Pluto and beyond.

2

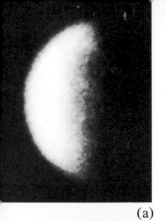
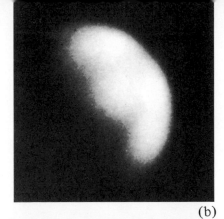

(a)　　　　　　　　　　　　(b)　　　　　　　　　　　　(c)

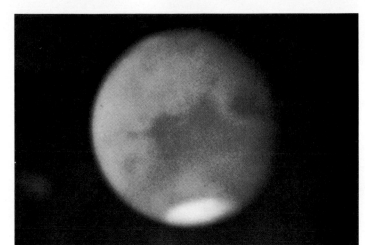

(d)

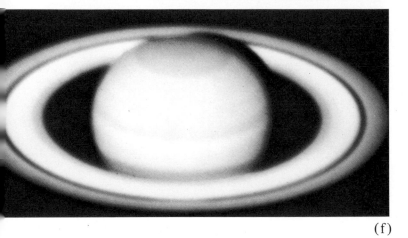
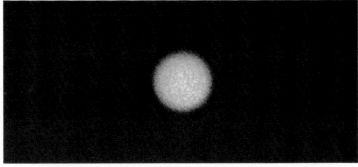

(e)

(f)

During the first decade of space exploration, scientists concentrated on the inner Solar System (Figure 1-1), but at the beginning of the second decade scientists and space technologists began to consider missions to the outer planets, particularly to the gaseous giants Jupiter and Saturn. These two planets are perhaps the most important in the Solar System because, after the Sun, they contain most of the matter in the Solar System. Jupiter alone accounts for over two-thirds of the planetary mass of the Solar System.

(g)

Figure 1-1. Planets of the Solar System consist of two types: small, dense inner planets with solid surfaces — Mercury, Venus, Earth with its Moon, and Mars — and large, mainly gaseous outer planets — Jupiter, Saturn, Uranus, and Neptune, some of which have satellites as large as the smaller inner planets. Pluto, the outermost known planet, has not been observed well enough from Earth to be accurately classified. Spacecraft have opened new vistas of our Solar System. Note the detail in the best ground-based photographs compared with the photographs of planets taken from spacecraft (continued next page).

    (a) Mercury (Pic du Midi Observatory)
    (b) Venus (Lick Observatory)
    (c) Moon, Tycho (Lick Observatory)
    (d) Mars (Catalina Observatory)
    (e) Jupiter (Catalina Observatory)
    (f) Saturn (Catalina Observatory)
    (g) Uranus (Catalina Observatory)

3

(h)

(i)

(k)

(j)

(m)

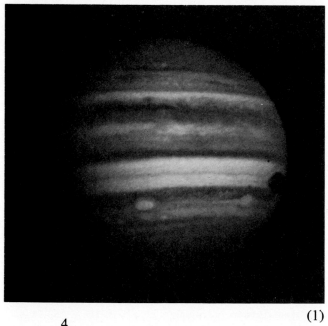

(l)

4

(h) Mercury (Mariner 10)
(i) Venus (Mariner 10)
(j) Moon, Tycho (Lunar Orbiter)
(k) Mars (Viking 1)
(l) Jupiter (Pioneer 10)
(m) Saturn (Pioneer 11)

Both giant planets (Figure 1-2) are unusual by terrestrial standards — the density of Jupiter is only slightly greater than water while that of Saturn is sufficiently low that the planet would float in water. Jupiter's mass is 317.8 times that of Earth. Its gravity affects the orbits of other planets and may have prevented the asteroids from coalescing into a planet. Jupiter's gravitational force pulls many comets into distorted orbits; some short-period comets appear to have become controlled by Jupiter so that their orbits at their most distant points from the Sun are about the distance of the Jovian orbit. Saturn also has collected a family of comets.

Despite their size, Jupiter and Saturn were not large enough to become stars. Their masses were insufficient to raise internal temperatures high enough to trigger nuclear reactions in their cores. However, had they been some 100 times larger, the Solar System might have been a triple star system, and nighttime would have been infrequent on Earth. As it is, both giant planets emit more energy than they absorb from the Sun, energy that is probably generated as these planets continue to cool following their primordial gravitational collapse eons ago soon after the Solar System formed.

In 1608, spectacle-maker, Hans Lippershey of Middleburgh, Holland, invented an astounding instrument. He happened to pick up two lenses and looked through them, discovering that objects viewed through the lenses appeared nearer. He experimented further with a convex and a concave lens at opposite ends of a tube. His spyglass engendered considerable excitement and word of his invention spread across Europe.

Two men, Galileo and Simon Marius, using the idea of Lippershey's spyglass, constructed a device — which came to be known as a telescope in about 1611 — and trained it on the heavens.

Figure 1-2. Jupiter and Saturn are dominant planets of our Solar System. The terrestrial planets Mercury, Venus, Earth, and Mars are relatively small compared with the planets of the outer Solar System, Jupiter, Saturn, Uranus, and Neptune.

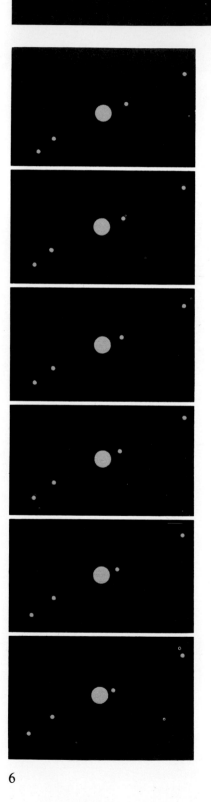

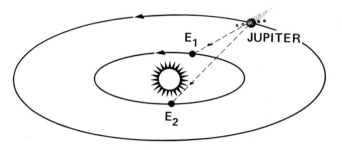

Figure 1-3. Jupiter and its four Galilean satellites. The photograph at top shows a typical configuration; right to left, the satellites Europa, Ganymede, and Callisto. Io is obscured by the planet. (*Photographs: Catalina Observatory, University of Arizona*)

Figure 1-4. Each year as Earth moves in its orbit away from Jupiter, the times of eclipse of Jupiter's satellites become late because light takes about 16 min longer to cross Earth's orbit. In 1675, the Danish astronomer Roemer determined the velocity of light from this effect.

The discovery of the satellites of Jupiter (Figure 1-3) is usually credited to Galileo, who published *The Starry Messenger* relating the results of observations he made at Padua on January 7, 1610. Galileo made a staggering number of observations at that time — "great, unusual, and remarkable spectacles, a host of stars." *The Starry Messenger* described what Galileo considered the most important discovery of all, the moons of Jupiter. Some historians, however, claim that Simon Marius of Auerbach, Germany, first discovered the Jovian satellites on December 29, 1609, but he did not publish his observations.

Both men, looking at Jupiter, were astounded to discover that the bright planet possessed a system of satellites — an undreamed of condition in the Aristotelian philosophy of an Earth-centered

6

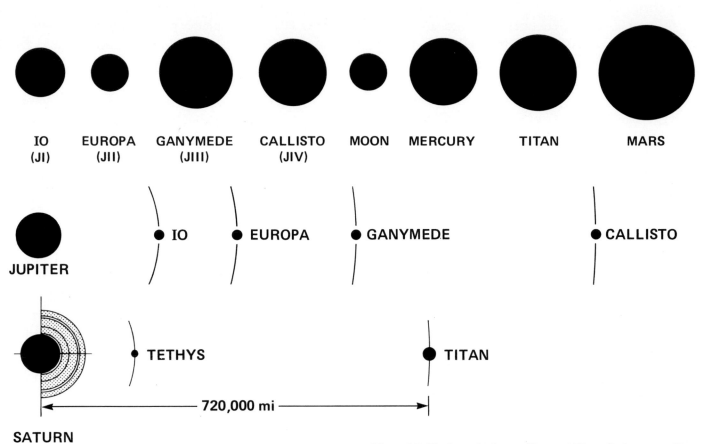

IO   EUROPA   GANYMEDE   CALLISTO   MOON   MERCURY   TITAN   MARS
(JI)   (JII)   (JIII)   (JIV)

JUPITER
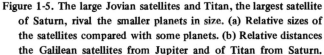
IO   EUROPA   GANYMEDE   CALLISTO

SATURN
TETHYS   TITAN

|← 720,000 mi →|

Figure 1-5. The large Jovian satellites and Titan, the largest satellite of Saturn, rival the smaller planets in size. (a) Relative sizes of the satellites compared with some planets. (b) Relative distances the Galilean satellites from Jupiter and of Titan from Saturn.

universe then holding sway over most human thought. In fact, some scientists of that day claimed the luminous objects were defects of the new instrument, not real objects. These satellites were later given the names Io, Europa, Ganymede, and Callisto by Marius, but are often referred to as the Galilean satellites. Today the satellites are frequently identified by the Roman numerals I, II, III, and IV, respectively.

In 1675, Ole Roemer, observing Jupiter's satellites, made one of the most important discoveries in physics. He noted that the eclipses of Jovian satellites occur progressively later as the Earth moves away from Jupiter and progressively earlier as it moves toward Jupiter. He explained that this effect is evidence for the finite velocity of light. Light traveling across Earth's orbit, when

Earth is farthest from Jupiter, takes 16 min and 40 sec to cover the additional distance. From this, he estimated the velocity of light to be about 300,000 km/sec (186,000 mps) (Figure 1-4).

The Jovian satellites are quite large — Callisto and Ganymede are about the size of the planet Mercury, while Io and Europa are larger than Earth's Moon (Figure 1-5). Viewed through a pair of good field glasses, all four satellites appear as starlike objects nearly in a straight line on either side of the disk of the planet because their orbits are viewed almost edgewise from Earth. These satellites have been sighted without the use of a telescope. The best viewing time is when the sky is faintly light following sunset, before the planet becomes overpoweringly brilliant in a black sky.

7

Almost three centuries later, in 1892, E. E. Barnard discovered a fifth satellite of Jupiter. Of the 14 Jovian satellites known today, 10 are much smaller than the 4 Galilean satellites. The Jovian system thus resembles a small solar system, except that the orbits of its four outermost satellites are traversed in the opposite sense to that of the other satellites, whereas all the planets orbit the Sun in the same sense, counterclockwise when viewed from the north ecliptic pole.

Saturn and its rings and satellites resemble a small solar system as well. But Saturn's satellites did not intrigue astronomers so much as other strange, unusual appendages during the years following the discovery of the telescope. In 1610, Galileo was mystified by two appendages, one on either side of Saturn (Figure 1-6). He was even more mystified when a few years later he could no longer see them. Many years later, Christian Huygens, who mastered the art of grinding tele-

scope lenses with higher precision than his contemporaries, observed a thin ring surrounding the planet inclined at a considerable angle to the plane of the ecliptic, sometimes seen open and bright and at other times invisible from Earth when viewed edge-on. At this same time, 1655, Huygens discovered a satellite of Saturn — Titan.

Astronomers had identified two bright rings of Saturn. But for many years, the nature of Saturn's rings remained an enigma. In June 1838, the astronomer Galle observed that from the inner ring a veil extended across half the dark space separating it from the planet. It was not until 1850 that Bond in the United States and Dawes in England showed that this effect was caused by a faint third "crepe" ring. Still the nature of Saturn's rings remained a mystery. Laplace and Herschel thought the rings were solid. In 1848, Edward Roche suggested they were probably small particles; Bond, in 1851, thought they must be fluid. Not until 1857 did James Clerk Maxwell, the Scottish physicist, prove mathematically that the rings consist of particles orbiting Saturn so closely crowded together as to appear as a continuous mass.

By the end of the 17th century, astronomers had discovered five satellites of Saturn, all but Titan being smaller than the Galilean satellites of Jupiter. In 1789, Herschel, with a new reflecting telescope, observed two more satellites. In the next century two more were discovered — at the time of the Pioneer missions to the giant planets nine known satellites orbited Saturn and two more were suspected.

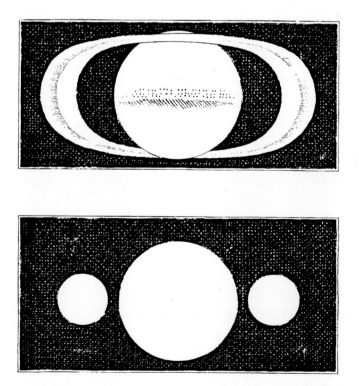

Figure 1-6. In the years following 1610, astronomers observed strange appendages on either side of Saturn that disappeared for a short while and then reappeared. It was many more years before these were correctly identified as the rings of Saturn.

Solar Orbits of the Giant Planets

Ancient astronomers observing the motions of the planets against a background of stars called them wandering stars. The word "planet" is derived from the Greek word "wanderer." All the planets, including Earth, orbit the Sun in near-circular paths. Jupiter and Saturn orbit the Sun

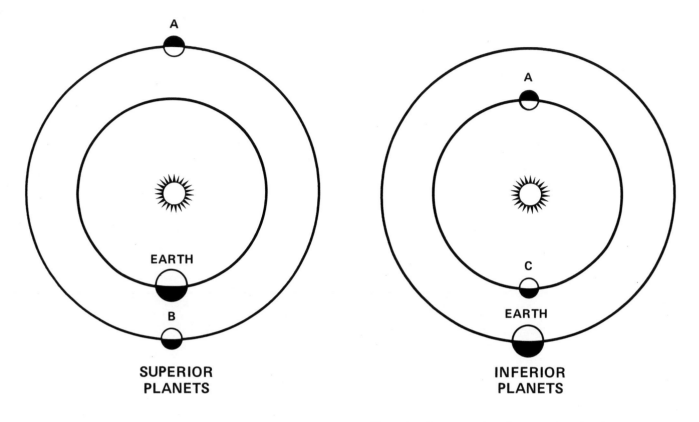

A

EARTH

B

SUPERIOR PLANETS

A

C

EARTH

INFERIOR PLANETS

Figure 1-7. When superior planets such as the giant planets are on the far side of the Sun as seen from Earth, they are said to be in conjunction (A). When opposite the Sun in Earth's skies, they are then closest to Earth and are said to be in opposition (B). Planets moving inside Earth's orbit are referred to as inferior planets. Mercury and Venus are such planets and can never be in opposition, but instead attain inferior conjunction when they are between Earth and the Sun (C).

outside the orbit of Earth — they are called superior planets. As seen from Earth they appear to move eastward on the average, nearly along the ecliptic. The ecliptic is the apparent yearly path of the Sun relative to the stars, which is the projection of the plane of Earth's orbit, the ecliptic plane, against the background of stars. Jupiter takes 11.86 Earth-years to orbit the Sun, Saturn, 29.46 years. So, as viewed from Earth, Jupiter and Saturn move along close to the ecliptic year by year progressively passing through the 12 zodiacal constellations.

When a superior planet is opposite the Sun in the sky, the planet is nearest Earth — and is in opposition (Figure 1-7). Consequently, the planet appears brightest at this time. At midnight it shines in the southern sky of the Northern Hemisphere, or in the northern sky of the Southern Hemisphere. Jupiter is in opposition every 13.1 months, Saturn every 12.4 months.

A planet is in conjunction when it lies in nearly the same direction as the Sun as seen from Earth. At this time, the planet is not visible in the night sky and is then most distant from Earth.

9

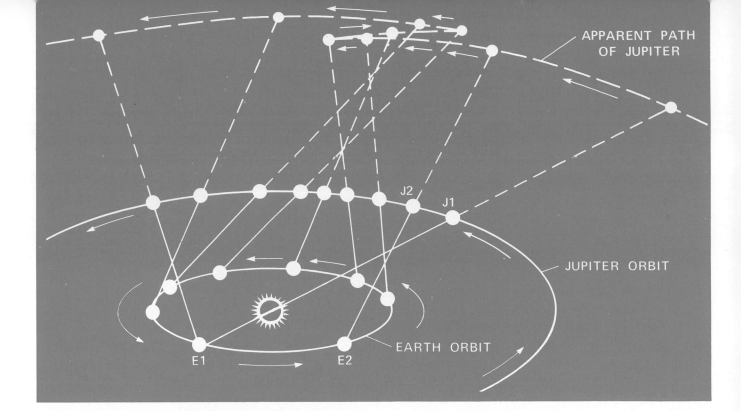

Figure 1-8. Because of the relative motions of Earth and an outer planet such as Jupiter or Saturn, Earth regularly "catches up" with the outer planet because Earth moves faster in its yearly orbit. Then, as seen from Earth, the outer planet appears to loop backward for several months. A typical loop motion of Jupiter (as shown) covers almost one-third of a zodiacal constellation; a loop of Saturn is smaller.

Because the orbit of a superior planet is outside Earth's orbit, and because Earth moves faster, each year around the date of opposition, a superior planet is "overtaken" by Earth and the planet appears to move backward relative to the background of stars — toward the west — in "retrograde motion" (Figure 1-8).

Jupiter as Observed from Earth

From pole to pole, Jupiter measures 134,000 km (83,270 miles) compared with Earth's 12,700 km (7,890 miles). Jupiter turns on its axis faster than any other planet in our Solar System,

once every 9 hr 55.5 min. Its equatorial regions rotate slightly faster than other regions, in 9 hr 50.5 min. Such rapid rotation has flattened the poles, and at its equator, Jupiter bulges to about 8,200 km (5,095 miles) greater than its polar diameter.

Although Jupiter's volume is 1317 times that of Earth, its mass is just under 318 times Earth's mass. Scientists have long known that Jupiter is not a solid body like Earth but consists mainly of gas and liquid with possibly a small rocky core (which is also liquid). By the 1950's, scientists realized that Jupiter's composition, predominantly hydrogen and helium, more closely resembles that of the Sun than of Earth.

Figure 1-9. In the best Earth-based photographs Jupiter is a magnif-
icently colored globe. The picture is even more magnificent
through a powerful telescope. Its various belts and zones are
clearly defined and the polar flattening is quite apparent.
(*Photograph: Catalina Observatory, University of Arizona*)

The sight of Jupiter, seen from Earth through a telescope, is magnificent (Figure 1-9) — stripes and bands of turbulent clouds parallel the planet's equator. Dusky amorphous areas cover each pole. The darker stripes or "belts" and the lighter bands between these belts called "zones" are permanent enough to be given names (Figure 1-10).

The colors of Jupiter appear soft and muted, yet quite definite. They change at different times — the zones vary from yellowish to white, the belts from gray to reddish brown. The intensity of the bands changes, fading and darkening. The bands also widen or become narrow and move up or down in latitude. Streaks, wisps, arches, loops, plumes, patches, lumps, spots, and festoons embellish the zones and bands. Astronomers have suggested that these smaller features are clusters of clouds, and that others are zones of turbulence between jet streams moving at different speeds. These small features are observed to change during the course of a day, sometimes within hours.

Cloud formations move around Jupiter at different rates. A great equatorial current, 20° wide, sweeps around Jupiter at 360 km/hr (225 mph) faster than surrounding regions.

In the southern hemisphere of Jupiter, a huge oval feature has intrigued astronomers since it was first observed in 1664 by the astronomer Robert Hooke. This Great Red Spot (Figure 1-11) is now about 24,000 km (15,000 miles) long, but at

11

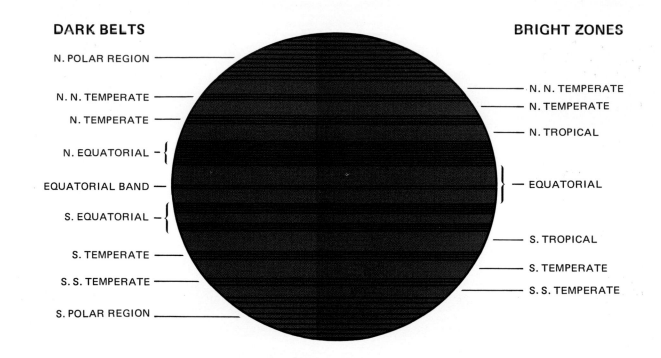

DARK BELTS

N. POLAR REGION

N. N. TEMPERATE

N. TEMPERATE

N. EQUATORIAL

EQUATORIAL BAND

S. EQUATORIAL

S. TEMPERATE

S. S. TEMPERATE

S. POLAR REGION

BRIGHT ZONES

N. N. TEMPERATE

N. TEMPERATE

N. TROPICAL

EQUATORIAL

S. TROPICAL

S. TEMPERATE

S. S. TEMPERATE

Figure 1-10. The belts and zones of Jupiter are permanent enough to be given names as shown here.

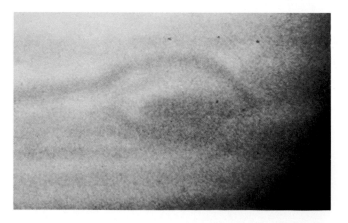

Figure 1-11. A Great Red Spot in the South Tropical Zone of Jupiter has intrigued astronomers for centuries. Speculation about the nature of the spot ranged from a floating island to a swirling column of gas anchored to some prominent feature on a solid core. (*Photograph: Catalina Observatory, University of Arizona*)

times has extended to almost 48,000 km (30,000 miles). The spot has, on occasion, faded almost completely. Many scientists have speculated on this marking, describing it as a high mountain peak or an island floating in the clouds. Small and less persistent red spots have been seen from time to time as well as relatively short-lived white spots (Figure 1-12).

After the Sun, Jupiter is the strongest source of radio signals in the Solar System. Three types of radiation received on Earth are emitted from Jupiter (Figure 1-13) — thermal, decimetric, and decametric. Thermal radio waves are produced by agitated molecules in the Jovian atmosphere. Decimetric radio waves are produced by electrons spiraling around lines of force in the planet's magnetic field. Decametric radio waves are produced by some remarkable type of electrical instability. Scientists have observed that decametric radiation is linked in some way to the orbital motion of Io, the closest large satellite of Jupiter.

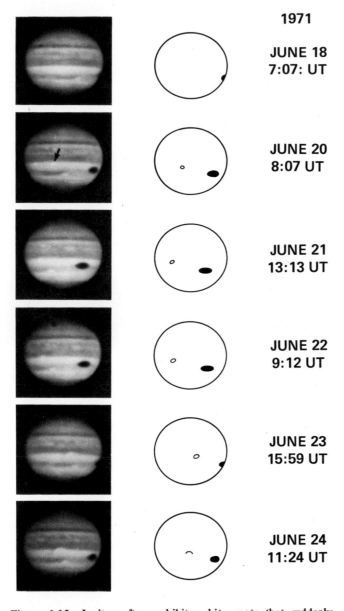

1971

JUNE 18
7:07: UT

JUNE 20
8:07 UT

JUNE 21
13:13 UT

JUNE 22
9:12 UT

JUNE 23
15:59 UT

JUNE 24
11:24 UT

Figure 1-12. Jupiter often exhibits white spots that suddenly appear, brighten, and then fade away. This set of ultraviolet photographs from the International Planetary Patrol Program shows the spectacular early growth of a major disturbance in Jupiter's South Equatorial Belt. North is at the top. At first, a tiny spot is barely detectable in ultraviolet light on June 18, but, in less than a week, the spot is comparable in size to the Great Red Spot. At age two days (indicated by arrow on the June 20 image), it stands out clearly. At that time, the disturbance was not yet detectable in red photographs of equal quality. The images in this particular sequence were obtained at the Mauna Kea and the Perth Observatories.

From observations of decimetric radio waves, scientists concluded that Jupiter has a magnetic field and radiation belts similar to Earth's belts within which charged particles are trapped and spiral around magnetic field lines. Because of the intensity of these radiation belts, scientists calculated that Jupiter's magnetic field is many times stronger than that of Earth.

Saturn Observed from Earth

From pole to pole, Saturn measures 107,000 km (66,490 miles). The planet spins on its axis once in about 10 hr 40 min. Saturn's equatorial regions rotate slightly faster than other regions, in 10 hr 14 min. This rapid rotation has flattened the poles and has bulged Saturn's equatorial diameter to about 12,000 km (7,456 miles) greater than the polar diameter.

Although Saturn's volume is 755 times that of Earth, its mass is just under 95.2 times Earth's mass. Saturn is not a solid body like Earth but is similar to Jupiter, consisting mainly of gas and liquid with possibly a small rocky (liquid) core. Like Jupiter, Saturn is composed predominantly of hydrogen and helium and is therefore more like

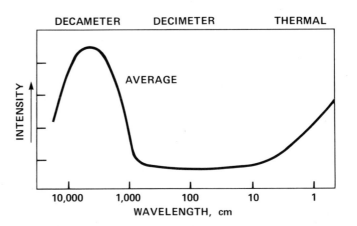

Figure 1-13. For over two decades, radio astronomers have recorded and measured radio waves emitted by Jupiter. These radio waves are of three main types: thermal, decimetric, and decametric, each having a different origin. The decimetric waves show that Jupiter has radiation belts of particles trapped in the planet's magnetic field.

13

Figure 1-14. The planet Saturn and its magnificent system of rings.
(Photograph: Catalina Observatory, University of Arizona)

the Sun than Earth. However, there is a striking difference between Jupiter and Saturn — the density of Saturn is only about half the mean density of Jupiter and about one-eighth that of Earth.

Viewed through a telescope from Earth, Saturn (Figure 1-14) is a spectacular sight — a dull, flattened globe surrounded by bright rings extending to a diameter of 274,200 km (170,400 miles). Faint bands on the globe suggest stripes of cloud paralleling the planet's equator. Large darker regions cover each pole, with dark stripes or "belts" and lighter bands between the belts called "zones."

The colors of Saturn are softer and more muted than those of Jupiter, varying from pale yellow to brownish yellow. The contrast between belts and zones is much less striking than on Jupiter.

Observations from Earth have revealed many interesting details. Of course, Saturn is much farther away and, viewed through a telescope,

appears as a disk whose diameter is less than half that of Jupiter. Light-colored spots have been observed on Saturn from time to time, but they do not last as long as those on Jupiter nor are their colors so intense. No feature of Saturn compares with Jupiter's Great Red Spot. In fact, only 10 conspicuous spots have been observed on Saturn during 300 years of telescopic observations from Earth.

From observations of such spots, astronomers have determined that clouds move around Saturn in 10 hr 37 min at 40° north and south latitudes, some 23 min longer than clouds at the equator. The variations in cloud speeds are believed to cause turbulence between belts and zones as on Jupiter.

Since no nonthermal radiation had been detected before the Pioneer mission, whether Saturn possessed a magnetic field could not be proved from radio data. However, because Saturn resembles Jupiter and spins rapidly on its axis, scientists thought it likely that Saturn has

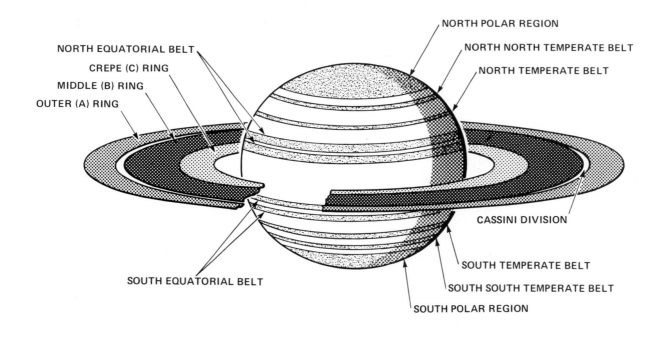

NORTH POLAR REGION
NORTH NORTH TEMPERATE BELT
NORTH TEMPERATE BELT
NORTH EQUATORIAL BELT
CREPE (C) RING
MIDDLE (B) RING
OUTER (A) RING
CASSINI DIVISION
SOUTH EQUATORIAL BELT
SOUTH TEMPERATE BELT
SOUTH SOUTH TEMPERATE BELT
SOUTH POLAR REGION

Figure 1-15. The various rings of Saturn and the gaps separating them as observed before Pioneer 11's flyby of the planet.

a magnetic field, but a flyby spacecraft would be needed to establish its presence and to measure its strength.

The ring system of Saturn (Figure 1-15) is a fascinating spectacle. These rings have divisions that were not thought to be empty space but regions where there were smaller numbers of particles. The most prominent division discovered by Cassini in 1675 is called Cassini's division. From Earth-based observations, astronomers believed it was about 6,000 km (3,730 miles) wide. It separates the two main bright rings — A for the outermost and B for the next inner visible ring — that comprise the bright visible system.

The B ring is the brighter — a golden yellow ring with a brighter rim near its outer circumference which stands out in high contrast against Cassini's division. The A ring is silvery, not so bright as the B ring. As discovered by Encke, the A ring also has a less clearly defined gap about one-fourth the width of Cassini's division. A faint inner "crepe"

ring, or C ring, has a milky transparency against the blackness of space or, when seen against the globe of the planet, it appears to be a dusky veil. The rings, being so thin, virtually disappear when seen edge on. These rings were estimated to be only 2 km thick.

Some observers claim to have observed faint rings inside the C ring and outside the A ring — an innermost D ring and an outermost E ring. Whether rings existed beyond the visible rings was an important consideration to scientists planning spacecraft trajectories to fly by Saturn.

Much of the evidence concerning Saturn's rings was conflicting. Both the composition and size of particles in the rings were disputed for many years. Just before the Pioneer mission, there were many speculative theories about the composition of the rings. One of these suggested that the rings consisted of ice or ice-coated rocks with diameters of at least 5 cm (2 in.) but not greater than several meters.

15

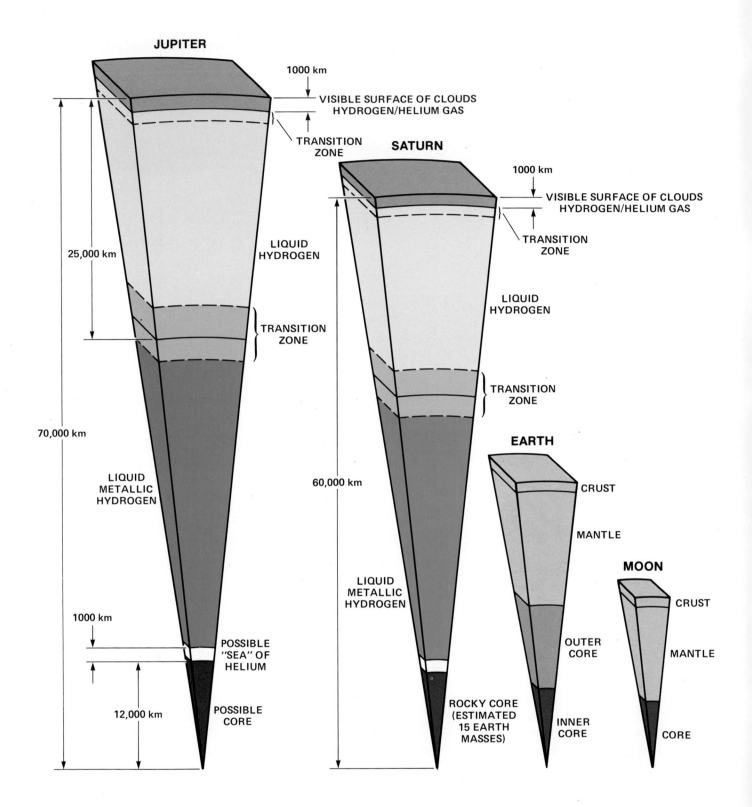

Figure 1-16. The interiors of the giant planets are quite different from the interiors of terrestrial bodies such as Earth and Moon.

16

Planetary Interiors

Astronomers believe that the interiors of Jupiter and Saturn are very similar to each other but quite different from those of the terrestrial planets such as Earth (Figure 1-16). It is believed that the giant planets consist of shells of increasing density. The outermost shell, the hydrogen atmosphere, has some helium and traces of heavier gases such as methane, ammonia, and water vapor. At depth within this atmosphere, the pressure becomes so great that the hydrogen liquifies. The next lower shell is of liquid hydrogen. Much deeper, the pressure is so great that liquid hydrogen becomes a special form called liquid metallic hydrogen, which behaves as a metal and readily conducts heat and electricity. Convective motions within this shell of metallic hydrogen could be responsible for the magnetic field of Jupiter and would be expected to produce a magnetic field for Saturn as well. Deep within each planet, highly compressed volatiles such as water, ammonia, and methane might surround a liquid metallic core with a mass perhaps 10 to 20 times greater than that of Earth. Each core might be extremely hot, exceeding the temperature at the surface of the Sun, because of the tremendous pressures at the planetary cores. Some models of planetary interiors suggest that, for Saturn, helium might separate from hydrogen to form another shell just above the core.

Planetary Evolution

The planets of the Solar System probably formed four to five billion years ago when hosts of small rocky particles and clouds of gas were drawn together by gravity. It is believed that as the Sun condensed from a primordial nebula, planets formed from concentrations of matter at various distances from the Sun. One speculation is that the planets that began early to aggregate material scooped up more matter than those planets that started later and had less free material to collect. The distribution of mass in the clouds probably contributed greatly to the resultant masses of the planets.

Photographs taken by spacecraft of the inner planets and their satellites, coupled with geological evidence on Earth and radar probing of the Venusian surface, show that the crusts of the terrestrial planets are densely cratered by many impacts. This cratering presents evidence of the final stages of planetary accretion (Figure 1-17). On Earth, subsequent changes to the surface through internal heat, plate tectonics, and weathering obliterated nearly all evidence of impact cratering. While such cratering would not, of course, have taken place on the gaseous giants, cratering on their satellites may offer clues about the distribution of the matter that impacted their surfaces.

Much of the primordial gas was hydrogen, the most common material in the Universe. The Sun, for example, is nearly all hydrogen, as are the stars. Vast clouds of hydrogen fill the spaces between the stars. Earth and the other inner planets may have possessed some hydrogen in their atmospheres for a very short time in the scale of planetary development. Energetic eruptions on the Sun during its early development may have swept hydrogen from the inner Solar System, depleting hydrogen from the atmospheres of the inner planets. The atmospheres of the outer planets still hold hydrogen. Jupiter and Saturn are thought to be predominantly hydrogen, and Uranus and Neptune are also believed to contain much of this very light gas.

Knowledge of the complex atmospheres of the outer planets should be helpful in understanding Earth's early atmosphere. From studies of duststorms in the thin, dry atmosphere of Mars and circulation patterns in the dense, hot atmosphere of Venus, meteorologists have gained a better understanding of planetary atmospheres in general. Information about the atmospheres of the giant planets is expected to add to this body of understanding.

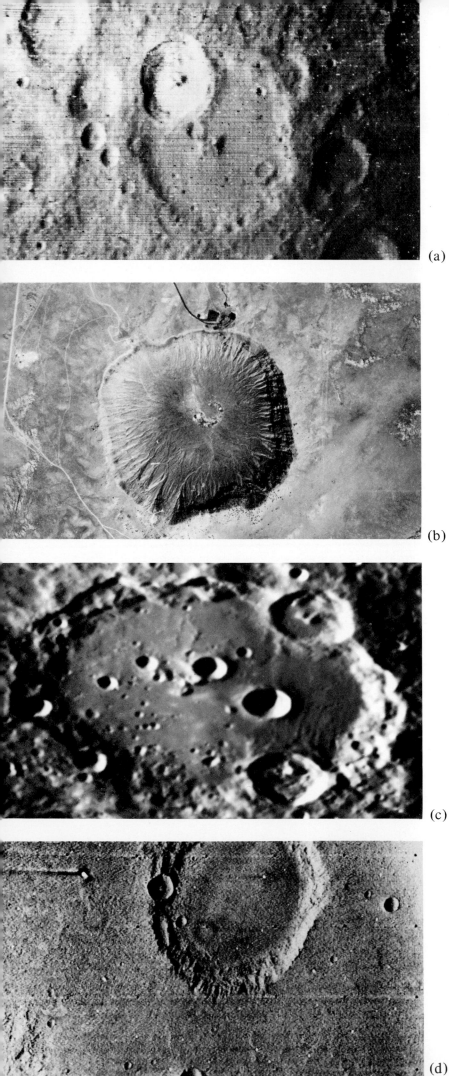

(a)

(b)

(c)

(d)

Figure 1-17. The planets are believed to have accreted from particles that condensed from a primordial solar nebula. Impact craters on the terrestrial planets are believed to be evidence of the final stages of accretion.

    (a) Mercury — Crater Kuiper (Mariner 10)
    (b) Earth — Meteor Crater, Arizona
        (*Photograph: U.S. Geological Survey*)
    (c) Moon — Clavius (Hale Observatories)
    (d) Mars — Unnamed large crater. Crater below and slightly to the left is comparable in size to Meteor Crater (Mariner 6)

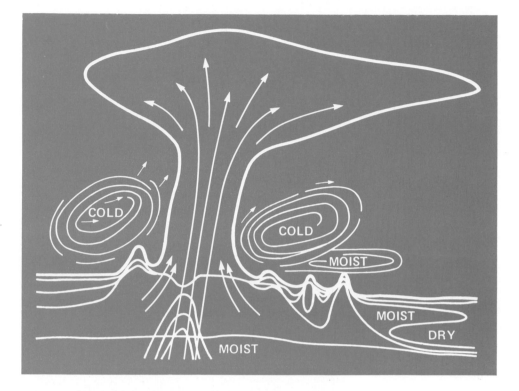

Figure 1-18. Heat in an atmosphere causes air masses to rise; on Earth this produces thunderstorms. As air cools in the upper atmosphere, it spreads sideways and the rotation of the planet creates swirling masses. The internal heat of Jupiter and Saturn may be producing huge thunderstorms that appear as spots such as the Great Red Spot.

At some level in the deep atmospheres of Jupiter and Saturn, the temperature should equal that on Earth. At this level ammonia crystals become liquid ammonia droplets and water condenses. These droplets would rain from the clouds, sometimes frozen into snows of water and ammonia. But the drops and snowflakes would never fall to a solid surface as on Earth. Instead, at the warm lower regions of the deep atmospheres of Jupiter and Saturn, these droplets would evaporate and return to the clouds.

Such a circulation pattern, somewhat analogous to those that create violent thunderstorms and tornadoes in Earth's atmosphere (Figure 1-18), would probably cause endless violent turbulence in the atmospheres of the giant planets, far more violent than Earth's thunderstorms. The electrical discharges that would accompany such turbulence would make Earth's flashes of lightning mere sparks by comparison. Thus vertical turmoil in the atmospheres of Jupiter and Saturn may provide examples of the most violent storms imaginable. Jet circulations in the cloud bands of these giants may be analogous to Earth's major atmospheric patterns such as the trade winds, tropical convergences, and jet streams.

It was long thought that Jupiter and Saturn might be inhospitable planets on which life could not survive. But since there are probably liquid water droplets in an atmosphere of hydrogen, methane, and ammonia, the atmospheres of the giant planets may provide the same primordial "soup" from which it has been suggested that life originated on Earth.

Life has been described as an unexplained ability to organize nonliving matter into a continuing system that perceives, reacts to, and evolves to cope with changes in the physical environment which threaten to destroy its organization. In 1953 a mixture of hydrogen, methane, ammonia, and water vapor — components of the atmospheres of Jupiter and Saturn — was bombarded by electrical discharges to simulate the effects of bolts of lightning. As a result, some of the gas molecules combined into more complex molecules of the type believed to be the building blocks of living systems (Figure 1-19).

At some point in Earth's history, postulated as being about 3.5 to 4 billion years ago, highly complex, carbon-based molecules became organized into living systems that were able to replicate

Figure 1-19. By passing electric sparks through a mixture of hydrogen, methane, ammonia, and water vapor, scientists have produced colored amino acids, the building blocks of organic life. The experiment was first performed by Stanley Miller in 1953. These photographs show an experiment at NASA-Ames Research Center's Chemical Evolution Branch. When methane or acetylene, both constituents of the Jovian atmosphere, is sparked in a chamber together with ammonia at the temperature of liquid nitrogen, reddish-brown polymeric material is synthesized. Such processes might be responsible for the colors in the atmospheres of Jupiter and Saturn.

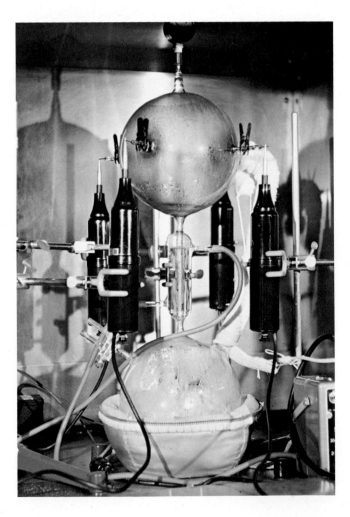

themselves — to reproduce. It is theorized that from this beginning through developmental changes in this biological chain, all the living creatures on Earth evolved.

But has life evolved in the atmospheres of Jupiter and Saturn? It is known that, on these planets, the temperature may be right and the gas mixture suitable, and that electrical discharges occur. Although the Pioneer spacecraft were not intended to search for evidence of such evolutionary processes, such missions could be precursors to more sophisticated ones, perhaps probing deep into the atmospheres of these intriguing planets.

Mission Objectives

The question of beginnings has always intrigued man. There are no satisfactory answers to how the Solar System condensed from charged atoms, energetic molecules, and electromagnetic forces of some primeval nebula. Nor is it known how the various planets evolved in their unique way. And more significant to man — how did life originate and flourish on Earth, a planet so different from all the others?

Earth itself reveals few answers because our planet can be studied only in its recent stages of evolution, a very short period in the long history of Earth as an astronomical body. From the available information, scientists cannot be sure about Earth's past, let alone its future. However, other planets have passed through evolutionary phases at different rates and some, such as the Moon and Mercury, have "fossilized" their ancient record of planetary evolution. But planets are much too far away to be studied in great detail by use of telescopes on Earth. Also, observations are limited by the screening and distorting effects of Earth's atmosphere (Figure 1-20).

With the planetary probes, astronomers have learned more about the planets during the first years of the space age than in all the previous centuries of observations from Earth. From this knowledge, man has gained a better understanding

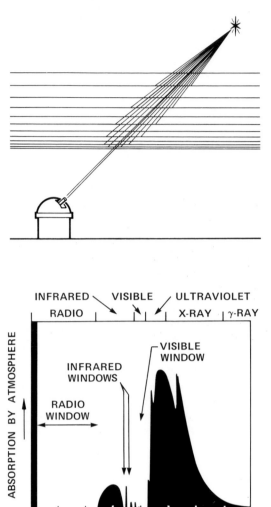

Figure 1-20. Because Earth's atmosphere selectively absorbs certain wavelengths of light, especially in the infrared and ultraviolet regions of the spectrum, astronomers can obtain only a partial view of planets from Earth.

of our planet Earth, its past and its future. Such knowledge and understanding are vital to the survival of all living species, for man must protect his tenuous environment while adapting to inevitable natural and man-made changes.

In many respects, the giant planets Jupiter and Saturn provide models of what is taking place in the entire Universe. Many processes within these

21

Figure 1-21. The gravity of Jupiter (or of Saturn), coupled with its orbital motion, can be used in a slingshot technique to speed spacecraft to the outer planets. But first NASA had to determine whether a spacecraft could penetrate the environment of Jupiter and the ring plane of Saturn without being destroyed.

planets may be similar to those in stars before nuclear reactions occur. The great turmoil in these processes, particularly those of Jupiter, coupled with the high-speed rotation of these planets, provide an opportunity for scientists to make comparative studies of jet streams and weather in quieter planetary atmospheres such as Earth's.

Each satellite system of the two giant planets represents a lesser solar system, even, as for Jupiter, to the densities of the satellite bodies which, like the planets, decrease with distance from the central body. Thus, their formation may have paralleled the formation of the Solar System.

The outer reaches of the Solar System were relatively unknown before the Pioneer odyssey to Jupiter and Saturn. Yet these great planets provide valuable information to help us understand the origins of the Solar System. Since they are so distant from the Sun, they require that spacecraft

depart Earth's orbit very fast to reach them in a reasonable time. For planets more distant than Jupiter, available launch vehicles cannot boost spacecraft of practical size to the necessary velocities. However, using the gravitational field and orbital motion of Jupiter in a slingshot technique, spacecraft can be hurtled into more energetic paths to carry them to the more distant planets and to escape from our Solar System (Figure 1-21).

But there was a danger: within Jupiter's strong magnetic field, radiation belts extend outward to great distances. These radiation belts must be explored to ascertain whether they will damage spacecraft if Jupiter is to be used as a gravity slingshot to the outer worlds. If these radiation belts prove to be a serious hazard, the exploration of the outer Solar System might have to await the development of more energetic propulsion systems than chemical rockets, perhaps decades hence.

22

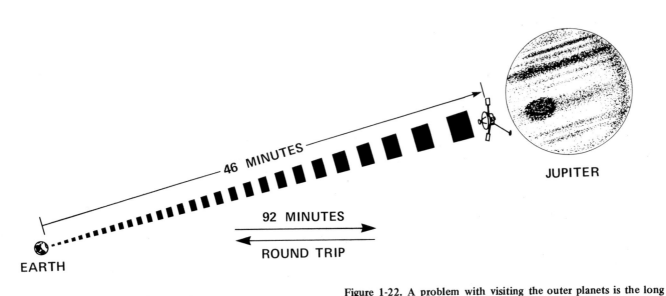

46 MINUTES

92 MINUTES

ROUND TRIP

EARTH

JUPITER

Figure 1-22. A problem with visiting the outer planets is the long time needed for radio waves, traveling at 300,000 km/sec (186,000 mps), to reach Earth from the spacecraft. It takes 92 min for a roundtrip by radio from Earth to Jupiter and back and nearly twice that for Saturn.

Whether Saturn can be used as a slingshot to reach Uranus and Neptune is in doubt until scientists can determine what hazards, if any, are presented by the ring particles outside the bright visible rings of the planet.

Although scientists have estimated from radio waves emitted by the Jovian radiation belts approximately how many electrons are trapped there, they have no way of knowing from Earth how many high-energy protons are trapped there — protons of the type that would be especially hazardous to spacecraft. Similarly, scientists cannot determine from Earth whether Saturn's rings extend far beyond the visible rings. Only with a spacecraft that could penetrate the radiation belts of Jupiter and, if it survived this journey, one that could then pass through the ring plane of Saturn near the visible rings, could scientists find out the answers.

The mission to Jupiter and Saturn posed many technical challenges. It would extend man's exploration of the Solar System to a new scale — 780 million kilometers (485 million miles) from the Sun to Jupiter and another 650 million kilometers (400 million miles) to Saturn, with a chance to explore interplanetary space far beyond the orbit of Uranus, although not in close proximity to that planet.

The vast distances to be covered by the spacecraft presented problems of communications — not only because of the weakness of radio signals but also because of the time delay in information traveling to Earth from the spacecraft and radio commands transmitted from Earth to the spacecraft (Figure 1-22). This delay required that controllers on Earth become adept at flying the spacecraft 90 min out of step with the spacecraft itself at Jupiter and 170 min out of step at Saturn.

Because of the great distance between the Sun and Jupiter, sunlight at Jupiter's orbit is only 1/27 as intense as at Earth's orbit; at the distance of Saturn, sunlight is only 1/90 as intense (Figure 1-23). Normally, a spacecraft's electrical power is supplied by converting sunlight to electricity. But a spacecraft bound for the outer Solar System must carry a nuclear energy source to generate electricity. Also, since the spacecraft must fly through space for several years before reaching its destination, the demands for a highly reliable spacecraft were more stringent than in previous

23

missions. Moreover, because of the high velocities required to reach Jupiter and Saturn, the spacecraft and its components and scientific instruments had to be lightweight.

SUN AS SEEN:

FROM EARTH   FROM JUPITER   FROM SATURN

Figure 1-23. Converting solar power to electricity is not practical for small spacecraft at the distances of the outer planets. At Jupiter, sunlight carries only 1/27 the energy it does at Earth, and at Saturn, only 1/90.

Additionally, between Mars and Jupiter stretches an asteroid belt (Figure 1-24) which some scientists thought might include abrasive dust, perhaps 280 million kilometers (175 million miles) wide, which might seriously damage a spacecraft crossing it.

Despite these obstacles, the opportunity to explore the outer Solar System beyond the orbit of Mars beckoned strongly, challenging the ingenuity of space technologists. The National Aeronautics and Space Administration accepted the challenge in a double-pronged exploratory mission: two spacecraft, Pioneers F and G, were to make the assault. Their journeys into the unknown to explore the far reaches of our Solar System began early in 1972 — incredible journeys to the planets Jupiter and Saturn, two spectacular points of light in the night skies of Earth that have held the attention of mankind for centuries.

Figure 1-24. If spacecraft are to visit the outer Solar System, they must cross the asteroid belt between Mars and Jupiter. The Pioneer mission was faced with the question of just how dangerous this asteroid belt would be to a spacecraft passing through it.

2
The Pioneer Jupiter/Saturn Mission

The Pioneer program began in 1957 when the Advanced Research Projects Agency authorized the launching of small unmanned spacecraft toward the Moon. In March 1958, Secretary of Defense McElroy announced that the United States Air Force would launch three such probes in an attempt to place a scientific payload in the vicinity of the Moon. The first successful Pioneer, launched 0342 EST October 11, 1958, traveled 117,100 km (72,765 miles) from Earth and returned scientific data for 48 hr. A magnetometer on board yielded evidence of complex geomagnetic effects thousands of kilometers from Earth. Another Pioneer, launched December 6, 1958, confirmed the existence of two Van Allen belts of trapped energetic particles. The first spin-scan image of any planet, in this case Earth, was obtained by one of these early Pioneers.

In May 1960, about a year after the National Aeronautics and Space Administration was formed, an informal study of solar probes was started at NASA's Ames Research Center. This study, led by Charles F. Hall, was to demonstrate the Center's potential for managing a space project. From this study, a new concept was presented — a small, simple, long-lived spacecraft to explore the interplanetary medium inside Earth's orbit. Smith J. DeFrance, then Center Director, was enthusiastic about this new space work for the Center. In September 1960, he organized a formal team; in 1961 and 1962, Charles Hall and others, including scientists, tried to stimulate interest in the concept at NASA Headquarters.

As a result of several presentations made to NASA Headquarters, Edgar M. Cortright, then Deputy Director of the Office of Space Science, invited Hall and his team to become involved in an interplanetary Pioneer spacecraft. Space Technology Laboratories, which had been involved in the first Pioneer spacecraft for the Air Force, was chosen to determine the feasibility of the spin-stabilized spacecraft concept they had evolved for the Interplanetary Pioneer mission; a project approval document was issued in June 1962. Space Technology Laboratories was selected over other competitors to build the spacecraft. The Pioneer project moved rapidly ahead for a first launch.

Pioneers 6 through 9, launched by Thor-Deltas in 1965 through 1968, explored interplanetary space in a band extending several million kilometers inside and outside Earth's orbit. Measurements made by these spacecraft greatly increased our knowledge of the interplanetary medium and the effects of solar activity upon the Earth. New information was gathered about the solar wind, solar cosmic rays, the structure of the Sun's plasma and magnetic fields, the physics of particles in space, and the nature of solar flares. These spacecraft continued to operate in space for many years. Several of the scientists involved with the Interplanetary Pioneers had been associated with the first Pioneers and continued with later Pioneer spacecraft missions to the outer planets, thereby devoting a major part of their professional lives to this program.

During the development of the Interplanetary Pioneers, an important series of meetings was held as part of the activities of NASA's Lunar and Planetary Missions Board. In 1967, an Outer Planets Panel associated with this Board and chaired by James Van Allen of the University of Iowa recommended that plans should be made for low-cost exploratory missions to the outer planets because such missions would make significant contributions to space science.

In June 1968, the Space Science Board of the National Academy of Sciences stated that Jupiter was probably the most interesting planet from a physical point of view and that it was at that time technically feasible to send space probes to that planet. The Board recommended that "Jupiter missions be given high priority, and that two exploratory probes in the Pioneer class be launched in 1972 or 1973."

In June 1969, in a further report, the Lunar and Planetary Missions Board emphasized the importance of obtaining more information about the outer giant planets and recommended that a long-term plan be developed to explore the outer Solar System. This report endorsed the earlier Space Science Board studies.

In previous years, a number of proposals and scientific papers had been presented about exploration of the outer planets, including missions to

several planets by one spacecraft using gravity assist from some of the planets. Several NASA centers and private companies had completed studies showing that the gravity field of Jupiter combined with the orbital motion of the planet could accelerate spacecraft to speeds that would enable them to complete missions to more distant planets in reasonable times and with useful scientific payloads.

In March 1967, for example, in a paper presented at the Fifth Goddard Memorial Symposium in Washington, D.C., several types of outer Solar System probes were discussed which could explore interplanetary space beyond the orbit of Mars, the solar wind and its interaction with deep space, and the Jovian environment. A Jupiter probe of this type would be accelerated sufficiently by the large planet to allow the spacecraft to escape completely from our Solar System into interstellar space. Such a mission would provide an opportunity to investigate how far the influence of the solar wind extends into the outer limits of our Solar System.

About this time, at the Goddard Space Center, a Galactic Jupiter Probe was studied as a means to explore solar, interplanetary, and galactic phenomena to as great a distance from our Sun as possible. Every 13 months, for a few weeks, the relative positions of Earth and Jupiter permit a spacecraft to be launched into a Jupiter-bound trajectory with a minimum launch energy. Launch energies required for the remainder of the 13 months are prohibitive. The study recommended that two spacecraft be launched to Jupiter in 1972 and 1973 by Atlas-Centaur launch vehicles. As each spacecraft passed through Jupiter's gravity field, it would obtain enough additional energy to carry it high above the ecliptic plane or to great distances from our Sun, hopefully into the interstellar medium. The spacecraft were to be spin-stabilized and would have an Earth-oriented antenna. Each spacecraft would receive its power from radioisotope thermoelectric generators.

A mission to Jupiter was officially approved by NASA Headquarters in February 1969, and the program was assigned to the Planetary Programs Office, Office of Space Science and Applications,

NASA Headquarters, Washington, D.C. The Pioneer Project Office at Ames Research Center, Moffett Field, California, was selected to manage the project, and TRW Systems Group, Redondo Beach, California, was awarded a contract to design and fabricate two identical Pioneer spacecraft for the mission.

In a scientific paper delivered to the American Astronautical Society's June 1969 meeting in Denver, Colorado, Howard F. Mathews and Charles F. Hall described the first mission to the outer planets as "an exciting era of exploration of the outer planets." The initial mission plan was to reach Jupiter. The mission was later extended when it became apparent that, without any change to its design, one of the spacecraft could reach Saturn.

From a consideration of the time needed to build the spacecraft, to select its scientific experiments, and to build instruments to perform these experiments, the first feasible launch opportunity for the mission appeared to be during late February through early March of 1972. The first spacecraft, Pioneer F, was scheduled to meet this launch opportunity. The second spacecraft, Pioneer G, was to be launched approximately 13 months later, during the 1973 opportunity. Before launch, all NASA spacecraft are given letter designations that are later changed to number designations after a successful launch — Pioneer F became Pioneer 10 and Pioneer G became Pioneer 11. The two spacecraft are hereafter referred to by their number designations.

Planning

Planning for the Pioneer mission to Jupiter and Saturn required a close involvement between NASA and industry. The Pioneer Program was managed at NASA Headquarters, first by Glenn A. Reiff and then by F. D. Kochendorfer.

At Ames Research Center, Charles F. Hall became Manager of the Pioneer Project. After the Pioneer 11 encounter with Saturn, Richard O. Fimmel became Project Manager. The experiments carried by the spacecraft were the responsibility of Joseph E. Lepetich, and the spacecraft system was the responsibility of Ralph W. Holtzclaw. The original Flight Operations Manager was Robert R. Nunamaker, then later Norman J. Martin. For the journey of Pioneer 11 from Jupiter to Saturn and for the encounter with Saturn, Robert P. Hogan was Flight Director. For the mission beyond Saturn, Robert W. Jackson was Flight Director and Dr. John H. Wolfe was Project Scientist; after Saturn encounter, Palmer Dyal became Project Scientist. Other members of the team were: Robert U. Hofstetter, Launch Vehicle and Trajectory Analysis Coordinator; Richard O. Fimmel, Science Chief; Gilbert A. Schroeder, Spacecraft Chief, and John W. Dyer, Chief, Mission Analysis.

The Jet Propulsion Laboratory of the California Institute of Technology, Pasadena, California, provided tracking and data system support with originally Alfred J. Siegmeth as the first Pioneer Tracking and Data Systems Manager and later Richard B. Miller. Goddard Space Flight Center, Greenbelt, Maryland, provided worldwide communications to the various stations of the Deep Space Network.

Lewis Research Center, Cleveland, Ohio, was responsible for the launch vehicle system, under the management of D. J. Shramo. John F. Kennedy Space Center, Florida, was responsible for launch operations, under J. W. Johnson.

At TRW Systems Group, Bernard J. O'Brien was Manager of the Pioneer Project, and William T. Dixon, the Systems Engineer. At the Atomic Energy Commission (now part of the Department of Energy, where Harold Jaffe manages the Isotope Flight Systems Office), B. Rock was Project Engineer for the SNAP-19 radioisotope thermoelectric generators built by Teledyne Isotopes. Bendix Field Engineering Corporation, under the management of Walter L. Natzic, then Thomas S. Goves, and later Patrick J. Barclay, supported the mission operations system. The responsibilities of the various individuals continue into the mission beyond Saturn until communications with the spacecraft stop as they move toward the outer fringes of the Solar System.

Mission Objectives

Initially, the objectives of the Pioneer mission to the giant planets, as defined by NASA, were:

- To explore the interplanetary medium beyond the orbit of Mars.

- To investigate the nature of the asteroid belt from a scientific standpoint and to assess the belt's possible hazards to missions to the outer planets.

- To explore the environment of Jupiter.

When the potential of the spacecraft to explore beyond Jupiter became clear, the objectives were extended:

- If the first spacecraft to fly by Jupiter attained its scientific objectives, the second would be targeted to fly by Jupiter in such a way that the spacecraft would enter a trajectory that would enable it to reach Saturn.

- The second spacecraft would then explore the Saturnian environment.

Ames Research Center was chosen for the mission because of its experience with earlier spin-stabilized spacecraft that are still exploring our inner Solar System.

The new Pioneer was required to utilize proven spacecraft modules of Pioneers 6 through 9 — it had to be a small, lightweight, magnetically clean, interplanetary spacecraft. To propel the 250-kg (550-lb) spacecraft to the tremendously high velocity needed to enter a transfer trajectory to Jupiter, the Atlas-Centaur launch vehicle (Figure 2-1) was equipped with an additional solid-propellant stage.

A series of planning meetings was held in the late 1960's. By early 1970, all scientific experiments had been selected:

- Magnetic fields and plasma in interplanetary space and planetary magnetic fields and trapped radiation in the magnetospheres of the planets were to be measured.

- Polarimetric measurements and images of Jupiter, possibly Saturn, and of several satellites were to be taken.

- Compositions of charged particle beams in space were to be determined.

- Cosmic rays were to be recorded.

- Planets were to be observed at ultraviolet and infrared wavelengths.

- Asteroids and meteoroids were to be detected and the distribution of meteoric dust observed.

- The intensity and distribution of the zodiacal light were to be observed.

- The radio communication signal was to be used to probe the planetary atmospheres during occultation.

- The radio communications signal would be used to learn about the planetary masses from analysis of Doppler residuals.

Principal investigators were selected for all experiments, and contracts were awarded to build the instruments and conduct the experiments. (Experiments are more fully described in chapter 4.)

Mission Overview

The two spacecraft for this mission were identical. Pioneer 10, the first, blazed the trail. If the asteroid belt or the Jovian magnetosphere had proved hazardous to Pioneer 10, Pioneer 11 would have been the backup spacecraft. Initially, Pioneer 11 was launched and targeted to follow the path of Pioneer 10. However, the capability existed and it was therefore planned that Pioneer 11 be retargeted as necessary on its way to Jupiter, based on the results from Pioneer 10's encounter with Jupiter. Pioneer 11 was retargeted to encounter

Figure 2-1. Missions to the giant planets required that the spacecraft reach the highest launch velocity yet achieved by any man-made object, over 51,500 km/hr (32,000 mph). An Atlas-Centaur launch vehicle was used, equipped with a third upper stage.

Figure 2-2. Each Pioneer spacecraft was designed for high reliability using space-proven components. For the mission to the giant planets, TRW Systems Group, Redondo Beach, California, designed and fabricated the two spacecraft.

Jupiter in a way that provided it with the capability of reaching Saturn.

The launch vehicle boosted each spacecraft in direct ascent, that is, with no parking orbit, to begin the flight to Jupiter at about 51,500 km/hr (32,000 mph). A trip of just under 600 days was the shortest time to Jupiter within the capabilities of the launch vehicle, and a trip of 748 days was the longest.

Several in-flight maneuvers were to be made during the Pioneer 10 mission to target the spacecraft so that it would arrive at Jupiter at a time and position best suited to observe the planet and several of its large satellites. For Pioneer 11, the in-flight

maneuvers were planned to preserve the option of continuing the mission to Saturn.

Pioneers 10 and 11 were designed to be compatible with the launch vehicle, and their communications systems were designed to be compatible with the Deep Space Network. Each Pioneer spacecraft had to provide a thermally controlled environment for its scientific instruments. The spacecraft were also designed to operate reliably in space for many years (Figure 2-2). Each carried a data system to sample the scientific instruments and to transmit scientific and engineering information to Earth about the "health" of the spacecraft and its instruments. The spacecraft also had to be capable of

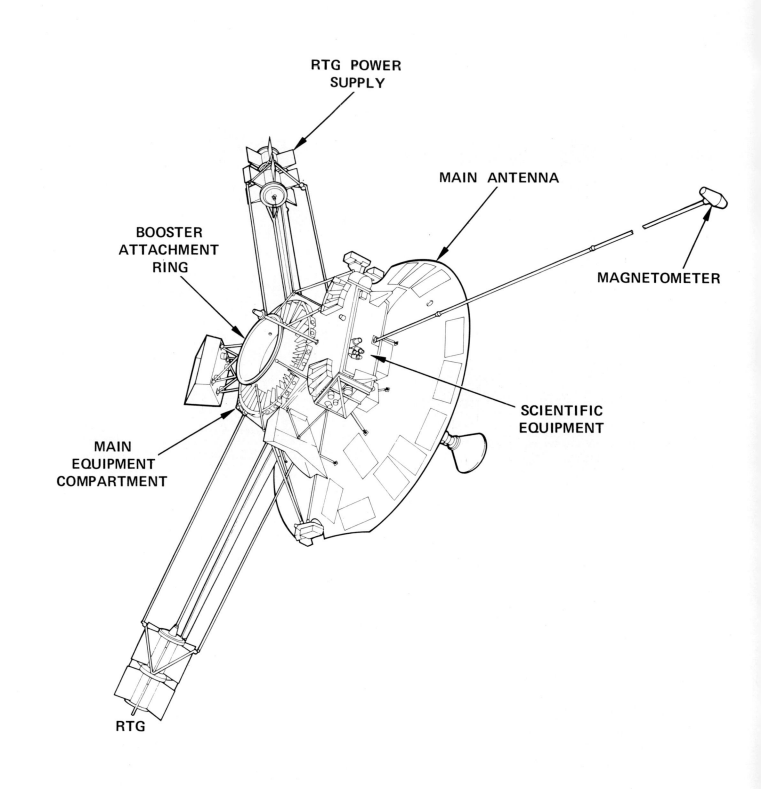

RTG POWER
SUPPLY

MAIN ANTENNA

MAGNETOMETER

BOOSTER
ATTACHMENT
RING

SCIENTIFIC
EQUIPMENT

MAIN
EQUIPMENT
COMPARTMENT

RTG

Figure 2-3. Each spacecraft, spin-stabilized in flight, carried various
scientific instruments and a large dish-shaped antenna that would
allow communications over great distances.

30

being commanded from Earth to perform their missions and to change the operating modes of onboard equipment (Figure 2-3).

Each Pioneer's curved path to Jupiter was about 1000 million kilometers (620 million miles) long, covering about 160° azimuthally around the Sun as the spacecraft traveled between the orbits of Earth and Jupiter. During each Pioneer's flight to Jupiter, Earth traveled almost twice around the Sun, while Jupiter moved only about 1/6 of its solar orbit.

There were options available in selecting the path to Jupiter. Certain arrival dates were unsuitable because the sensors on the spacecraft would have been unable to perform the desired scientific experiments. Other arrival dates were unsuitable because they would have clashed with the arrival of another spacecraft, Mariner 10, at Venus or Mercury and would have caused conflict in the use of the large 64-m (210-ft) antennas of the Deep Space Network.

Pioneer 10 could have been launched from February 25 to March 20, 1972, to arrive at Jupiter some time between mid-October 1973 and late July 1974. The arrival of Pioneer had to be timed so that Jupiter and the spacecraft would not appear too close to the Sun as observed from Earth. About 300-325 days and 700-725 days after launch, the motions of Earth and the spacecraft put them on opposite sides of the Sun. Thus it was impractical for Pioneer 10 to arrive at Jupiter more than 700 days after launch. During the earlier passage of the spacecraft behind the Sun, just over 300 days after launch while the spacecraft was en route to Jupiter, communications with the spacecraft were interrupted, but not at a critical period of the mission. Similar options applied to Pioneer 11 for its launching 1 year later.

There were critical targeting options at Jupiter: how close should the spacecraft be allowed to approach the planet, how much should the trajectory be inclined to Jupiter's equatorial plane, and at what point should the closest approach be relative to Jupiter's equatorial plane?

An early decision was made that the encounter trajectory of Pioneer 10 (Figure 2-4) should be one

to provide the maximum information about the radiation environment of Jupiter to the smallest feasible radial distance, even if, by the spacecraft following such a trajectory, its systems were damaged by radiation and the mission ended at Jupiter. Hence, images of Jupiter could only be assured before closest approach. An approach trajectory was selected so as to view a well-illuminated planet before encounter and a partially illuminated crescent planet after the encounter. At first it seemed desirable that occultation of the spacecraft by Jupiter should be avoided, but an occultation was selected because the information it could provide about the Jovian atmosphere could not be obtained any other way.

Because Jupiter has radiation belts trapped within its magnetic field, scientists wanted to know

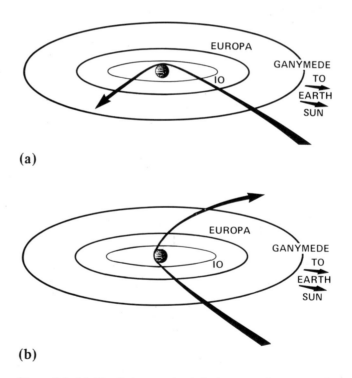

(a)

(b)

Figure 2-4. (a) The first encounter trajectory was chosen to probe the radiation belts of Jupiter and to ensure that the spacecraft would have opportunities to obtain images of the terminator, the Great Red Spot, and several satellites, and would be occulted by Io as seen from Earth. (b) The second encounter trajectory was chosen to allow the spacecraft to continue to Saturn after its encounter with Jupiter, and to provide options to pass inside or outside the rings of Saturn and to approach Titan, Saturn's largest satellite.

31

how close a spacecraft could safely approach Jupiter to take advantage of the gravity slingshot effect without damage to the spacecraft's electronic and optical equipment. Obtaining an answer to this question was one of the primary objectives of the first mission to Jupiter.

In July 1971, scientists at a workshop held at the Jet Propulsion Laboratory defined the Jovian environment in terms of the best available information. With slight modifications, this environment was accepted as the design environment for the Pioneer spacecraft and its scientific instruments. No one could be sure that this environment, although based on the very best observations from Earth, was the actual environment of Jupiter — it was a task of the Pioneer mission to determine the true Jovian environment. The environment of Saturn was considered less hazardous than Jupiter's, at least from the standpoint of radiation damage.

A tradeoff for the Pioneer mission was that, although a closer approach to Jupiter would increase the intensity of radiation encountered, the spacecraft would fly by Jupiter more quickly and would therefore be exposed to radiation for less time. These two factors, which determine the integrated or total radiation dosage, were carefully considered before the final flyby path was selected.

Generally, the mission was designed so that Pioneer 10 would fly by Jupiter at three times the radius of the planet (referred to as $3R_J$), that is, twice the Jovian radius above the cloudtops. Although it was possible to target Pioneer 10 at a closer approach, this trajectory was selected because, from available information, the spacecraft might have been seriously damaged by radiation had it been sent closer to the planet. When the mission was being planned, the ephemeris of Jupiter was uncertain — to about 2000 km (1250 miles) — but, navigationally, the spacecraft could have been sent to within 3/8 Jupiter radii above the cloudtops. Navigation to Jupiter is simplified somewhat because the intense gravitational pull of the planet provides a focusing effect. Such gravity focusing would reduce an aiming error of 1600 km (1000 miles) to an encounter error of 480 km (300 miles)

After the approach was chosen the electronic equipment and science sensors were designed to survive the level of radiation expected while Pioneer 10 passed through the radiation belts.

The amount of propellant carried on Pioneer 10 permitted the time of arrival at Jupiter to be changed by several days, thereby allowing mission planners to direct the spacecraft to fly close enough to a Jovian satellite to obtain a spin-scan image of it or to be occulted by a satellite.

Hazards of the Mission

In 1800, Johann Elert Bode called a meeting of astronomers at the Schröter Observatory in Lilienthal, Germany. He asked them to search for a planet believed to be orbiting between Mars and Jupiter. On January 1, 1801, Giuseppe Piazzi, director of the Observatory of Palermo, Italy, discovered a small planetary object, 1022 km (635 miles) in diameter, which he named Ceres. But soon after it was discovered, Ceres, moving along its orbit, was lost in the glare of the Sun.

The great mathematician, Friedrich Gauss, developed a theory for determining the orbits of planetary bodies based on a minimum number of observations. He calculated the orbit of Ceres and showed where it would emerge from the solar glare. While observing Ceres again in 1802, Heinrich Olbers discovered a second planetary body smaller than Ceres, measuring only 560 km (348 miles) across, which he named Pallas. Other surprising discoveries were made by Karl Ludwig Harding in 1804, Juno, 226 km (141 miles) in diameter; and by Olbers in 1807, Vesta, 504 km (313 miles) in diameter — the brightest of these minor planets. These small planetary bodies (Figure 2-5), called "asteroids" by William Herschel, were regarded as fragments of a trans-Martian planet.

At least 8 other asteroids larger than Juno are known today, but they were not discovered until

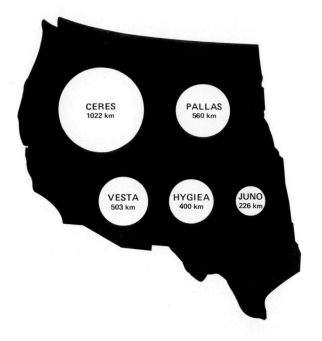

Figure 2-5. Asteroids, or minor planets, are relatively small bodies on a planetary scale. Here five of the largest asteroids are shown relative to a map of the western United States.

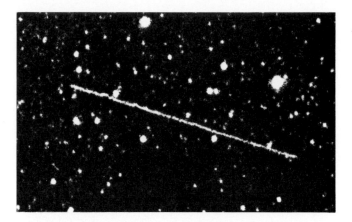

Figure 2-6. Asteroids are shown in thousands by photographs that reveal them in a time exposure as streaks among the "fixed" stars. The peculiar white streak on this photograph is an Apollo asteroid (taken by Eleanor Helin, of the California Institute of Technology, with the 18-inch Schmidt telescope at Palomar, in July 1973). It was traveling 97,000 km/hr (60,000 mph) in relation to Earth, 13.7 million kilometers (8.5 million miles) away from Earth. The exposure time was about 2 hr. It was calculated that the asteroid is 6.5 to 7 km (4 to 4.5 miles) in diameter. (*Photograph: Hale Observatories*)

almost 50 years after the discovery of the first four. The year 1845 marked the beginning of discoveries of great numbers of minor planets — today 40,000 to 100,000 such bodies are postulated. Many have been discovered photographically (Figure 2-6). Most are found between the orbits of Mars and Jupiter, while others stray closer to or farther from the Sun in more elliptical orbits. Several have approached Earth; one at least approaches the orbit of Mercury and another, that of Saturn (Figure 2-7).

The orbits of the larger asteroids have been cataloged, but many of the asteroids move in unknown orbits. Although the risk of a spacecraft colliding with a charted asteroid was negligible, there was no way to estimate how many particles the size of a grain of sand might be present in the asteroid belt to collide with the spacecraft and seriously damage it.

At the beginning of the Pioneer program, scientists did not know whether the first Pioneer would survive passage through the asteroid belt on its way to Jupiter. But before other missions to the outer planets could be considered, at least one spacecraft

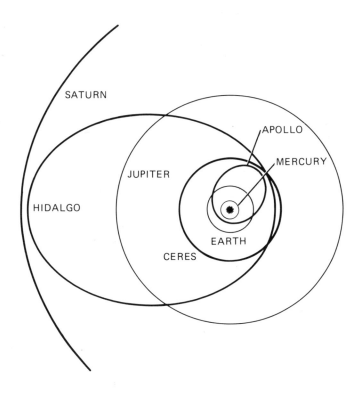

Figure 2-7. While asteroids such as Ceres are generally concentrated between the orbits of Mars and Jupiter, some stray to the orbit of Mercury (e.g., Apollo) and to the orbit of Saturn (e.g., Hidalgo). Several have passed relatively near Earth.

had to penetrate this region and survive the passage.

Another problem had to be faced by the Pioneer mission planners: how to supply electrical power to the spacecraft at such great distances from the Sun. Solar cells were considered during early planning of the mission because radioisotope power generators had not then been tested over the long lifetimes required for such a mission and the radiation from them would have a mildly deleterious effect on certain scientific instruments. However, since sunlight at Jupiter carries only 1/27 the energy it does at Earth, very large arrays of solar cells would be required. Also, damage to solar cells by the Jovian radiation belts could be serious. Therefore, radioisotope thermoelectric generators were judged to be a better engineering choice and were adopted for the Pioneer spacecraft.

Because of the tremendous speed required to carry the spacecraft from Earth to Jupiter, the pay-load weight was severely restricted — complicated onboard computing systems would be much too heavy. The Pioneer spacecraft had to be virtually "flown from the ground," despite the long delays in communicating over the vast distances to Jupiter, Saturn, and beyond.

The long timespan of the mission and the weight limitations imposed on the spacecraft also required that all spacecraft components be reliable to an unprecedented degree. Such a level of reliability was achieved by making the spacecraft as simple as possible, leaving as much as possible of the complexity on the ground. Such vital items as transmitters and receivers were duplicated, and only systems and components that had been flight-proven on other spacecraft were used. Electronic components were "burned in" before they were assembled on the spacecraft so that components likely to fail were eliminated before the flight. The success of the mission depended heavily on an

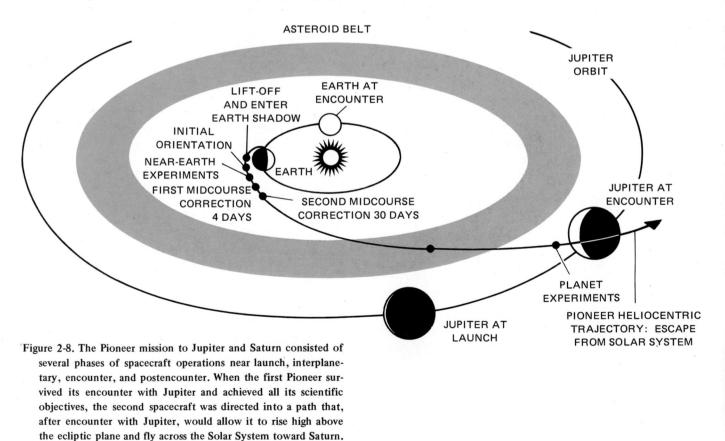

Figure 2-8. The Pioneer mission to Jupiter and Saturn consisted of several phases of spacecraft operations near launch, interplanetary, encounter, and postencounter. When the first Pioneer survived its encounter with Jupiter and achieved all its scientific objectives, the second spacecraft was directed into a path that, after encounter with Jupiter, would allow it to rise high above the ecliptic plane and fly across the Solar System toward Saturn. Both spacecraft reached sufficiently high velocities from their planetary encounters to fly completely out of the Solar System.

34

advanced command, control, and communications system to link Earth-based computers and human controllers to the spacecraft.

Command, Control, and Communications

Mission Phases — Five distinct phases of command and control characterized the Pioneer mission to Jupiter, Saturn, and beyond (Figure 2-8). Each phase required different approaches and techniques. Two phases — Earth launch and planetary encounter — were critical from the standpoint of controllers having to quickly make corrections if any problems arose. For the other three interplanetary phases — travel from Earth to Jupiter, from Jupiter to Saturn, and beyond planetary encounters — time was not so critical.

During prelaunch and launch at John F. Kennedy Space Center, launch teams from Ames Research Center and Lewis Research Center controlled the spacecraft and launch vehicle, respectively. Shortly after the spacecraft separated from the launch vehicle and entered the transfer orbit to Jupiter, control of the spacecraft was transferred to the Ames flight operations team at the Jet Propulsion Laboratory (Figure 2-9). Simultaneously, control of the scientific instruments within the spacecraft was transferred to the Pioneer Mission Operations Center (PMOC) at Ames Research Center (Figure 2-10). This period of split control between engineering at the Jet Propulsion Laboratory and science at the Pioneer Mission Operations Center was arranged to take advantage of the multiple consoles and backup computers at the Jet Propulsion Laboratory for the critical first days of Pioneer's epoch-making flights to the outer Solar System. Engineer specialists were thereby able to simultaneously monitor all subsystems, such as telemetry, power, thermal, attitude control, data handling, and command.

As Pioneer 10 moved away from Earth, passing the orbit of the Moon less than 11 hr after liftoff (compared with 3 days for the Apollo spacecraft to reach the Moon), the monitoring activities changed from assessing the "health" of the spacecraft and

Figure 2-9. From immediately after liftoff until the Pioneer spacecraft had settled down and had been thoroughly checked out, the major facilities of the Space Flight Operations Facility (SFOF) at the Jet Propulsion Laboratory, Pasadena, California, were used.

Figure 2-10. Afterward, the Pioneer Mission Operations Center at NASA's Ames Research Center assumed control, with continued support from the SFOF.

its scientific instruments to readying Pioneer for its momentous voyage to Jupiter and beyond.

Several days after liftoff and after midcourse maneuvers, with all equipment and scientific instruments performing well, the mission crews left the Jet Propulsion Laboratory and John F. Kennedy Space Center and returned to Ames Research Center — now the control center for the entire mission.

As the spacecraft settled into the interplanetary mode, the task for those monitoring the Pioneer became one of watching and waiting, and becoming familiar with the unavoidable and increasing delays for signals to travel to the spacecraft and from the spacecraft to Earth. During the interplanetary "cruise" phase, a team of five to seven scientists with supporting personnel at the Pioneer Mission Operations Center monitored the spacecraft. During this phase, and in the subsequent flight of Pioneer 11 from Jupiter to Saturn and beyond the planetary encounters for both spacecraft, all data received from the spacecraft were continually monitored by computers and by personnel (Figure 2-11) to alert ground control to any malfunction at the earliest possible moment — an important consideration if corrective action were required. A computer at Ames Research Center monitored telemetry signals on critical aspects of both spacecraft and their payloads. If a voltage or temperature were to rise or fall too much, or if the status of an instrument were to change without being commanded to do so, the computer sounded an alarm and printed out a message. Day or night, whenever the situation required it, the duty operator immediately notified the cognizant engineer or scientist, who then resolved the problem. The mission controllers were given specific procedures to cover any emergency and they were advised where to obtain specialized technical help if it were needed.

During the long voyage through interplanetary space, data from each scientific instrument were sampled periodically to assess how well the instrument was functioning, in both a scientific as well as an engineering sense. Controllers, engineers, and

Figure 2-11. Duty operators kept constant vigil during the many years of flight, observing the performance of the spacecraft and their scientific instruments.

scientists watched for any need to change bias voltages, to adjust the range or sensitivity of instruments, or to switch modes of operations.

When each Pioneer reached the edge of the Jovian system, quick action again became the mode of operation — but action quite different from that during the Earth launch phase. Since the Pioneer spacecraft were then over 800 million kilometers (500 million miles) from Earth, radio signals took 92 min for the round trip to the spacecraft and back. When Pioneer 11 reached Saturn, the round-trip time was 173 min. All commands to the spacecraft had to be planned well in advance because of the delay in communication.

The most critical piece of equipment in this respect was the imaging photopolarimeter (IPP) (described in detail in Appendix 1). It required long sequences of commands during the planetary encounters to best utilize the time when the spacecraft passed by the planets and their satellites. A sequence of contingency commands was designed to reconfigure the Pioneer spacecraft and their instruments should spurious commands be gener-

36

Figure 2-12. Communications with the two Pioneer spacecraft at unprecedented distances relied on the large antennas of the Deep Space Network, such as this one at Goldstone in the Mojave Desert of California.

ated by the accumulation of electrical charges or by intense radiation during close approach to Jupiter.

The fourth phase of command and control, which applied to Pioneer 11 during its voyage from Jupiter to Saturn, was a quiet period as the spacecraft flew high across the Solar System above the plane of the ecliptic. During this period, project personnel were busy planning how the spacecraft should penetrate Saturn's ring plane and were executing maneuvers of the spacecraft to allow a close look at Titan, Saturn's largest satellite, while ensuring an encounter with Saturn on the far side of the Sun from Earth early enough to prevent too much interference from the Sun itself.

The Pioneers entered the final phase of command and control as they passed beyond planetary encounter. As the Pioneers continue to move farther away, their received signals become fainter and fainter and take longer and longer to reach Earth. Ultimately, somewhere beyond the orbit of Neptune, contact with these tiny emissaries from Earth will be lost as both spacecraft continue to move out of our Solar System and into interstellar space.

Tracking and Data Acquisition Support — The NASA Communications Network operated by Goddard Space Flight Center provided worldwide ground communications circuits and facilities to link Earth terminals that receive signals from the spacecraft with control centers on the west coast of the United States.

Extending around the world, the Deep Space Network (operated for NASA by the Jet Propul-

37

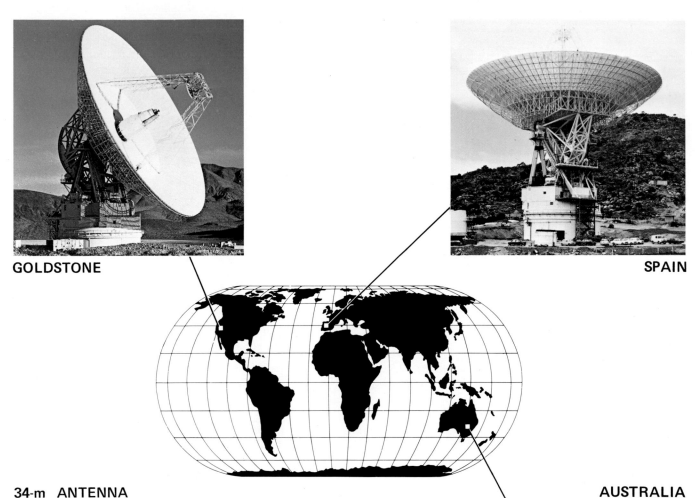

GOLDSTONE

SPAIN

34-m ANTENNA

AUSTRALIA

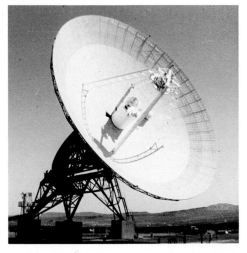

Figure 2-13. A worldwide network of antennas and communications ensured that, as Earth turned on its axis, communication was maintained with the distant spacecraft through the Deep Space Network. Encounter of Pioneer 11 with Saturn was timed so that two of the large antennas received the data simultaneously from the spacecraft during this critical period.

38

sion Laboratory) provided deep space tracking, telemetry data acquisition, and commanding capabilities through the 26-m (85-ft) and 64-m (210-ft) diameter antennas (Figure 2-12) at Goldstone, California, and in Spain, South Africa (until July 1, 1974), and Australia. During the later phases of the mission, some of the smaller antennas were enlarged to 34-m (112-ft) diameter dishes; then each of the three stations had one of each size of antenna. As Earth turned on its axis, the controllers maintained contact with the spacecraft using stations in Goldstone, Australia, Spain, or, for part of the Pioneer 10 mission, South Africa, operating in turn each day. As each Pioneer spacecraft began to set at one station, the next station acquired it (Figure 2-13), with periods of overlapping coverage. The encounter with Saturn was timed so that signals from Pioneer were received at both the Madrid and Goldstone stations during the most critical period of the encounter to reduce the chance that vital data might be lost.

Telecommunications — Communications over the vast distances to Jupiter and Saturn and beyond presented problems never before encountered in our space program. Transmitters and antennas onboard the spacecraft had to be designed to conserve power and to be as lightweight as possible. Communications with Earth relied heavily on the extremely sensitive 64-m (210-ft) antennas of the Deep Space Network and their advanced receiving systems. During the long interplanetary cruises, the spacecraft used the 26-m (85-ft) diameter antennas when the larger antennas were required for other space missions, but with the smaller antennas, information had to be transferred from the spacecraft to Earth at a lower rate.

When used to transmit commands to the spacecraft, the 64-m (210-ft) antennas were so precise in directing their radio beams and provided such a high radiated power (up to 400,000 W at Goldstone) that these commands could be received by the spacecraft at greater distances (to several hundred times the distance between Earth and the Sun) than those at which messages from the space-craft could be received at Earth (perhaps 40 times the distance between Earth and the Sun).

The spacecraft carried three antennas to receive and to send signals — low gain (omnidirectional), medium gain, and high gain (beamed). It also carried two redundant receivers (for commands from Earth) and two redundant transmitters. The redundancy provided a back-up in the event of a failure during the journeys of the two Pioneers which lasted more than two decades.

The amount of energy received at Earth from the spacecraft via radio links from Jupiter's distance is incredibly small: from the distance of Saturn the amount is smaller still by more than two-thirds. A 26-m (85-ft) diameter antenna collecting this energy from the distance of Jupiter would require 17 million years to gather enough energy to light a 7.5-W nightlamp for a mere one-thousandth of a second. From Saturn it would require nearly 56 million years. Only the sophisticated data coding and signal modulation techniques, coupled with the large antennas and the advanced, ultra-cold receiving devices attached to them made it possible to receive and record these faint signals from the two Pioneer spacecraft. All the pictures of Jupiter and Saturn reproduced in this volume, all the information from space to beyond the orbit of Uranus, all the information about the environment of the two planets, all the engineering data about the spacecraft and their many scientific instruments, all the tracking of the spacecraft to 2 billion miles from Earth derived from these incredibly weak radio signals. The communications system of the Pioneer spacecraft and the Deep Space Network are truly great technological achievements.

The rate at which information is passed over a radio link is expressed in bits/second, where a bit is defined as a unit of information analogous to the dots and dashes of the Morse code. Onboard each spacecraft, a data-handling system converted science and engineering information into an organized stream of data bits for transmission to Earth. Just as a streetlamp shining at night appears fainter and fainter with increasing distance, radio signals

39

from a spacecraft also become fainter with distance. Also, natural background radio signals create interference, and even the components of the electronic apparatus generate radio noise by the movement of electrons within them. As signals become fainter with distance they tend to be drowned out by this background of noise. Therefore, sophisticated techniques and equipment had to be developed to receive information from these extreme distances.

As the Pioneer spacecraft moved farther into our Solar System, their signals became weaker and weaker at Earth. The telemetry system adjusted to these weaker signals by commanding a change in the rate at which information was transmitted to Earth. Power per unit of information depends on the rate at which the information is sent — the bit rate. To extract information from a radio signal, the energy level of the signal must exceed the energy of the background noise. As the spacecraft moved farther and farther away, the bit rate was reduced so that less information was sent per second. Each bit of information lasted longer and thereby possessed more energy, so that it could be detected above the radio noise.

By reducing the bit rate, controllers compensated for the fainter signals received from the Pioneer spacecraft. When each spacecraft was on its way to Jupiter, the communication system could pass a maximum of 2048 bits of information to Earth every second, using the 26-m (85-ft) antennas. But at Jupiter, because of the increased distance, the maximum rate was only 1024 bits/sec, using the 64-m (210-ft) antennas. Near Saturn the maximum rate was maintained at 1024 bits/sec with the larger antennas because their sensitivity had been improved during the five years the Pioneer spacecraft took to travel from Jupiter to Saturn. Because of the increased sensitivity of the Deep Space Network, communication between Earth and the two Pioneers far exceeded original expectations. At Saturn encounter, however, proximity to superior conjunction with the Sun forced a reduction in the transmitting rate from 1024 to 512 bits/sec for part of each station's view period.

A digital telemetry unit onboard each spacecraft prepared the data for transmission in one of 13 data formats at one of 8 bit rates from 16 to 2,048 bits/sec. An onboard data storage unit was able to store 49,152 data bits for later transmission to Earth. This storage capability allowed data to be gathered by the spacecraft during important parts of the mission faster than the data could be sent to Earth. It also stored data when the data could not be transmitted at all, for example, when the spacecraft was passing behind Jupiter or Saturn. The data were later transmitted in response to ground command.

Command and Control — At Pioneer Mission Operations Control, 222 different commands were used to operate the Pioneer spacecraft. The command system consisted of two command decoders and a command distribution unit within each spacecraft. Commands were transmitted from Earth at 1 bit/sec. Since each command message consisted of 22 bits, a command required 22 sec to transmit.

Each spacecraft also carried a small command memory that could store five commands. When a series of up to five commands had to be executed in less time than was needed to transmit them from Earth at the command rate, that is, 22 sec for each command, this memory was used. The command memory with time delay was also used to command the spacecraft when it was behind Jupiter and Saturn and out of touch with Earth.

A command distribution unit in each spacecraft routed the commands within the spacecraft: 73 commands to operate experiments and 149 to control subsystems of the spacecraft. Science commands, for example, included those to calibrate instruments, change modes, move the photopolarimeter telescope, and change instrument data types. Spacecraft commands included firing the rocket thrusters and changing from one component to another redundant component, selecting different antennas, and changing the modes of the data-handling subsystems.

Any command not properly verified by the decoder in the spacecraft was not acted on by the command distribution unit. Thus, precautions were taken against the spacecraft accepting wrong commands. Commands were also verified on Earth by a computer and by controllers before the commands were transmitted. A Pioneer Encounter Planning Team, headed by the Project Science Chief, considered many possible contingencies that might arise during the weeks when each Pioneer spacecraft was passing through the systems of the giant planets, and they developed command sequences to meet such contingencies.

The decision early in the planning stages to "fly" the Pioneer spacecraft by command required constant scrutiny and diligence on the part of the controllers well in advance of any commanded events taking place on the spacecraft. Indeed, two years of careful planning preceded the first encounter with Jupiter. All commands (e.g., more than 16,000 total for the first Pioneer) were meticulously sequenced, checked, and stored in a ground-based computer in 8-hr-long files suitable for transmission during the time that a ground station would be in contact with the distant spacecraft. Most of these commands were transmitted to the spacecraft in a four-week period. Personnel at the Pioneer Mission Operations Center, the Ground Data System, and the Deep Space Network met all the demands of the mission — sending commands on time, with the high level of reliability the mission demanded. This performance was repeated for the encounter of the second Pioneer with Jupiter and, five years later, with Saturn.

3
The Pioneer Spacecraft

The Pioneer spacecraft were designed to fit within the 3-m (10-ft) shroud of the Atlas-Centaur launch vehicle. Each spacecraft was stowed with its booms retracted and its antenna dish facing forward (i.e., upward on the launch pad). Basically, the two spacecraft had to be extremely reliable and lightweight; their communications systems had to transmit information over extreme distances; and each had nonsolar heat sources to supply electrical power.

Each Pioneer spacecraft comprised several distinct subsystems: a general structure, an attitude control and propulsion system, a communications system, thermal control system, electrical power system, navigation system, and most important to the scientific mission, a payload of 11 sophisticated instruments for scientific observations and measurements (Figure 3-1).

ATTITUDE CONTROL & PROPULSION

GENERAL STRUCTURE

Figure 3-1. A Pioneer outer planet spacecraft and its major subsystems.

44

VIGATION

THERMAL CONTROL

SCIENCE EXPERIMENTS

ECTRICAL POWER

COMMUNICATIONS

To communicate over the great distances from the outer Solar System, the dish-shaped antennas of the spacecraft had to be pointed toward Earth. The simplest and least expensive way to do this was to spin-stabilize each spacecraft, keeping its spin axis pointing toward Earth (Figure 3-2).

General Structure

From its cone-shaped, medium-gain antenna to the adapter ring that fastened the spacecraft to stage three of its launch vehicle, each spacecraft was 2.9 m (9.5 ft) long. The structure of each spacecraft centered around a 36-cm (14-in.) deep, flat, equipment compartment, the top and bottom of which consisted of regular hexagons with sides 71 cm (28 in.) long. Attached to one side of this hexagon was a smaller "squashed" hexagon compartment that carried most of the instruments for the scientific experiments.

A 2.74-m (9-ft) diameter, 46-cm (18-in.) deep, parabolic, dish-shaped, high-gain antenna of aluminum honeycomb sandwich material was attached to the front of the equipment compartment. Its feed was topped with a medium-gain antenna mounted on three struts which projected about 1.2 m (4 ft) forward. A low-gain, omni-directional antenna extended about 0.76 m (2.5 ft) behind the equipment compartment mounted below the dish of the high-gain antenna. Two three-rod trusses, 120° apart, projected from two sides of the equipment compartment. At their ends, radioisotope thermoelectric generators were held about 3 m (10 ft) from the center of the spacecraft. A third single-rod boom, 120° from the two trusses, projected from the experiment compartment to position a magnetometer sensor about 6.6 m (21.5 ft) from the center of the spacecraft. All three appendages were extended after launch.

Attitude Control and Propulsion

A starlight sensor on each spacecraft provided a reference on the bright southern star Canopus,

Figure 3-2. Each Pioneer spacecraft was stabilized by rotation, as shown in this photograph of a spacecraft under spin test.

and two sunlight sensors provided a reference to the Sun. Attitude was calculated from the reference directions to Earth and the Sun, with the known direction to Canopus provided as backup. Before Pioneer 11 was launched, the gain and threshold settings of its starlight sensor were modified to improve performance on the basis of experience gained during the first few months of Pioneer 10's flight.

Three pairs of rocket thrusters located near the rim of the antenna dish (Figure 3-3) were used to direct the spin axis of each spacecraft, to keep it spinning at the desired rate of 4.8 rpm, and to change the velocity of the spacecraft for in-flight maneuvers. The system's six thrusters could be commanded to fire steadily or in pulses. Each thruster developed its propulsive jet from the

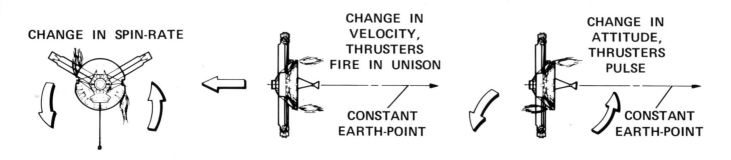

CHANGE IN SPIN-RATE

CHANGE IN VELOCITY, THRUSTERS FIRE IN UNISON

CONSTANT EARTH-POINT

CHANGE IN ATTITUDE, THRUSTERS PULSE

CONSTANT EARTH-POINT

Figure 3-3. Thrusters were used to control the spin of the spacecraft, its attitude, and its velocity.

decomposition of liquid hydrazine by a catalyst in a small rocket thrust chamber to which the nozzles of the thruster were attached.

Attitude and velocity were changed by two thruster pairs mounted on opposite sides of the rim of the antenna dish. One thruster of each pair pointed forward, the other aft. To change attitude, the spin axis of the spacecraft was precessed in the desired direction by firing two thrusters, one on each side of the antenna dish. One thruster was fired forward, one aft, in brief pulses of thrust at a precisely timed position in the cycle of rotation of the spacecraft. Each thrust pulse, timed to the rotation, precessed the spin axis a few tenths of a degree until the desired attitude was reached.

To change velocity, the spin axis was first precessed until it pointed in the direction along which the correcting velocity had to be applied. Then two thrusters, one on each side of the antenna dish, were fired continuously, both in the same direction (i.e., forward or aft, to apply the correcting velocity in the desired direction). For example, if the spacecraft's spin axis were aligned to its flightpath, the correcting velocity would be applied forward to increase its velocity along its flightpath and aft to decrease it.

To adjust the spin rate of the spacecraft, two more pairs of thrusters, also set along the rim of the antenna dish, were used. These thrusters were aligned tangentially to the antenna rim, one pointing against the direction of spin and the other pointing with it. Thus, to reduce spin rate, two

thrusters were fired against the direction of spin. To increase spin rate, they were fired with the spin direction.

Communications

Each Pioneer spacecraft, in its journey to explore the giant outer planets, carried two identical receivers. The omnidirectional and medium-gain antennas operated together and were connected to one receiver, while the high-gain antenna was connected to the other. The receivers did not operate at the same time, but were interchanged by command or, if there was a period of inactivity, they were switched automatically. Thus, if a receiver had failed during the mission, the other would have automatically taken over.

Two radio transmitters, coupled to two traveling-wave-tube power amplifiers, each produced 8 W of transmitted power at S-band. The communications frequency uplink from Earth to the spacecraft was at 2110 MHz, the downlink to Earth, at 2292 MHz. The turnaround ratio, downlink to uplink, was precisely controlled to be compatible with the Deep Space Network.

The data system of each spacecraft converted scientific and engineering information into a specially coded stream of data bits for transmission by radio to Earth. A convolutional encoder arranged the data in a form that allowed most errors to be detected and corrected by ground computer at the receiving site of the Deep Space

Network. There were 11 data formats divided into scientific and engineering data groups. Some science formats were optimized for interplanetary data, others for the encounters with Jupiter and Saturn. Engineering data formats specialized in data handling, electrical, communications, orientation, and propulsion data. All formats were selected by command from Earth.

Thermal Control

Temperature was held between $-23°$ and $38°$ C ($-10°$ and $100°$ F) inside the scientific instrument compartment, and at various other levels elsewhere so that the scientific equipment onboard the spacecraft operated satisfactorily.

The system of temperature control was designed to adapt to the gradual decrease in solar heating as the spacecraft moved away from the Sun, and to those frigid periods when the spacecraft passed through Earth's shadow soon after launch and when it passed through Jupiter's or Saturn's shadow during planetary encounters. The temperature control system also controlled the effects of heat from the third-stage engine, atmospheric friction during launch, spacecraft thermoelectric power generators, and from other equipment.

Equipment compartments were insulated by multilayered blankets of aluminized plastic. Temperature-responsive louvers at the bottom of the equipment compartment, opened by temperature-sensitive bimetallic springs, controlled the amount of excess heat allowed to escape. Other equipment was individually thermally insulated and was warmed as required by electric heaters and twelve 1-W radioisotope heaters fueled with plutonium-238.

Electrical Power

Nuclear-fueled electric power for the Pioneer spacecraft was derived from SNAP-19-type radioisotope thermoelectric generators (RTGs), developed by the Atomic Energy Commission, similar to those that had been used successfully to power

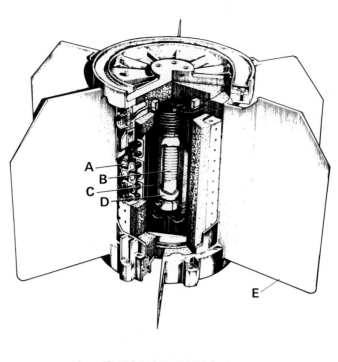

A   **THERMOELECTRICS**
B   **FUEL CAPSULE**
C   **REENTRY HEAT SHIELD**
D   **FUEL DISCS**
E   **HEAT RADIATING FINS**

Figure 3-4. Four radioisotope thermoelectric generators (RTGs) provided electrical power in each Pioneer spacecraft.

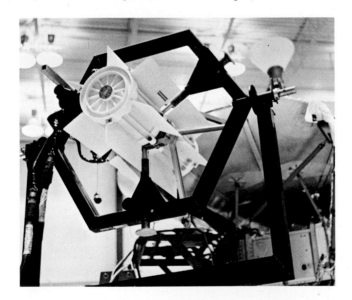

Figure 3-5. Two RTGs were mounted at the end of each of two extended booms. Here the effects on the sensitive scientific instruments of radiation emitted from the nuclear fuel of the RTGs were much reduced.

the Nimbus-3 meteorological satellite. These units converted heat from the radioactive decay of plutonium-238 into electricity (Figure 3-4).

The RTGs (Figure 3-5) were located on the opposite side of the spacecraft from the scientific instruments to reduce the effects of neutron radiation. Mounted in pairs on the end of each three-rod truss, these four RTGs developed about 155 W of electrical power for each spacecraft at launch. By the time each spacecraft reached Jupiter, the power output had decreased to about 140 W. It continued to decrease, but at a slower rate, as Pioneers 10 and 11 proceeded on their long journeys after Jupiter encounter. The depletion of power was not caused by the isotope source itself, but resulted from a deterioration in the junctions of the thermocouples which converted heat into electricity within each unit. The RTGs supplied adequate power for the mission because each spacecraft needed only 100 W to operate all its systems and experiments. The scientific instruments consumed only 25 W. Any excess power from the RTGs not required by the spacecraft was dissipated into space in the form of heat by a shunt resistor radiator. Alternatively, any excess power was used to charge a battery that automatically supplied additional power for short periods when the spacecraft required more than the output of the RTGs.

Navigation

Throughout the mission, the axis of the high-gain antenna was slightly offset from, but parallel to, the spin axis of each spacecraft within close tolerances. Except during the early stages of the flight near Earth and when adjustments were made to realign the spacecraft to make course corrections, the spin axis of each spacecraft always pointed toward Earth, within a tolerance of 1°, to provide best communication.

Analysts used the shift in frequency of the radio signals from the spacecraft together with angle tracking by the antennas of the Deep Space Network to calculate the speed, distance, and

direction of the spacecraft from Earth. The motion of the spacecraft away from Earth caused the frequency of the spacecraft's signals to drop and their wavelength to increase. This effect — known as the Doppler shift — allowed the speed of the spacecraft to be calculated from measurements of the change in frequency of the signal received at Earth. As the spacecraft continued outward, angle tracking became less important. Pioneer's path was calculated by use of celestial mechanics, and the radio data were used to determine just how close the spacecraft was to its calculated path. Residual Doppler data (i.e., the difference between the Doppler shifts expected and those observed) provided information to keep the trajectory updated and to determine the masses of planetary bodies the Pioneers encountered.

The radio beam to Earth was offset 1° from the spin axis of the spacecraft. As a result, when the spin axis was not directed exactly toward Earth, uplink signals received by Pioneer from Earth varied in intensity synchronously with the rotation of the spacecraft. A system on the spacecraft, known as conical scan (CONSCAN) (Figure 3-6), was originally intended to automatically change the attitude of the spacecraft in a direction that would reduce such variations in signal strength,

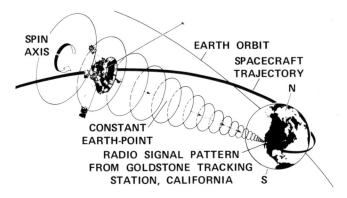

Figure 3-6. An automated system in each spacecraft — CONSCAN — could be used to point the spin axis of Pioneer toward Earth. It relied on a slight offset in the antenna feed axis to produce a wobbling signal when the antenna was not pointing exactly toward Earth. Controllers, directing the spacecraft so that its antenna drifted past the optimum point, conserved thruster propellant. CONSCAN could have automatically pointed the spacecraft's axis, but with a greater expenditure of propellant.

thereby returning the spin axis to align with the direction of Earth to within a threshold of 0.3°. However, flight operations personnel developed and used a direct command technique that allowed them to conserve the gas supply of each spacecraft so that the mission could be extended beyond the encounters with Jupiter and Saturn.

Scientific Payload

The Pioneer spacecraft, as they moved through interplanetary space on their way to Jupiter and Saturn and beyond, were to investigate magnetic fields, cosmic rays (fast-moving parts of atoms from the Sun and from the Galaxy), the solar wind (a flow of charged particles from the Sun) and its relationships with the interplanetary magnetic field and cosmic rays, and any interplanetary dust concentrations they might encounter in the asteroid belt.

At Jupiter and Saturn, Pioneer investigated their planetary systems in four main ways: by measuring particles, fields, and radiation; by spin-scan imaging the planets and some of their satellites; by accurately observing the paths of the spacecraft and measuring the gravitational forces of the planets and their major satellites acting on them; and by observing changes in the frequency of the S-band radio signal before and after occultation to study the structures of their ionospheres and atmospheres.

4
Pioneer Science at New Frontiers

The scientific payloads of Pioneers 10 and 11 for the missions to Jupiter and Saturn were virtually identical. They were designed to gather new knowledge about interplanetary space beyond Mars and about the Jovian and Saturnian systems. Several of the science instruments measured particles, fields, and radiation, while an imaging photopolarimeter provided spin-scan imaging and analysis of scattered light. Additionally, the radio signals from the spacecraft were used to measure the gravitational fields of Jupiter and Saturn and their major satellites and to investigate the atmospheres of the two planets. The Pioneers performed several experiments in interplanetary space between Earth and the target planets and beyond:

- Mapped the magnetic field in interplanetary space.
- Determined how the solar wind changed with distance from the Sun and, during the flight of Pioneer 11 to Saturn, how the solar wind changed high above the plane of the ecliptic.
- Measured solar and galactic cosmic ray particles.

- Studied interactions among the interplanetary magnetic field, the solar wind, and cosmic rays.
- Searched for a transition region of the heliosphere — the region where the influence of the Sun on interplanetary space ends — in two opposite directions.
- Measured the amount of neutral atomic hydrogen in interplanetary space and near Jupiter and Saturn.
- Ascertained the distribution of dust particles in interplanetary space in the outer Solar System.
- Determined the sizes, masses, fluxes, and velocities of small particles in the asteroid belt, thus providing information on the probability of damage by such particles to spacecraft passing through this region.
- Searched for gravitational radiation impinging on the Solar System by means of its effects on the spacecraft's velocity as revealed on the microwave radio link between Earth and the spacecraft.

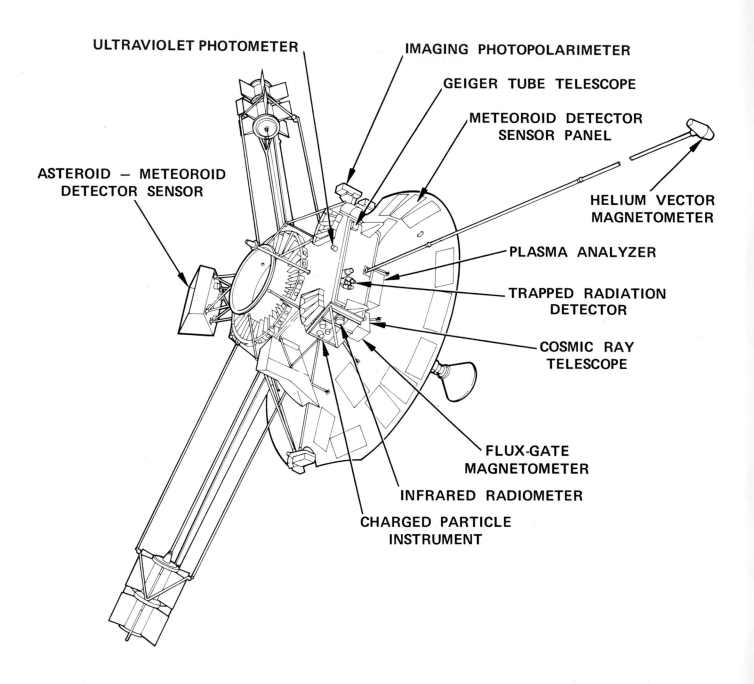

ULTRAVIOLET PHOTOMETER

IMAGING PHOTOPOLARIMETER

GEIGER TUBE TELESCOPE

METEOROID DETECTOR
SENSOR PANEL

ASTEROID — METEOROID
DETECTOR SENSOR

HELIUM VECTOR
MAGNETOMETER

PLASMA ANALYZER

TRAPPED RADIATION
DETECTOR

COSMIC RAY
TELESCOPE

FLUX-GATE
MAGNETOMETER

INFRARED RADIOMETER

CHARGED PARTICLE
INSTRUMENT

Figure 4-1. These scientific instruments were carried onboard Pioneers 10 and 11; only Pioneer 11 carried the flux-gate magnetometer.

- Searched for the gravitational effects of large undiscovered objects orbiting the Sun.

Within the systems of Jupiter and Saturn, the Pioneer spacecraft performed a more involved series of experiments:

- Mapped the magnetic fields of the planets — their intensity, direction, and structure.

- Determined how many electrons and protons of various energies were distributed along the trajectory of each spacecraft through the planetary magnetospheres and, for Saturn, determined how the rings affect the distribution of those particles; for both planets, determined how the particles were affected by the satellites.

- Searched for auroras in the polar atmospheres of the two planets.

- Obtained information to help interpret the observed characteristics of the two main types of radio waves from Jupiter — decimetric and decametric.

- Mapped how the two planets interact with the solar wind.

- Measured the temperature of the atmospheres of the two planets and of those of some of their larger satellites.

- Determined the structure of the upper atmospheres of Jupiter and Saturn, where molecules are ionized by solar radiation to produce an ionosphere.

- Mapped the thermal structure of the two planets by measuring their infrared radiation, and deduced how much more heat each planet radiates into space than it absorbs from the Sun.

- Obtained spin-scan images of Jupiter and Saturn in two colors during the encounter sequences, and close-up images of special planetary features (the Great Red Spot and polar regions of Jupiter and the rings of Saturn); made polarimetry measurements of Jupiter and Saturn and of some of their large satellites.

- Probed the upper atmospheres of Jupiter and Saturn with S-band radio waves at occultation; similarly, probed the Galilean satellite Io to establish whether it has an atmosphere.

- Investigated, at relatively close range, several of the Galilean satellites of Jupiter, and Saturn's largest satellite, Titan, by spin-scan imaging and other measurements to determine their sizes and other physical characteristics.

- Determined the shape of the external gravitational fields of Jupiter and Saturn and inferred the internal mass distribution and structure of those fields.

- Determined more precisely the masses of Jupiter and its Galilean satellites, and the masses of Saturn, the rings of Saturn, and of the Saturnian satellites, Rhea, Iapetus, and Titan, by accurate observations of the effects of their gravitational fields on the motion of the spacecraft.

- Provided information to calculate with greater precision the orbits and ephemerides of Jupiter and its Galilean satellites, and of Saturn and Titan.

- Determined the maximum radiation dosage for planning future missions.

Eleven scientific instruments and experiments (Figure 4-1) were selected from more than 150 proposals submitted to NASA Headquarters in response to the original request for proposed onboard experiments for the original Pioneer mission to Jupiter. These instruments, and two non-instrumented experiments, are described in the following subsections. In addition, a high-field magnetometer was later selected for Pioneer 11 to ensure adequate coverage of higher magnetic field strengths that might be encountered. This instrument — a flux-gate magnetometer — is also described.

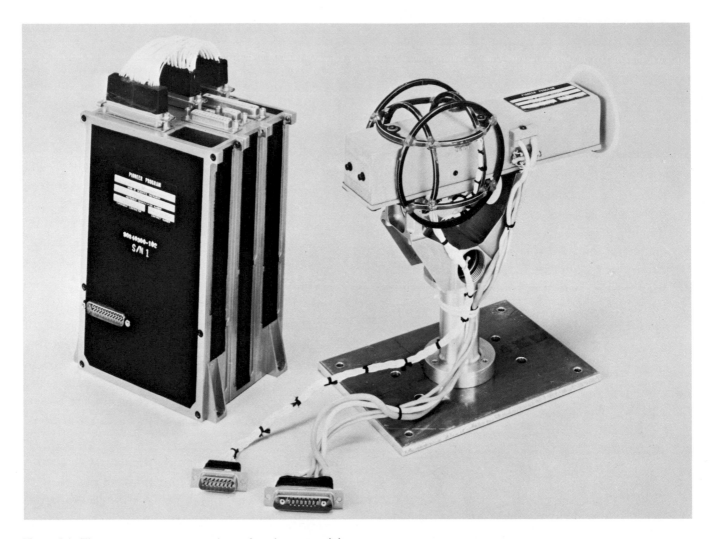

Figure 4-2. The magnetometer, mounted on a long boom to minimize interference from spacecraft magnetic fields, measured
magnetic fields in interplanetary space and near Jupiter and
Saturn. The electronics shown at the left of the magnetometer
were mounted within the spacecraft.

Magnetic Fields

Magnetic fields permeate the plasma of electrically charged particles in interplanetary space as it
spreads out from the Sun across the Solar System.
Before the Pioneer missions to Jupiter and Saturn,
these effects had been observed and measured only
to the orbit of Mars. Scientists were still uncertain
about many specific details concerning the interplanetary medium and particularly the configuration of the magnetic field beyond the orbit of Mars
to the outer regions of the Solar System. The outer

boundaries of the Sun's influence were, and still
are, vague, and interactions between the plasma
and the magnetic fields of the Solar System and
those of the nearby interstellar medium still puzzle
scientists. Pioneers 10 and 11 will continue to
explore the regions beyond the orbit of Saturn and
will provide data that will help define the transition region of the solar influence, or the heliopause.

Of even greater importance was the objective of
measuring the detailed magnetic fields of Jupiter

and Saturn and the configurations throughout the magnetospheres of these planets.

Principal Investigator:

Edward J. Smith
Jet Propulsion Laboratory, Pasadena, California

Coinvestigators:

Palmer Dyal and David S. Colburn
Ames Research Center, NASA, Moffett Field, California

Charles P. Sonett
University of Arizona, Tucson, Arizona

Douglas E. Jones
Brigham Young University, Provo, Utah

Paul J. Coleman, Jr.
University of California at Los Angeles

Leverett Davis, Jr.
California Institute of Technology, Pasadena, California

This experiment used a sensitive magnetometer (Figure 4-2) mounted on the tip of a lightweight boom extending 6.6 m (21.5 ft) from the center of the spacecraft to reduce the effects of even the minute amount of residual magnetic field of the spacecraft and to help balance the spin-stabilized Pioneer spacecraft. The helium vector magnetometer measured the fine structure of the interplanetary field, mapped the fields of Jupiter and Saturn, and provided field measurements to evaluate the interaction of the solar wind with the two planets. The magnetometer operated in any one of eight ranges, the lowest of which covered magnetic field strengths from ±0.01 to ±4.0 γ ($1\gamma = 10^{-5}$ gauss); the highest measured field strengths up to $\pm140{,}000$ γ (i.e., ±1.4 gauss). (The surface field of Earth is about 0.5 gauss.) The ranges were selected by ground command or automatically by the instrument as it reached the limits of a given range.

The sensor for the magnetometer consisted of a cell filled with helium that was excited by electri-cal discharge at radio frequencies and by infrared optical pumping. Changes in helium absorption caused by magnetic fields passing through the magnetometer were measured by an infrared optical detector.

Flux-Gate Magnetometer Experiment

Pioneer 11 carried another instrument for measuring the magnetic field, a flux-gate magnetometer. This instrument was designed to measure the intense planetary fields of Jupiter and Saturn and to extend the measuring capability of the spacecraft beyond the range provided by the helium vector magnetometer. The scientific objectives were to study the intrinsic magnetic fields of Jupiter and Saturn by carrying out measurements during the closest approach phases of the Pioneer 11 mission. The knowledge acquired allowed a comprehensive study of the general problem of how planets, including Earth, generate their magnetic fields, and a determination of the detailed geometry of their inner magnetospheres.

Principal Investigator:

Mario H. Acuna
Goddard Space Flight Center, NASA, Greenbelt, Maryland

Coinvestigator:

Norman F. Ness
Goddard Space Flight Center, NASA

The instrument (Figure 4-3), mounted on the main body of the spacecraft, used two magnetic ring cores that were driven to saturation by associated oscillators at a frequency of 8 kHz. The presence of an external magnetic field created an imbalance in the sensors which was detected by four coil windings; the coil windings were oriented perpendicular to each other. The instrument had a single dynamic range with a compressed response that provided a maximum field measurement capability of ±10 gauss (0.001 tesla) and a resolution of ±0.05 gauss for external fields of less than 2 gauss.

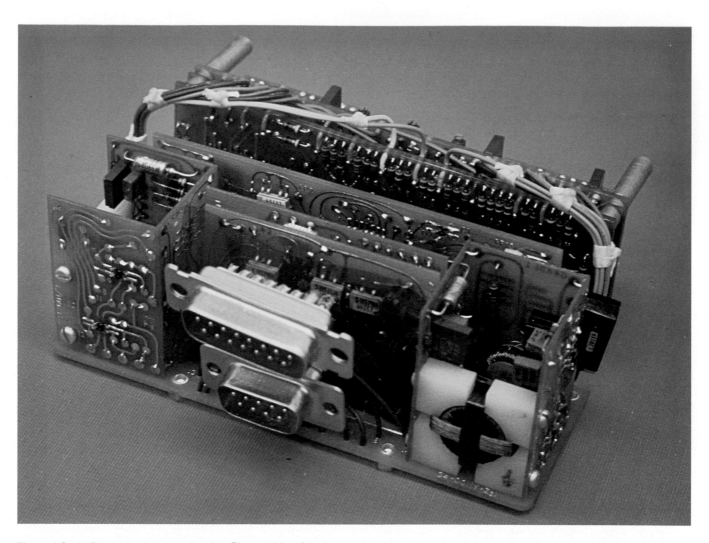

Figure 4-3. A flux-gate magnetometer (on Pioneer 11 only) was used to measure high-intensity magnetic fields in the inner magnetospheres of Jupiter and Saturn.

Interplanetary Solar Wind and Heliosphere

The solar wind consists of streams of protons, electrons, and some helium nuclei emitted by the Sun in all directions. Particles in the solar wind affect electrical and communication systems on Earth and may give rise to long-term weather cycles. This wind was unknown until spacecraft began to explore space beyond Earth's magnetosphere less than 20 years ago. Some of the charged particles of the solar wind become trapped in radiation belts by Earth's magnetic field. They also account for the aurora borealis, the aurora

australis, and other phenomena that baffled scientists until the radiation belts were discovered by experiments carried out by Earth satellites.

The behavior of the solar wind at great distances from the Sun could only be conjectured before the flight of Pioneer 10 to the outer planets. Until the Pioneer 10 mission, instruments on spacecraft had measured the wind only as far as the orbit of Mars. And virtually nothing was known of the interaction of the solar wind with Jupiter and Saturn or about the effects of Saturn's rings on the wind.

Principal Investigator:

John H. Wolfe (Jupiter/Saturn)
Ames Research Center, NASA, Moffett Field, California

Aaron Barnes (Post-Saturn)
Ames Research Center, NASA, Moffett Field, California

Coinvestigators:

John Mihalov, H. Collard, and D. D. McKibbin
Ames Research Center, NASA

Louis A. Frank
University of Iowa, Iowa City

Reimar Lüst
Max Planck Institut fur Physik und Astrophysik, Garching,
Germany

Devrie Intriligator
University of Southern California, Los Angeles

William C. Feldman
Los Alamos Scientific Laboratory, New Mexico

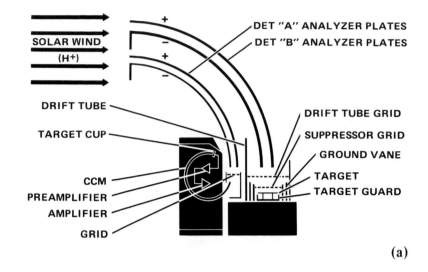

(a)

The Pioneer spacecraft each carried a plasma analyzer (Figure 4-4) to evaluate the solar wind. It looked toward the Sun through a hole in each spacecraft's large dish-shaped antenna. The solar wind particles entered the plasma analyzer's apertures between two quadraspherical plates where the direction of arrival, the energy (speed), and the number of ions and electrons making up the solar wind were measured.

A voltage was applied across the quadraspherical plates in a maximum of 64 steps, at a rate of one step/revolution of the spacecraft, to count particles in discrete energy ranges. The direction of particle travel was determined from instrument orientation and by knowing which of the detector targets the particle struck. The instrument had a high-resolution analyzer and a medium-resolution analyzer to detect particles of different energy levels. The high-resolution analyzer had 26 continuous channel multipliers (CCM) to measure the number

(b)

Figure 4-4. A plasma analyzer was aimed toward the Sun through a hole in the large dish antenna of each Pioneer spacecraft; its purpose was to map the density and energy of the solar wind. (a) Diagram of the plasma analyzer. (b) Plasma analyzer ready for installation in the spacecraft.

of ions per second with energies from 100 to 8000 eV. The medium-resolution analyzer had 5 electrometers to count ions in the energy range from 100 to 18,000 eV and electrons from 1 to 500 eV.

57

Figure 4-5. Charged particle detectors were used to study the life history of cosmic rays in the Solar System and to study radiation trapped in the Jovian and Saturnian magnetospheres.

Figure 4-6. A combination of cosmic ray telescopes was used to determine the composition of solar and galactic cosmic ray particles and their energy ranges.

Charged Particle Composition

The charged particle detector (Figure 4-5) had four measuring systems: two particle telescopes that operated in interplanetary space and two that measured the trapped electrons and protons inside the radiation belts of Jupiter and Saturn.

Principal Investigator:

John A. Simpson
University of Chicago

Coinvestigators:

Joseph J. O'Gallagher
University of Chicago

Anthony J. Tuzzolino and R. Bruce McKibben
University of Chicago

During the interplanetary phase of the mission, before and after encounter with Jupiter and Saturn, this experiment sought to identify the chemical elements hydrogen, helium, lithium, beryllium, boron, carbon, nitrogen, and oxygen, and to separate hydrogen, deuterium, helium-3, and helium-4 in an attempt to differentiate between particles emanating from the Sun and those from the Galaxy. The instrument was also used to determine how streams of high-energy particles from the Sun travel through interplanetary space.

The main telescope of seven solid-state detectors measured the composition of cosmic rays from 1 to 500 MeV, and a three-element, low-energy telescope measured 0.4- to 10-MeV protons and helium nuclei.

Two new types of sensors were developed to cope with the extremely high intensities of trapped particles in the Jovian magnetosphere. A solid-state electron current detector, operating below $-40°$ C ($-40°$ F), detected those electrons above 3.3 MeV that generate the decimetric radio waves emitted by Jupiter and similar electrons in the radiation environment of Saturn. A trapped proton detector contained a foil of thorium, the atoms of which underwent nuclear fission when hit by protons with energies above 35 MeV; the foil was insensitive to electrons.

Energy Spectra of Cosmic Rays

The cosmic ray telescope used for this experiment (Figure 4-6) was designed to monitor solar and galactic cosmic ray particles and to track the high-energy particles from the Sun. The instrument could determine which nuclei of the 10 lightest elements are the cosmic ray particles. Before saturation by radiation when near Jupiter and Saturn, the cosmic ray telescope measured high-energy particles in the radiation belts of these planets.

Principal Investigator:

Frank B. McDonald
Goddard Space Flight Center, NASA, Greenbelt, Maryland

Coinvestigators:

Kenneth G. McCracken
Minerals Research Laboratory, North Ryde, Australia

William R. Webber and Edmond C. Roelof
University of New Hampshire, Durham

Bonnard J. Teegarden and James H. Trainor
Goddard Space Flight Center, NASA

The instrument consisted of three three-element solid-state telescopes. The high-energy telescope measured the flux of protons between 56 and 800 MeV. The medium-energy telescope measured protons with energies between 3 and 22 MeV and identified the 10 elements from hydrogen to neon. The low-energy telescope measured the flux of electrons between 0.05 and 1 MeV and of protons between 0.05 and 20 MeV.

Charged Particles in the Jovian and Saturnian Systems and in Interplanetary Space

This instrument (Figure 4-7) measured the intensities, energy spectra, and angular distribution of

Figure 4-7. Other telescopes measured various characteristics of the electrons and protons in the radiation belts of Jupiter and Saturn.

energetic electrons and protons in interplanetary space and near Jupiter and Saturn. On Pioneer 10, the instrument used an array of seven miniature Geiger-Müller tubes, collectively known as a Geiger tube telescope (GTT). Each tube was a small gas-filled cylinder. When a charged particle passed through the gas, an electrical pulse was generated by the applied voltage. Individual pulses from five of the tubes and coincident pulses from three combinations of the seven tubes were transmitted. Protons of energy greater than 5 MeV and electrons with energies greater than 40 keV were detected.

On Pioneer 11, one Geiger-Müller tube was replaced by a thin silicon wafer to detect protons in the specific energy range 0.61 to 3.41 MeV.

Other minor changes were made to improve the characteristics of the detector system.

Principal Investigator:

James A. Van Allen
University of Iowa, Iowa City, Iowa

Collaborators:

Daniel N. Baker, Bruce A. Randall, Michelle F. Thomsen, Roger F. Randall, Christopher K. Goertz, Davis D. Sentman, and Mark E. Pesses
University of Iowa, Iowa City, Iowa

The trains of pulses were passed through quasi-logarithmic data processors and then to the radio telemetry system of the spacecraft. Angular distributions were measured as the spacecraft rotated.

Trapped Radiation in the Planetary Systems

Telescopes different from those described in the previous experiment were used in a trapped radiation detector covering a broader range of electron and proton energies. The greater range of this instrument was obtained through use of several different kinds of detectors. An unfocused Cerenkov counter detected the light emitted in a particular direction as particles passed through it. It recorded electrons with energies from 0.5 to 12 MeV. An electron scatter detector was activated by electrons with energies from 100 to 400 keV.

Principal Investigator:

R. Walker Fillius
University of California at San Diego

Coinvestigator:

Carl E. McIlwain
University of California at San Diego

The instrument also included a minimum ionizing detector consisting of a solid-state diode that measured minimum ionizing particles (i.e., less than 3 MeV) and protons in the range 50 to 350 MeV. Sensitive materials of different types in

60

two scintillation detectors distinguished between electrons of less than 5 keV and protons of less than 50 keV. These five different "eyes" of the instrument (Figure 4-8) provided basic information about several of the fundamental features of the planetary radiation belts, including the types of particles within the belts, their distribution, energy, and intensity.

Particles and Dust in Space

This investigation consisted of two distinct experiments, using different experimental techniques. One technique detected light reflected from particles, the other detected particle impacts.

The instrument for the first experiment (Figure 4-9) consisted of four nonimaging telescopes that detected sunlight reflected from meteoroids passing through their fields of view. Each telescope had a 20-cm (8-in.) diameter primary mirror, secondary optics, and a photomultiplier tube that converted light to electrical signals. When a particle passed through the telescope's 8° field of view, reflected light from it was detected by the photomultiplier tube. The fields of view for the four telescopes overlapped slightly. If a particle was "seen" simultaneously by any three of the telescopes, the instrument recorded an event. From these data, the particle's distance, trajectory, velocity, and relative size were calculated.

These telescopes could detect objects ranging from distant asteroids (miles in diameter) to minute sunlit particles of dust several feet from the telescope.

Meteoroid-Asteroid Detector

Principal Investigator:

Robert K. Soberman
General Electric Company, Philadelphia, Pennsylvania

Coinvestigator:

Herbert A. Zook
Johnson Space Center, NASA, Houston, Texas

Figure 4-8. A trapped radiation detector measured, over a very broad range, the energies of electrons and protons trapped by the magnetic fields of Jupiter and Saturn.

Meteoroid Detector

Principal Investigator:

William H. Kinard
Langley Research Center, NASA, Hampton, Virginia

Coinvestigators:

José M. Alverez, Robert L. O'Neal, Donald H. Humes, and Richard E. Turner
Langley Research Center, NASA

The second experiment consisted of 13 panels, each containing 18 pressurized cells; the cells were filled with a mixture of argon and nitrogen. These panels had an area of 0.605 m² (6.5 ft²) and were mounted on the back of the dish antenna (Figure 4-10).

When a cell was punctured by a particle in interplanetary space, it lost gas at a rate proportional to the size of the hole made in the cell wall. The loss in pressure was detected when the pressure reached a certain threshold value. Cells on Pioneer 10 recorded impacts with particles with masses as small as 1 billionth of a gram; on Pioneer 11 the cell walls were thicker so that only more massive particles would be detected.

Ultraviolet Photometry

The ultraviolet photometer carried onboard Pioneers 10 and 11 (Figure 4-11) measured the scattering of solar ultraviolet light or emission of ultraviolet light from interplanetary hydrogen, helium, and dust; from the atmospheres of Jupiter and Saturn; and from some of their satellites.

Principal Investigator:

Darrell L. Judge
University of Southern California, Los Angeles

Coinvestigator:

Robert W. Carlson
University of Southern California, Los Angeles

Radiotelescopes have shown that the Solar System is immersed in and traveling through an interstellar gas cloud of cold, neutral (uncharged)

(b)

(a)

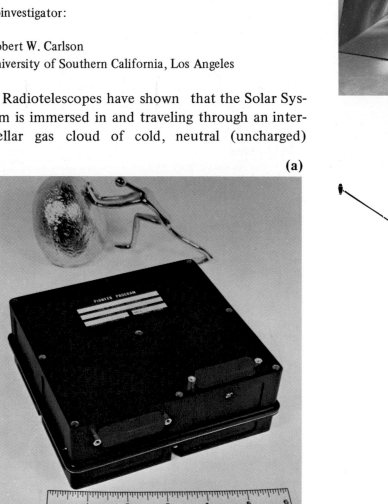

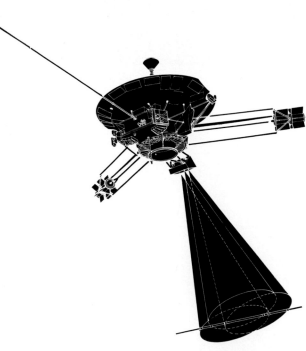

(c)

Figure 4-9. The meteoroid-asteroid detector used four nonimaging telescopes to track and characterize interplanetary objects ranging from bits of dust to distant large asteroids. (a) Electronics. (b) Nonimaging telescopes. (c) Instrument installation.

62

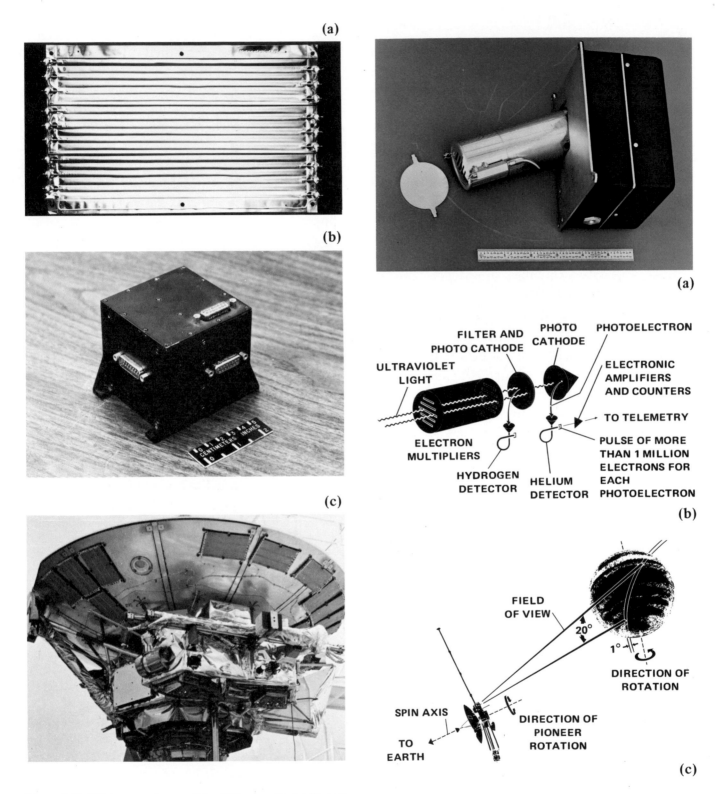

(a)

(b)

(c)

FILTER AND
PHOTO CATHODE

PHOTO
CATHODE

PHOTOELECTRON

ULTRAVIOLET
LIGHT

ELECTRONIC
AMPLIFIERS
AND COUNTERS

TO TELEMETRY

ELECTRON
MULTIPLIERS

PULSE OF MORE
THAN 1 MILLION
ELECTRONS FOR
EACH
PHOTOELECTRON

HYDROGEN
DETECTOR

HELIUM
DETECTOR

FIELD
OF VIEW

20°

1°

DIRECTION OF
ROTATION

SPIN AXIS

DIRECTION OF
PIONEER
ROTATION

TO
EARTH

Figure 4-10. Thirteen panels comprising 234 pressurized cells were mounted on the back of the spacecraft's main dish antenna. When penetrated and depressurized by impact with small meteoroids, the cells served to measure meteoroid distribution. (a) Pressure-cell panel. (b) Panel electronics. (c) Panel installation.

Figure 4-11. Scattering of ultraviolet light was measured by the ultraviolet photometer to determine the quantities of hydrogen and helium in space and on Jupiter and Saturn. (a) Ultraviolet photometer. (b) Diagram of the photometer. (c) How the photometer scanned Jupiter.

63

hydrogen. By measuring the scattering of the Sun's ultraviolet light in space, the ultraviolet photometer measured the amount of neutral hydrogen in the heliosphere. The presence of neutral hydrogen (already measured near Earth) could be the result of the neutralization of fast solar-wind hydrogen ions at the boundary of the heliosphere, their conversion into fast uncharged hydrogen atoms, and diffusion of these neutral atoms back into the heliosphere. Or the source of the neutral hydrogen might be in the Galaxy itself. The hydrogen penetrates the Solar System as a result of the System's relative velocity to the interstellar gas of 73,000 km/hr (45,000 mph).

The experiment was intended to gather data to resolve the origin of the neutral hydrogen and to establish the boundaries of the heliosphere. From measurements of the interplanetary helium, experimenters hoped to determine also the percentage of helium in the interstellar medium. This was expected to throw more light on the question of whether the universe originated in a "big bang," a single creative event, or is a continuous creation still going on.

The viewing angle of the ultraviolet photometer was fixed so that the spin of the spacecraft caused the photometer to scan the celestial sphere. When near Jupiter and Saturn, the photometer scanned the medium above the cloudtops. By measuring the changes in intensity of ultraviolet light reflected into two photocathodes of the instrument — one measuring radiation at 1216 Å, the other at 584 Å — the photometer detected light emitted by excited hydrogen and helium atoms, respectively.

Within the systems of Jupiter and Saturn, the instrument measured the scattering of solar ultraviolet light by the atmospheres of the planets. This scattering provided information about the amount of atomic hydrogen in the upper atmospheres, the mixing rates within the atmospheres, the amount of helium in each, and therefore the helium/hydrogen ratio within the atmospheres of these huge gas giants. Virtually all theories of the origin

of these two planets and their subsequent development make assumptions about the amount of helium in the planetary atmospheres, but before the Pioneer missions, helium had not been identified in the atmosphere of either Jupiter or Saturn.

By measuring changes in the ultraviolet light glow, the instrument checked to see if Jupiter and Saturn had polar auroras at the times of flyby. Such auroras are bright, glowing regions in the upper atmospheres caused by precipitation of particles along magnetic field lines from space toward the poles of the planet.

Infrared Radiometry

Infrared emissions from Jupiter have been measured successfully from Earth. Maps of the planet at infrared wavelengths show belts and bands similar to those on photographs of the planet in visible light. But most of Jupiter's infrared radiation, and that from Saturn, is emitted at 20 to 40 μm, wavelengths that can be observed effectively only from a spacecraft (because Earth's atmosphere readily absorbs them, blocking the 40-μm region entirely). The infrared radiometer was designed to measure radiation from Jupiter and Saturn at wavelengths of 20 and 40 μm.

Principal Investigator:

(Jupiter) Guido Munch
California Institute of Technology, Pasadena

(Saturn) Andrew P. Ingersoll
California Institute of Technology, Pasadena

Coinvestigators:

Gerry Neugebauer
California Institute of Technology

Stillman C. Chase
Santa Barbara Research Center, California

Laurence M. Trafton
University of Texas, Austin

Figure 4-12. The infrared radiometer measured the amount and distribution of heat energy from Jupiter and Saturn and provided information on temperature distributions in the outer atmospheres.

Glenn S. Orton
Jet Propulsion Laboratory, Pasadena, California

An important question about Jupiter and Saturn is that concerning their heat balances — the balance between the radiation emitted by each planet and absorbed sunlight. Observations from Earth had shown that Jupiter is hot enough to emit more heat than it absorbs. The infrared radiometer provided a more accurate measurement of the net heat energy outputs of both Saturn and Jupiter. (The output from Saturn is even more difficult to ascertain from Earth-based observations.)

The two-channel radiometer (Figure 4-12) measured infrared radiation in the wavelength ranges of 14–25 μm and 26–56 μm. The instrument not only determined the temperature across the disks of Jupiter and Saturn and its ring system, but also provided important information to aid in determining the thermal structure and chemical composition of each planet's atmosphere.

Like the ultraviolet photometer, the infrared radiometer used a fixed telescope that scanned the surface of the planetary cloudtops as the spacecraft rotated. Because of the fixed viewing angle, the infrared instrument could view the planets for only limited times during approach.

Designed with a 7.6-cm (3-in.) diameter Cassegrain optical system, the instrument relied on 88-element, thin-film, bimetallic thermopiles to detect infrared radiation. Its field of view was about 725 by 2400 km (450 by 1500 miles) on Jupiter's cloud surface at about the time of closest approach. Its resolution at the distance of closest approach was about 2400 km (1500 miles).

Celestial Mechanics Experiment

Deep space tracking of the Pioneer spacecraft determined their velocities along the Earth-spacecraft line to within a fraction of a millimeter per second. This information was obtained once per minute during tracking periods.

The two-way Doppler tracking data, augmented by optical and radar position data about the planets, were used to determine the planetary masses from their perturbations on the path of the spacecraft. Computer calculations, based on the spacecraft's trajectory and known planetary and satellite orbital characteristics, provided a fivefold reduction, for example, in the uncertainty of Jupiter's mass (Figure 4-13). Masses of the four large satellites of Jupiter (Io, Europa, Ganymede, and Callisto) were determined to an accuracy of better than 1%. The experiment also determined the polar flattening of the planets to great precision (within 0.8 km (0.5 mile) for Jupiter).

The gravitational fields of the planets were determined, and their response to a relatively rapid rotation was used to construct new models for the planetary interiors. The equations of state for hydrogen, helium, and rocks under high pressures were used for the models.

Thus, this celestial mechanics experiment made use of the spacecraft itself as a sensitive instrument affected by the gravitational fields of Jupiter, Saturn, and the large satellites of the two planets.

Principal Investigator:

John D. Anderson
Jet Propulsion Laboratory, Pasadena, California

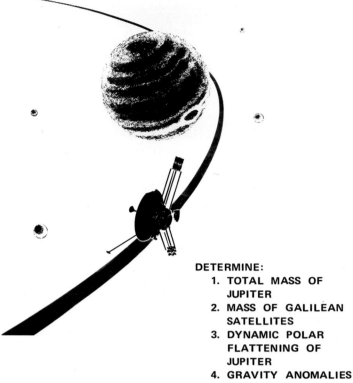

DETERMINE:
1. TOTAL MASS OF JUPITER
2. MASS OF GALILEAN SATELLITES
3. DYNAMIC POLAR FLATTENING OF JUPITER
4. GRAVITY ANOMALIES ON JUPITER

Figure 4-13. A celestial mechanics experiment determined the masses of Jupiter and its Galilean satellites (Io, Europa, Ganymede, and Callisto); of Saturn and its largest satellite, Titan; and of Saturn's rings. Also, previous findings about the polar flattening of Jupiter and Saturn were verified. This diagram shows the experiment for Jupiter.

Coinvestigator:

George W. Null
Jet Propulsion Laboratory

William B. Hubbard
University of Arizona, Tucson, Arizona

Occultation Experiment

The radio signals from the spacecraft were used in another experiment to probe the atmospheres of Jupiter and Saturn and the innermost large satellite of Jupiter, Io (Figure 4-14). Passage of each spacecraft's S-band radio signal through the atmospheres

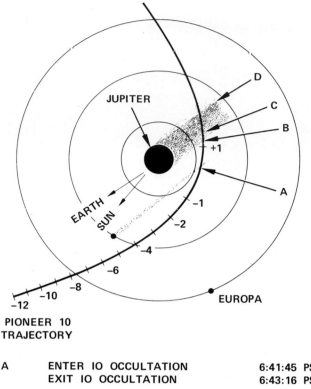

PIONEER 10 TRAJECTORY

A	ENTER IO OCCULTATION	6:41:45 PST
	EXIT IO OCCULTATION	6:43:16 PST
B	ENTER JUPITER OCCULTATION	7:42:25 PST
C	ENTER SUN SHADOW	8:15:35 PST
D	EXIT JUPITER OCCULTATION	8:47:21 PST

Figure 4-14. As the spacecraft flew behind the planets (and Pioneer 10 behind a satellite of Jupiter), radio signals from the spacecraft had to pass through the planetary (and satellite) atmospheres on their way to Earth. This diagram illustrates how this experiment was performed at the encounter of the Pioneer 10 spacecraft with Jupiter. As the spacecraft flew behind Io and Jupiter, its radio signals were modified by the ionosphere and then cut off by the surface of Io and by the dense atmosphere of Jupiter. Changes in the radio signals as they passed through the atmospheres of these bodies provided valuable information about atmospheric structures, temperatures, compositions, and charged particles.

of the planets when the Pioneers swung behind them as viewed from Earth directly measured the vertical structure of their ionospheres and provided information on the density of the atmospheres to a pressure level of about 1/10 Earth's atmosphere.

Figure 4-15. A special instrument, the imaging photopolarimeter, measured the faint glows in interplanetary space of the zodiacal light, the Gegenschein (or counterglow), and integrated starlight. This same instrument scanned the planets and satellites to examine their reflective properties and to provide spin-scan images.

Principal Investigator:

Arvydas J. Kliore
Jet Propulsion Laboratory, Pasadena, California

Coinvestigators:

Gunnar Fjeldbo Lindal, Dan L. Cain, and Boris L. Seidel
Jet Propulsion Laboratory

S. Ichtiaque Rasool
NASA Headquarters, Washington, D.C.

Similar analyses have been made from Earth using the light of stars occulted by Jupiter, but Pioneer's S-band signal is a precisely controlled monochromatic source capable of providing very accurate measurements. Refraction of the radio signal provided measurement of the electron density structure of the ionospheres and, used in conjunction with infrared temperature measurements, allowed inferences to be made about the hydrogen/helium ratio in the atmospheres of each of the two planets. It was shown, for example, that the amount of helium in the atmosphere of Saturn is somewhat depleted compared with that of Jupiter. As Pioneer 10 swung behind Io, a similar experiment resulted in the discovery of a tenuous atmosphere on that satellite.

Imaging Photopolarimetry Experiment

The imaging photopolarimeter used in this experiment (Figure 4-15) is described in detail in appendix A. The photopolarimeter operated in three modes, which differed mainly in their sensitivity and instantaneous fields of view.

67

Principal Investigator:

Tom Gehrels
University of Arizona, Tucson

Coinvestigators:

(Jupiter) Charles Blenman, Jr., Arthur Clements, Jyrki
Hameen-Antilla, Charles E. KenKnight, William Swindell,
and Martin G. Tomasko
University of Arizona

David L. Coffeen
Goddard Institute for Space Studies, New York City

Robert F. Hummer
Santa Barbara Research Center, California

(Zodiacal Light) Jerry Weinberg and Martha Hanner
Space Astronomy Laboratory, State University of
New York, Albany

(Saturn) Charles Blenman, Jr., James J. Burke, Lyn R.
Doose, Charles E. KenKnight, and Martin G. Tomasko
University of Arizona

David L. Coffeen
Goddard Institute for Space Studies

The most sensitive operating mode of the instrument was used during the interplanetary phase of Pioneer's mission to measure the zodiacal light, Gegenschein (counterglow), and integrated starlight from our Galaxy. This mode was not used during planetary encounter. The other two modes gathered photometric and polarimetric data on Jupiter and Saturn over a wide range of phase angles and distances, to provide new knowledge about the shape, size, and refractive index of cloud particles and the abundance of gas above the clouds. Information was also gathered about the ring system of Saturn and the larger satellites of the two planets. The photometric mode also provided data that were processed by computer into images of the planets and some of their satellites and the ring system of Saturn.

The imaging experiment relied on the spin of the spacecraft to sweep a small telescope across the planet being viewed. The instrument scanned strips of the planet's surface that were only 0.03° wide, in red and blue light. The strips were then processed to reconstruct images of the planets.

5
First into the Outer Solar System

An announcement of the experiments that would be carried aboard the Pioneer spacecraft on their missions to Jupiter and Saturn was a press release addressed to editors in the San Francisco Bay area:

On Thursday, May 7 [1970], the 13 experimenters participating in the first mission to Jupiter will be at NASA's Ames Research Center, Mountain View, for a project coordination meeting. The Pioneer . . . scientific spacecraft . . . are scheduled for launch to the vicinity of Jupiter in 1972 and 1973. At 11:30 a.m. we will present a review and question and answer session for news media on the mission and experiments.

Several hundred scientists and engineers met in the Main Auditorium at Ames Research Center to plan trajectories to Jupiter. A tentative launch date in early 1972 had been chosen. Questions raised by scientists in connection with their experiments were pondered by celestial dynamicists and spacecraft engineers: "The ultraviolet experiment needs to look at the sunlit side of the planet. It would be important to look at the solar wind outside the ecliptic plane — Could the trajectory to Jupiter provide for this? Can Pioneer reach the region of space, perhaps 30 to 100 times Earth's distance from our Sun, where the solar wind stops? Does 15 times Earth's distance from the Sun represent the limit of communication with Pioneer?"

These and other questions sparked the first of a series of coordination meetings to plan the Pioneer mission. It was stressed that one of the prime purposes of the Pioneer mission to the outer planets was to provide information on the environment of Jupiter, the largest planet in the Solar System, information that would aid scientists in planning more sophisticated spacecraft for later missions to all the outer planets.

Among matters debated by scientists was whether to have the spacecraft pass over a pole of Jupiter, where the Jovian atmosphere seemed to be more transparent than over regions nearer the equator. From a path over the planet's pole, Pioneer might be able to look deeper than it could over equatorial regions into the 138,000-km (86,000 mile) diameter ball of hydrogen that Jupiter is. Although considered, the polar passage was rejected for the first Pioneer in favor of an objective to gain as much information as possible about the radiation belts of Jupiter, which were believed to be concentrated equatorially.

What the effects of nuclear-powered, radioisotope thermoelectric generators (RTGs) might be on the scientific instruments carried by Pioneer was discussed. The Pioneers were designed to be as electromagnetically clean as possible so they could measure very weak magnetic fields in deep space. The radiation from the RTGs could "dirty" the spacecraft with neutrons and other subatomic particles, thereby making the instruments less sensitive to the space measurements. Representatives of the Atomic Energy Commission explained how the radiation from the RTGs might be reduced by eliminating impurities from the radioactive fuel

69

elements and they described ways in which purification techniques were being tested.

At a press conference following the technical meetings, the exploratory and ambitious nature of the mission to the two giant planets was emphasized. The duration of each of the two flights (Pioneers 10 and 11) would be much greater than that of any other space project to date. There were many unknowns in the environment between Mars and Jupiter and in close approach to Jupiter itself. And if the mission were successful enough for one Pioneer spacecraft to continue to Saturn, there were many unknowns about passage close to that ringed planet. Moreover, as pointed out by Glenn A. Reiff, then Pioneer Program Manager at NASA Headquarters: "The telecommunications network will be stretched to the limits of its capabilities."

Charles F. Hall, Project Manager at Ames Research Center, confirmed that the spacecraft design had been completed, and that construction of the first of the two spacecraft was under way at TRW Systems, Redondo Beach, California. "Experimenters and staffs are here to discuss the design of the scientific equipment to integrate with the spacecraft and its mission profile." Everything was on schedule. He pointed out how the mission schedule was constrained by the launch window — the interval of time during which conditions would be favorable for launching the spacecraft. For Pioneer 10, that window would be open for only 18 days in 1972.

Almost a year after that first press conference and meeting in May 1970, a similar meeting was held in the Main Auditorium at TRW Systems. Scientists at the March 1971 meeting reported that the RTGs were generating higher radiation than had been expected at the time of the 1970 meeting, but that instruments had been adapted to the more intense radiative environment. Details of the science experiments showed the wealth of data expected from the mission in space and at the planets. Scientific equipment, as well as the spacecraft, was being readied on schedule. Because scientists could only make considered guesses about conditions in the asteroid belt and within

the Jovian system, instruments had to be designed with a wide range of capabilities.

Meanwhile, trajectory analysts continued their work. They evaluated various approaches to Jupiter that would be best suited to Pioneer's information-gathering experiments and that would make the most of the spacecraft's capabilities, if it survived the encounter and was still functioning. Targeting so that the spacecraft would be occulted by a satellite of Jupiter during the encounter would cause its radio signals to Earth to pass through any atmosphere held by the occulting satellite. Changes in the radio signals as they pass through an atmosphere provide valuable data on the atmosphere's density and distribution. Io, one of Jupiter's Galilean satellites, was the prime candidate for such an experiment because it was known that Io modulated radio waves from the Jovian system. The other Galilean satellites — Europa, Ganymede, and Callisto — were also of interest.

On November 16, 1971, Ralph W. Holtzclaw, Space Systems Manager at Ames Research Center, discussed the need to make the spacecraft reliable for their long mission. "No single component failure can be catastrophic to the mission," he insisted. He pointed out that the Pioneer mission was quite different from earlier space missions. Scientists had to spend several years planning the experiments. Then the spacecraft would operate for 7 or 8 years more in space, possibly even longer. Scientists were thus being asked, in effect, to dedicate some part of their time for 10 years or more to a single experiment.

All the mission preparations went well. From contract award to the scheduled launch date in early March 1972 was 1 month less than 2½ yr. But the thousands of people upon whom the success of the Pioneer missions to Jupiter and Saturn depended performed on schedule to meet the critical time of the launch window (Figure 5-1).

Figure 5-1. Thousands of people contributed to the development and fabrication of the Pioneer spacecraft destined to journey to Jupiter and Saturn. Their dedication made it possible to meet the tight schedule for the launch windows.

70

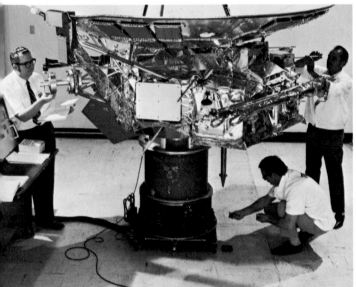

DR. F.B. McDONALD   DR. J.A. VAN ALLEN   R. J. A. SIM

Charles F. Hall praised those who had made the program possible:

It is most appropriate to compliment the many dedicated people who have worked so hard to reach this first goal of the Pioneer . . . mission to Jupiter and to congratulate all for a job well done. I estimate that at the time of the Pioneer [10] launch, more than 15 million man-hours will have been expended to make this goal possible. I am sure that you all feel as I do that a successful mission wherein we will be exploring new frontiers in space will be a just compensation for this large effort and that we are, indeed, a fortunate, select group which has been given the opportunity to participate in and contribute to the Pioneer . . . mission.

By December 22, 1971, the Atlas/Centaur launch vehicle stood ready on Launch Complex 36A at the John F. Kennedy Space Center, Florida. The Pioneer 10 spacecraft was airlifted from TRW Systems, California, to Florida on January 14, 1972, with its full complement of scientific instruments, but without its RTGs.

To ensure operational readiness of the spacecraft and its science instruments for launch, it was tested through a simulated countdown in Building AO (Figure 5-2). The RTGs were installed and the spacecraft loaded with propellant. Finally, it was mated to the third stage of the launch vehicle and encapsulated within a protective nose shroud for its journey through Earth's atmosphere. The entire assembly was then transferred to the launch pad and mated to the Atlas/Centaur.

When the launch window opened on February 27, 1972, blockhouse electrical power failed within 59 min of the planned liftoff time of 8:52 p.m. EST. High winds delayed the launch until March 2. On March 2, 1972, at 8:49 p.m. EST, the Atlas/Centaur lifted from the launch pad (Figure 5-3) carrying Earth's first space probe to an outer planet. The grandeur of the night launch

72

Figure 5-2. A simulated countdown at Kennedy Space Center thoroughly tested each spacecraft before launch.

Figure 5-3. At 8:49 p.m. EST, March 2, 1972, Pioneer 10 began its journey to Jupiter, the first mission to the giant planet, then on toward the boundaries of our Solar System and into interstellar space.

from Cape Kennedy was enhanced by distant thunder and by lightning flashes on the cloudtops as the brilliant light of the Atlas engines' exhaust jets rose through the clouds.

Following the launch, telemetered data poured into the control centers by radio from the launch vehicle and from the spacecraft. Any malfunctions would have required immediate corrective action if the spacecraft and its scientific payload were to be saved. Pioneer withstood the launch without ill effect. After 17 min of powered flight, Pioneer 10 had been accelerated to 51,682 km/hr (32,114 mph), almost 11,300 km/hr (7,000 mph) faster than any previous manmade object. After the Atlas had exhausted its propellants and dropped behind, the Centaur engines took over and continued to thrust the Pioneer into space. But the tiny ball of brilliant white fire began to disappear into the black void of the night sky — Pioneer 10 soon disappeared, on its way to Jupiter, and beyond, for it would ultimately escape the Solar System and journey among the distant stars.

Shortly after separation from the upper stages, the spacecraft deployed its RTG power units at the end of their two booms, thereby slowing its rotation rate. Then the third boom, tipped with a sensitive magnetometer, was slowly extended to its full length of 5.2 m (17 ft).

The launch of Pioneer 10 was so accurate that a correction of only 50.4 km/hr (31.3 mph) to the spacecraft's velocity was required. This correction was commanded and took place on March 7. Pioneer 10 could have reached Jupiter without the correction, but it was needed to assure a time of arrival better suited to some of the experiments.

After Pioneer 10 separated from its launch vehicle, a sequencer activated the attitude control system to turn the spacecraft around and orient it for its long voyage so that the big dish antenna pointed toward Earth. Actually, while near Earth, Pioneer 10's orientation was such that sunlight illuminated it from the side, which caused heating problems for several weeks after launch. To reduce these temperature problems, the spacecraft was commanded to point slightly away from Earth so

Figure 5-4. Only 11 hr after launch, Pioneer 10 passed the orbit of the Moon, shown in this artist's conception. Actually, the spacecraft did not pass near the Moon because the Moon was at another part of its orbit.

that the shadow of the dish antenna would shield vulnerable parts (such as the battery) from solar heat.

Only 11 hr after launch, Pioneer 10 passed the orbit of the Moon (Figure 5-4).

The plasma analyzer was the only instrument onboard Pioneer 10 designed to look directly at the Sun. Some of the others could not be pointed sunward without risking serious damage. In the early stages of the flight, therefore, when the Sun illuminated the spacecraft from the side, several instruments were left unenergized and others were suitably shielded from the Sun. Instruments such as the magnetometer and charged particle detectors were not affected by sunlight. They were turned on quickly so they could be calibrated in-flight as they passed through the well-known magnetic and radiation environments surrounding Earth.

Two days after liftoff, the cosmic ray telescope was turned on; then, sequentially over the next few days, the ultraviolet photometer, asteroid-meteoroid detector, imaging photopolarimeter, and plasma analyzer were turned on. All scientific instruments had been turned on by 10 days after launch.

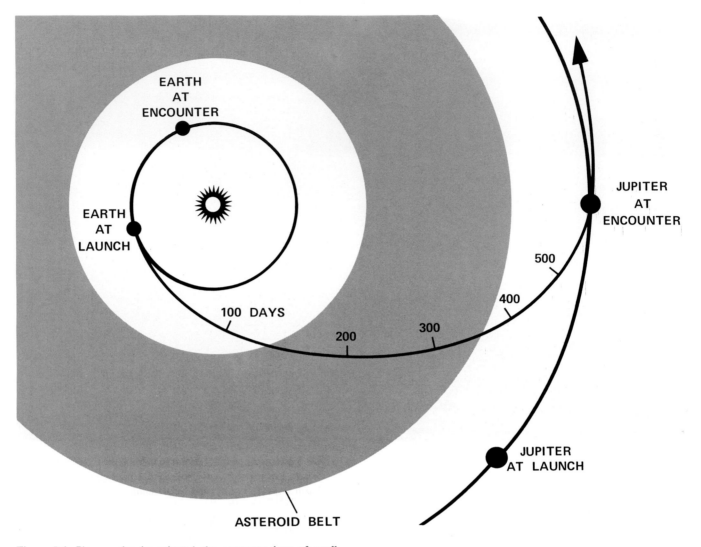

EARTH
AT
ENCOUNTER

EARTH
AT
LAUNCH

100 DAYS

200

300

400

500

JUPITER
AT
ENCOUNTER

JUPITER
AT LAUNCH

ASTEROID BELT

Figure 5-6. Pioneer also investigated the concentrations of small meteoroids in space, especially those within the asteroid belt where a hazard to space flight might have been encountered. Pioneer found that the number of these bodies varies somewhat with distance from the Sun, but not entirely as had been expected. Pioneer 10, and later Pioneer 11, penetrated the asteroid belt and emerged from it undamaged.

was a 90% chance that Pioneer 10 would pass through the belt undamaged.

Pioneer 10 was 322 million kilometers (200 million miles) from Earth on September 1, 1972 — then deep in the asteroid belt and still undamaged (Figure 5-6). At this time it took 36 min for a radio signal to travel from Earth to the spacecraft and for a reply to be received at Earth. Ten of the scientific experiments onboard were operating. The remaining experiment — the infrared radiometer —

was not needed until the spacecraft reached Jupiter; nevertheless, the radiometer had been turned on monthly to check that it was operating correctly.

In August 1972, several unprecedented storms on the Sun (Figure 5-7) provided Pioneer 10 with a unique opportunity to measure the solar wind and solar energetic particles at much greater interplanetary distances than ever before. A huge area of the Sun's photosphere unexpectedly erupted to produce three enormous storms on August 2 and another on August 7. The event on August 7 generated in 1 hr enough energy to furnish all the electrical power that would be consumed (at the present rate) in the United States over the next 100 million years.

Effects of the solar storm were severe in Canada, the northern United States, Sweden, and Alaska because the solar wind warped Earth's magnetic field and caused magnetic disturbances and black-outs of power and communications.

Pioneer 10's measurements of the effects of the storms in space were correlated with those from a series of earlier Pioneers still in orbit around the Sun. These four spacecraft — Pioneers 6, 7, 8, and 9 — were located at different azimuthal positions from Earth, but at solar distances only slightly different from that of Earth. The Pioneers measured the solar wind and its magnetic fields as it swept through space (Figure 5-8). Pioneer 9, close to Earth, saw the highest solar wind speeds ever recorded: 3.6 million km/hr (2.24 million mph). But, in crossing the 214 million kilometers (133 million miles) to Pioneer 10 in just 76 hr, the wind lost about half the velocity it had possessed when close to Earth.

Pioneer 10 measured the enormous temperature equivalent of the solar wind: 2 million K, which is similar to that of the solar corona itself.

Dr. John Wolfe, Pioneer Project Scientist, explained at the time:

> The velocity of the solar wind in the interplanetary medium is dependent on the temperature of the solar corona, and from a temperature point of view, the solar corona is quite inhomogeneous. Thus, the Sun emits both fast- and slow-moving plasma. The energy density of the solar wind is 100 times that of the interplanetary magnetic field, so the solar wind drags along and carries the magnetic field with it. This magnetic field not only screens incoming cosmic rays and prevents those with low energy originating outside the Solar System

Figure 5-7. In August 1972, an unprecendented event on the Sun allowed Pioneer 10 a unique opportunity to observe the solar wind and energetic solar particles. A series of immense flares erupted on the Sun and sprayed interplanetary space with highly energetic particles. (*Photo: National Oceanic and Atmospheric Administration*)

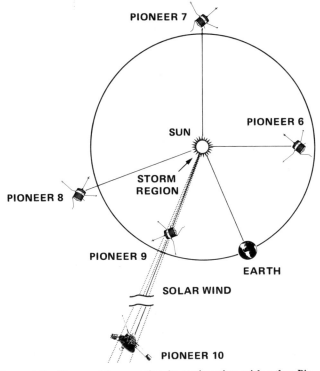

Figure 5-8. Pioneer 10, operating in conjunction with other Pioneer spacecraft closer to Earth, observed the distribution of the solar wind from these flares and how its characteristics change with increasing distance from the Sun.

Figure 5-10. Shifts of people maintained around-the-clock vigil on the Pioneer spacecraft for the several weeks during each encounter with Jupiter and Saturn.

Center, told newsmen gathered in the Main Auditorium at Ames for the historic Jupiter encounter (Figure 5-11):

This is an unusual event. The planet Jupiter, as you know, is an object that has been the subject of fairly extensive observation for almost 400 years. Galileo, who looked at the planet through his primitive telescope in 1610, discovered . . . the four brilliant moons that surround the planet. This observation provided, I think, the first really visible proof, as it were, that the Copernican model of the Solar System wasn't exactly the way it looks. Jupiter, there-

fore, served, perhaps, the function of quite profoundly changing the way we think about the Universe.

Charles F. Hall added: "We are really only twelve generations away from Galileo and his first crude look at the planet. Twelve generations later, we are actually there measuring many of the characteristics of the planet itself." (See Figure 5-12.)

Pioneer 10 had, by this time, already passed through the bow shock where Jupiter's magnetic field affects the solar wind. This took place about noon on November 16, at a distance of about 108.9 Jupiter radii, or about 6.4 million kilometers (4 million miles) — farther out than had been anticipated. The spacecraft's crossing of the shock was

80

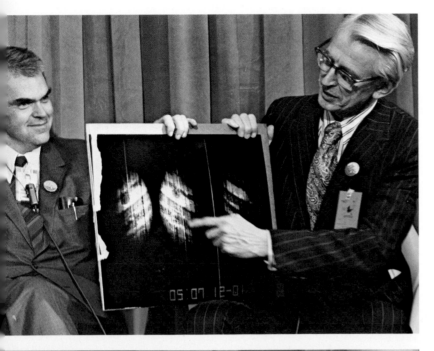

Figure 5-11. Dr. James C. Fletcher, NASA Administrator at the time of the first encounter of a spacecraft with giant Jupiter, and Dr. Hans Mark, then Director of Ames Research Center, briefed newsmen and visiting scientists gathered in the Main Auditorium at Ames Research Center.

Figure 5-12. Twelve generations after Galileo's first telescopic look at Jupiter, we are actually there making measurements, commented Charles F. Hall, then Pioneer Project Manager.

Figure 5-13. Dr. John H. Wolfe, Project Scientist, explained observations made by Pioneer 10 as it traversed the Jovian system.

indicated by an approximate 50% drop in solar wind speed, as recorded by Pioneer's instruments. This information, of course, arrived at Earth 45 min after the spacecraft measured the change in velocity. Before Pioneer encountered the shock, the solar wind blew on the spacecraft at 451 km/sec (280 miles/sec). Immediately after crossing the shock, the spacecraft's instruments showed that the velocity of the solar wind had dropped to about 225 km/sec (140 miles/sec), and its temperature rose from about 50,000 to 500,000 K. The spacecraft itself did not experience this temperature, of course; the highly rarefied plasma, although incredibly hot, had too little mass per unit volume to transfer significant quantities of heat to the spacecraft.

A day later, at noon on November 27, 1973, Pioneer 10 crossed the boundary between the shocked solar wind and the magnetic field of Jupiter — the magnetopause. The distance was 96.4 Jupiter radii. Explained Dr. John Wolfe (see Figure 5-13):

> The observation is that this is the point at which the pressure of plasma coming from the Sun, after it has gone through the shock wave, becomes equal to the pressure of Jupiter's magnetic field, and the plasma which is contained within that field. So the solar wind stopped at this point.

Although similar to that of Earth, this environment of Jupiter was discovered by Pioneer to be in some ways quite different. Near the boundary of Earth's magnetic field, all that holds off the solar wind is the strength of Earth's field. But for Jupiter, Pioneer found much plasma within Jupiter's magnetic field near the boundary, where it helps to hold off the solar wind. This additional barrier was found to be about equal to Jupiter's magnetic field. Pioneer also discovered that the magnetopause was relatively close to the bow shock.

Pioneer 10's instruments confirmed what radio astronomers had already postulated about the magnetic field of Jupiter: that it is inverted relative to that of Earth — its magnetic north pole is to the south. The science experiments showed, too, that the magnetosphere of Jupiter is markedly different from that of Earth, being flattened in its outer regions. This was inferred from the way Jupiter's magnetic field lines were stretched out from the planet in the outer regions. The Jovian magnetic field was also shown to be tilted from the planet's axis of rotation so that, at any point in space around the planet, the field appears to move up and down; the disk of the outer magnetosphere wobbles relative to the surrounding space.

As for Pioneer 10, none of its redundant circuits had yet been needed. So mission planners were optimistic that, even if some of the spacecraft's equipment were damaged during passage through the Jovian environment, there would still be backup equipment available for the flight beyond Jupiter.

The spacecraft had speeded up slightly over its anticipated course, however, and would arrive at Jupiter 1 min early — because Jupiter turned out to be slightly more massive than expected; as a result, its gravitational field was slightly stronger than had been calculated from Earth-based observations.

In the previous 24 days, thousands of commands had been transmitted to Pioneer 10. During that time, only one ground data system failed: a computer became overloaded but it recovered within 2 min. By this time, the numbers of commands were increasing daily from 400 to 2000 per day as Pioneer moved toward its closest approach to Jupiter. A special command sequence was developed to reconfigure the imaging photopolarimeter regardless of any spurious command functions that might be activated by the radiation. Also, a sequence of contingency commands was periodically transmitted so that the spacecraft could be corrected even before the telemetry signals telling of spurious commands could be received at Earth.

During the encounter, only one scientific objective was missed because of false commands generated by Jupiter's intense radiation — the close-in imaging of the satellite Io. The imaging photopolar-imeter responded to spurious commands 10 times, but the reconfiguration countered those commands so that only the image of Io and a few partial close-ups of Jupiter were lost.

Pictures of Jupiter had by this time been coming back for several days, each one built up from a number of scans as the rotating spacecraft swept the imaging photopolarimeter's narrow-angle telescope system's field of view across the disk of Jupiter. Twelve pictures of Jupiter were received at Earth on November 26, and many more on subsequent days. Images were returned in two colors, red and blue, from which a detailed color picture of the planet could be reconstructed later.

Quick-look pictures from the spacecraft were displayed on television screens in the Main Auditorium at Ames Research Center by the Pioneer Image Converter System (PICS). As the scans of data from the spacecraft arrived, they were placed alongside each other on the screen as a series of bars until the complete picture of the planet was assembled.

The PICS was developed by L. Ralph Baker of the University of Arizona. The system was designed to present a real-time display of Pioneer spin-scan images to allow scientists to monitor operation of the imaging photopolarimeter during encounter, and also to provide a video signal so that the images could be displayed to the press and made available to television networks. Thus, the public was able to view the results of this first flyby of Jupiter as it took place half a billion miles from Earth.

The imaging photopolarimeter scanned the planet in two colors, red and blue. But these colors, although chosen to get best scientific results from Jupiter, were not sufficient to produce a visually satisfactory image. If the red and blue images from Pioneer 10 had been simply mixed together, they would have produced a magenta image, quite unlike Jupiter and most unnatural to the human eye. Instead, the red and blue signals were used to make a synthetic green image so that a normal three-color combination could then be obtained (Figure 5-14).

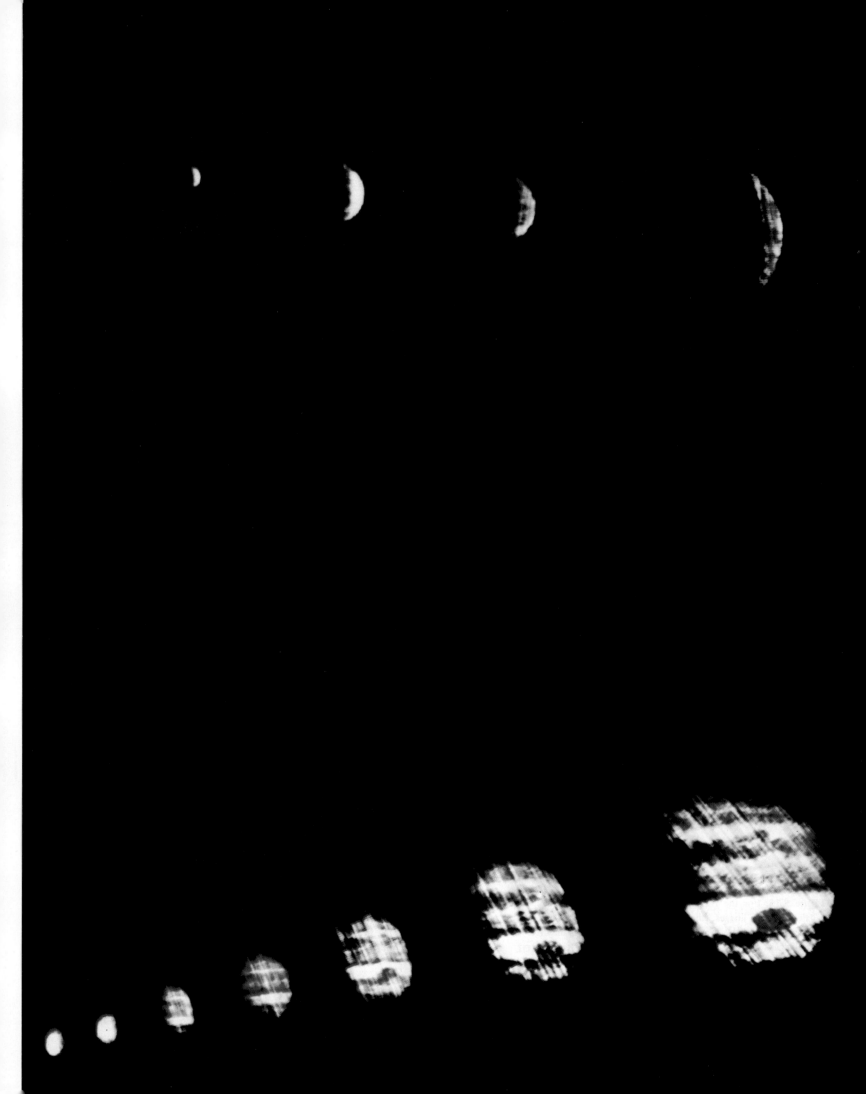

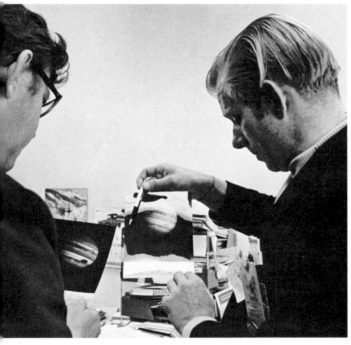

The following hours produced more unique crescent images of Jupiter as Pioneer 10 headed away from the planet. All other equipment performed as expected. Ultraviolet and infrared scans and meteoroid dust sampling proceeded according to plan.

Immediately after the close encounter, Robert Kraemer commented:

> The mission, by all standards, is written down right now as 100 percent successful. It is very hard to see how it (Pioneer 10) could have done its job any better. All elements went beyond the project team's expectations — getting off to a good launch a couple of years ago, tracking the spacecraft, getting all the data back, has been just a beautiful effort.

The spacecraft contractor's Project Manager from TRW Systems, B. J. O'Brien, said:

> We did see the radiation effects at about the points we predicted . . . the small indications of . . . failures . . . were precisely in those areas we would have predicted, namely, the power. We feel a little bit like Professor Higgins in Pygmalion who said, "We did it."

Project Science Chief, Richard O. Fimmel, commented: "This has been the most exciting day of my life!" Many of the principal investigators agreed wholeheartedly.

Pioneer 10 did what it was supposed to do: determine whether spacecraft could explore Jupiter despite the hazards of the Jovian environment. Pioneer 10 measured the severity of Jupiter's

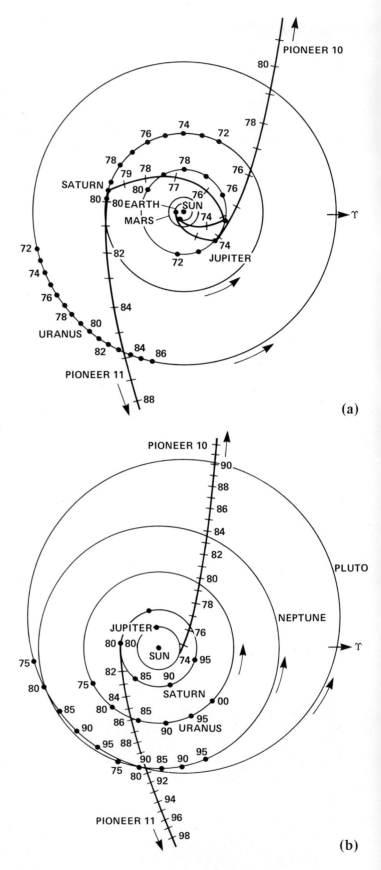

(a)

(b)

Figure 5-17. Sun-centered trajectories of Pioneer 10 and 11. (a) Time marks along each trajectory and on the orbits of the planets (to Uranus) represent the positions at 1-yr intervals. (b) The Solar System is shown on a smaller scale. The paths of the two Pioneer spacecraft are drawn beyond the orbit of Pluto. The planet's positions are shown here at 5-yr intervals. Closest approaches of Pioneer 11 to the outermost planets are: Uranus (6.2 AU) in 1985, Neptune (12.2 AU) in 1989, and Pluto (17.0 AU) in 1985. (An astronomical unit is Earth's mean distance from the Sun.)

environment and provided enough new data to whet our appetites for further exploration of the giant planets of the Solar System.

Afterward, Pioneer 10 headed for the outer reaches of the Solar System. It would cross the orbit of Saturn in 1976 and that of Uranus in 1979. By 1990, the spacecraft will cross the orbit of Pluto and then continue at over 40,000 km/hr (25,000 mph) into interstellar space. On its way out of our Solar System, Pioneer 10 will gather additional information about the behavior of the solar wind at extreme distances from the Sun.

Meanwhile, Pioneer 11 had been following Pioneer 10 on its way to a rendezvous with Jupiter. On April 11, 1973, the course of the spacecraft was changed slightly by an Earth-line velocity change maneuver. This correction aimed Pioneer 11 to pass to the left of Jupiter as viewed from Earth and about 20,000 km (12,400 miles) above the cloudtops. This aiming point was chosen to provide several flyby options, including a continued journey beyond Jupiter to Saturn, the choice of option to be made later in the mission by another maneuver.

With the spacecraft 11 million kilometers (7 million miles) along its way, the solar wind and cosmic ray instruments were sending valuable data about the interplanetary medium.

The trajectories of Pioneer 10 and Pioneer 11 as seen from the celestial north pole projected onto the ecliptic plane are shown in Figure 5-17 (drawn to two scales). During encounter with Jupiter, the flyby trajectory was such that the speed of Pioneer 11 would be almost doubled. The transfer of energy from Jupiter to the spacecraft boosted the spacecraft's speed just as effectively as a large rocket engine and flung Pioneer 11 toward Saturn. Pioneer 11's trajectory from Jupiter to Saturn was about three times longer than its path from the Earth to Jupiter. Along that trajectory to Saturn, Pioneer 11 would fly high above the plane of the ecliptic, reaching a height of 160 million kilometers (100 million miles) in the early part of 1976. Pioneer 11 would be the first spacecraft to probe deep space far from the ecliptic plane.

Pioneer 11 passed safely through the asteroid belt on March 20, 1974. The experiments on Pioneer 11 confirmed the findings of Pioneer 10 about the numbers of particles in the asteroid belt. As the second spacecraft traveled from Earth's orbit outward in the Solar System, the smallest particles (0.001 mm) detected by the spacecraft's instruments appeared to decline in number. Somewhat larger particles (0.01 to 0.1 mm) seemed to be evenly distributed all the way from Earth's orbit through the asteroid belt itself, with no increase within the belt. Still larger particles (0.1 to 1.0 mm) were found to be three times more numerous in the center of the belt as they are near Earth.

The modified, meteoroid-impact detector instrument onboard Pioneer 11 reported some findings that were different from those of Pioneer 10. The walls of the gas cells of the detector panels mounted behind the dish antenna were thicker on the Pioneer 11 instrument than on that of Pioneer 10. Because of the thicker cell walls, more massive particles were required to penetrate the walls on impact. Therefore, only particles from 0.02 to 0.1 mm in diameter (100-millionths to one-millionth of a gram) would be recorded.

For such particles, about half as many more gas-cell penetrations were found near Earth by Pioneer 11 than by Pioneer 10, which seemed to suggest that about equal numbers of small and large particles were present. However, between 180 million and 344 million kilometers (112 million and 214 million miles) from the Sun, Pioneer 11 encountered virtually no larger particles — its detector recorded only one penetration. In the asteroid belt, the larger particles appeared again, but only about one-sixth as many as in the total range measured by Pioneer 10. This appears to mean that, in the asteroid belt, smaller particles, 0.01 to 0.1 mm, are three times more common than larger particles.

Between Earth and the outer edge of the asteroid belt, Pioneer 11 counted 20 penetrations, 7 of them while the spacecraft was within the belt. The larger asteroidal particles, measured by the asteroid-meteoroid telescope, were mostly in the size range of 0.1 to 1.0 mm in diameter, one-millionth to one-thousandth of a gram. A few of the particles seen by Pioneer 10 were as large as 10 to 20 cm (4 to 8 in.). Analysis of the Pioneer 10 data suggested that there are almost three times more large particles inside the asteroid belt as between Earth and the belt. The data from Pioneer 11 confirmed this finding.

Particles in the center of the belt, which orbit the Sun at about 61,200 km/hr (38,000 mph), would penetrate 1-cm-thick aluminum, even if the particle weighed only 0.001 gm. But most of the particles seen by Pioneer 10 and Pioneer 11 were smaller, and the total number of such particles was found to be far lower than had been predicted before the Pioneer mission. Although the belt contains quite large bodies as well as tiny dust particles, dangerous concentrations of high-velocity dust particles, which would be hazardous to spacecraft, were not encountered by the two Pioneer spacecraft. This finding was confirmed when two much larger Voyager spacecraft crossed the belt in subsequent years on their way to Jupiter and Saturn.

Just after Pioneer 11 emerged from the asteroid belt, its trajectory was modified by command from Earth. On April 19, 1974, thrusters on the spacecraft were commanded to add another 63.7 m/sec (210.2 ft/sec) to the spacecraft's velocity, thereby correcting the aiming point at Jupiter to 43,000 km (26,725 miles) above the cloudtops. The main mission of Pioneer 11 at Jupiter was to penetrate deeper into the radiation belts. The inner radiation belt of the planet could easily destroy the electronics onboard the spacecraft if the intensity of particles continued to increase beyond the maximum measured by Pioneer 10 at its closest approach. (The closest approach of Pioneer 10 was 2.86 Jovian radii, that is, 132,252 km (82,000 miles) above the cloudtops.) Pioneer 11 was directed to approach to less than one-third the distance of Pioneer 10, from which distance it could make unique observations of both Jupiter and its environment. The close approach also

allowed the spacecraft to be accelerated by Jupiter to a velocity 55 times that of the muzzle velocity of a high-speed rifle bullet — 173,000 km/hr (108,000 mph) — so that it would be carried across the Solar System some 2.4 billion kilometers (1.5 billion miles) to Saturn.

Meanwhile, as Pioneer 11 cruised toward Jupiter, interest in this giant planet, sparked by the findings of Pioneer 10, was producing new discoveries from Earth-based observations.

Charles Kowal, a research assistant in astronomy at California Institute of Technology, Pasadena, developed a new technique to search for small objects near Jupiter. Using the Palomar Schmidt telescope's enormous light-gathering power, a special screen to mask the glare of Jupiter, and photographic plates baked in nitrogen gas to increase their sensitivity, Kowal discovered a thirteenth satellite of Jupiter in September 1974. A fourteenth satellite was discovered a year later while Pioneer 11 was on its way to Saturn. These satellites were too small to be seen by the imaging systems of the Pioneer spacecraft.

The trajectory of Pioneer 11 had been selected so that the spacecraft would approach Jupiter on the left side (as viewed from Earth) and in the planet's southern hemisphere, and then hurtle almost straight up through the intense radiation belts, thereby reducing the time it would be exposed to the radiation (Figure 5-18). B. J. O'Brien, Pioneer Project Manager at TRW Systems, where the Pioneer spacecraft were built, told the press just before encounter that the total radiation dosage Pioneer would be expected to receive would be less than that of Pioneer 10's, ". . . and we're betting that's what counts."

The problem was that the billions of electrons and protons trapped in Jupiter's magnetic field bombarded the spacecraft. Some of those particles traveled fast enough to dislodge electrons from atoms, and even whole atoms from molecules, within the spacecraft. When this happened to a critical part of the spacecraft's electronics, spurious

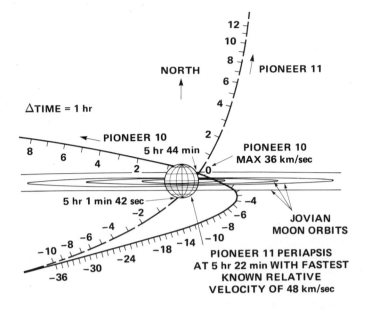

Figure 5-18. Pioneer 10 and 11 encounters with Jupiter as viewed from Earth. The hour time marks show the locations of the spacecraft relative to the periapsis target point, that is, the closest approach of each spacecraft to Jupiter.

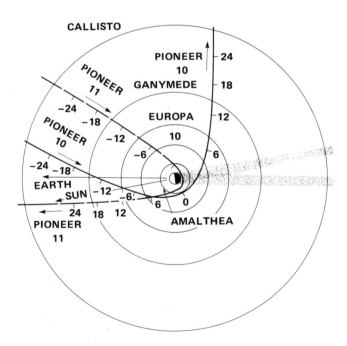

Figure 5-19. The encounter trajectories of Pioneers 10 and 11 with Jupiter as viewed from the celestial north pole. Pioneer 10 swung around Jupiter in a counterclockwise direction, but Pioneer 11 moved around along a clockwise course. Jupiter rotates counterclockwise in this view. The numbers alongside each trajectory show the time (in hr) before and after closest approach.

information could be generated or the electronics would fail completely. Explained O'Brien:

Pioneer 10 passed along the magnetic equator, where most energetic particles appear to concentrate. The spacecraft took lots of hits over a [relatively] long time. But Pioneer 11 will go in slowly, slip through the area of maximum radiation fast, and come out in the clear pretty quickly. The radiation counts will probably soar at a pace that will scare us half to death just before closest approach, but the total dose Pioneer 11 receives won't be as great as Pioneer 10 took because the time [of exposure] will be much shorter.

Pioneer 11 will be out of communication with Earth at the time of closest approach. It will have gone behind Jupiter at 9:01 p.m., 21 minutes before closest approach. Its onboard magnetic memory will be recording data for later transmission to Earth. Then we sit and wait . . . and fidget. At 9:44 p.m., 22 minutes after closest approach, Pioneer 11 will come out from behind Jupiter. But we have another 40 minutes wait before we hear anything because of the signal's travel time from the distance of Jupiter to the Earth. So, at 10:24 p.m., if Pioneer is still working, we'll hear that we made it.

The close path by Jupiter also provided a bonus in that it permitted images of the polar regions of the giant planet to be obtained by the spin-scan imaging system and the infrared radiometer, thereby providing views of Jupiter that could never be obtained by observation from Earth. Thus, Pioneer 11 was able to satisfy the need for a polar view of Jupiter as expressed at the first science meeting in 1970. And, unlike Pioneer 10, Pioneer 11 was directed to fly by Jupiter against the direction of the planet's rotation (Figure 5-19).

93

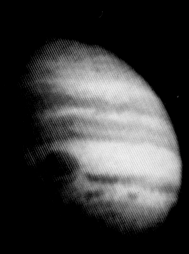

Figure 5-20. This series of PICS images shows views of Jupiter as
Pioneer 11 approached the planet from the south, flew by, and then
rose high above the north polar region.

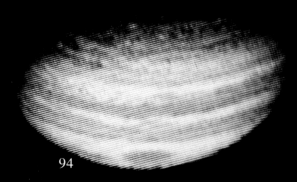

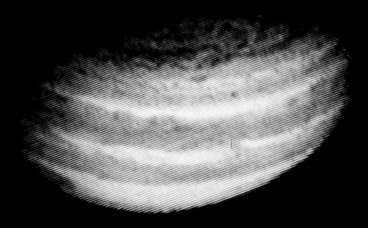

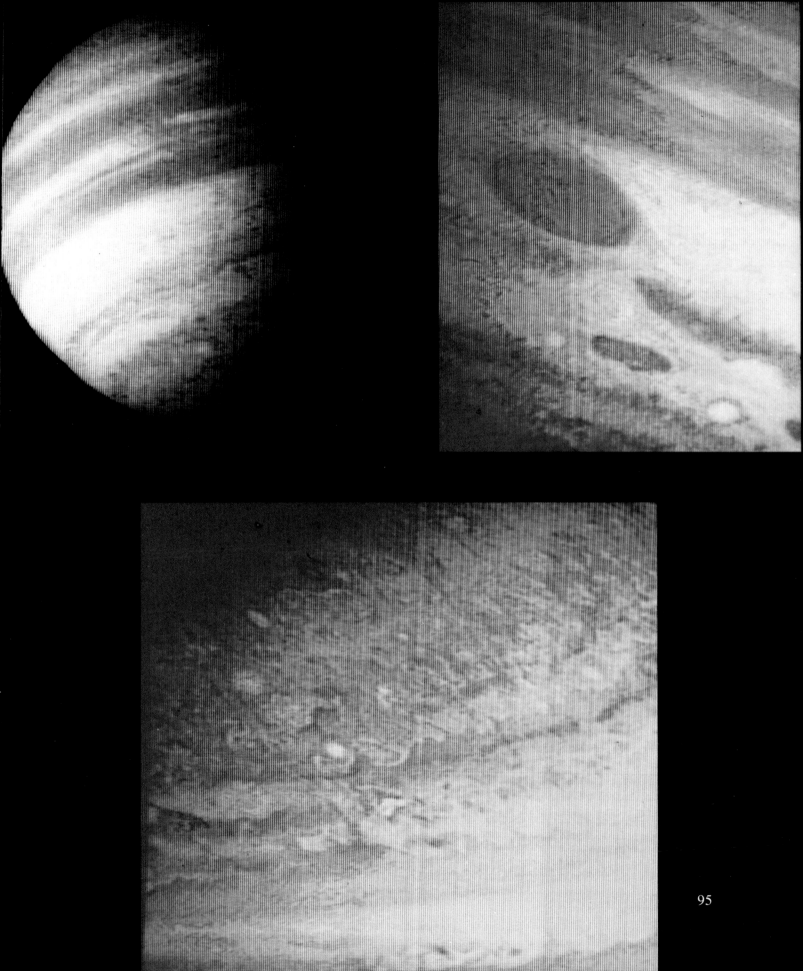

95

After passing in front of Jupiter as the planet moved along its orbit around the Sun, the spacecraft then went around the dark side of Jupiter and completed a circuit of the planet by crossing the spacecraft's own incoming trajectory before heading for Saturn.

The PICS images of Jupiter returned from the spacecraft (Figure 5-20) were displayed live to thousands of interested people over cable television in the San Francisco Bay area. During the encounter, several public halls, to which the television images and a running commentary by Apollo 15 astronaut Colonel A. Worden were relayed, were jammed for many hours.

Before its closest approach to Jupiter, the spacecraft's view of the planet showed the terminator near the left-hand edge of the disk. After closest approach, the spacecraft's view showed the terminator very near the upper right-hand edge of the disk. The south polar regions were seen before closest approach and the north polar regions afterward.

As with Pioneer 10, there were five phases to the encounter. The first lasted about 3 weeks, starting November 3, 1974, when the spacecraft passed from interplanetary space into the Jovian system, and covered the distance from about 24 million to 10 million kilometers (15 million to 6 million miles) from the planet.

The second phase covered entry of Pioneer 11 into the inner system, after penetration of the bow shock in the solar wind created by the interaction of Jupiter's magnetic field with the wind, on November 25, 1974, at 10:00 p.m. PST. At 9:00 p.m. PST on November 26, the spacecraft entered the magnetosphere where the magnetic field of Jupiter prevents the solar wind from approaching close to the planet. Pioneer 11 was by that time 7 million kilometers (4.3 million miles) from Jupiter. But at 10:20 a.m. PST on November 27, at a distance of 6.6 million kilometers (4.1 million miles), Pioneer 11 was overtaken by the inward-moving bow shock and was outside the magnetosphere for 5.5 hr before it crossed the bow shock again and returned to the magneto-

sphere at a distance of 6.44 million kilometers (4.0 million miles) from Jupiter. These repeated crossings of the bow shock, first experienced by Pioneer 10, confirmed the model of the Jovian magnetosphere that likened it to an unstable soft balloon buffeted by the solar wind and often squeezed in toward Jupiter on the side facing the Sun.

The third phase of the encounter was when Pioneer 11 continued flying through the outer magnetosphere from about 4.8 to 3.2 million kilometers (3 million to 2 million miles) from the planet.

Phase four, the period around closest approach, covered the day and a half before and after periapsis, during which the spacecraft's most detailed measurements and better spin-scan images of Jupiter and the large satellites were obtained.

During phase five, Pioneer 11 left Jupiter behind and repeated many of the earlier observations, but in reverse sequence.

On November 7, Pioneer crossed the orbit of Sinope, the outermost satellite of Jupiter. In the following few days, the spacecraft successively crossed the orbits of Pan (renamed Carame) and Andrastea (renamed Ananke). By November 21, Pioneer 11 had crossed the orbit of Hera (renamed Elara) at just over 11.75 million kilometers (7 million miles) from Jupiter; it later crossed the orbits of Demeter (renamed Lysithea) and Hestia (renamed Himalia). But the Jovian system is so large that, despite Pioneer 11's enormous speed, it was not until December 1, the day before closest approach, that the spacecraft began to cross the orbits of the Galilean satellites. There were no really close approaches to those satellites. Pioneer 11 came within 786,000 km (488,420 miles) of Callisto, within 692,200 km (430,130 miles) of Ganymede, and within 265,500 km (164,981 miles) of Io. The spacecraft passed within 587,000 km (364,760 miles) of Europa and within 127,000 km (78,920 miles) of the innermost satellite, Amalthea. Spin-scan images were obtained of several of these satellites (see chapter 9).

By the time Pioneer 11 entered the orbits of the

inner satellites, television screens at Ames Research Center were displaying good-sized images of Jupiter showing an orange and gray-white striped sphere with detailed cloud features and a prominent Great Red Spot (see figure 5-20).

The excellent image of the Great Red Spot (shown in chapter 9) was obtained as a result of quick revision to the command sequences for the spacecraft. Pioneer 11 was flying by Jupiter at high speed and in opposite direction to the planet's rotation. The combination of these two rapid motions made it mandatory that the timing of a close-in image of the spot be extremely precise.

Months before the encounter, Lyn R. Doose of the University of Arizona, working with the imaging photopolarimetry team, contacted ground-based observatories to determine the spot's position and drift rate to estimate where it would be at the precise time of Pioneer 11's flyby. When a final position had been established, a series of computer-generated drawings was prepared, simulating how the planet would appear to the spacecraft at 1-hr intervals during the close encounter. From these drawings, the best observing opportunity was selected and reserved for imaging the Great Red Spot; other activity of the imaging photopolarimeter was arranged around the timing for the Great Red Spot image.

Just before the encounter, Doose explained:

A somewhat different approach from that used on Pioneer 10 would be employed. The Great Red Spot would be scanned nearer to the center of the planet's illuminated hemisphere so that it would not be foreshortened and would be well away from the terminator and evenly illuminated.

The commands to the imaging photopolarimeter were written, rewritten, checked, and rechecked. Only days before the flyby we discovered an error. The time for obtaining the best image of the spot as derived from the computer-generated drawings was referenced to where the telescope should execute the

commands, but had been interpreted as being when the commands should be transmitted.

The rotation of Jupiter, coupled with the motion of the spacecraft, would have put the Great Red Spot outside the field of view of the image.

For 2 days the imaging command sequence for the several hours before closest approach was revised. New commands were written and command files were prepared for transmission to the spacecraft in the tight command sequence. With these last-minute changes, the Great Red Spot sequence worked perfectly and a unique image of the Great Red Spot was obtained (see Figure 9-11).

In addition to presenting higher latitudes to the spin-scan imaging system, the flyby trajectory chosen for Pioneer 11 allowed the magnetic field and radiation environment to be explored to higher latitudes of the magnetosphere. Also, in contrast to Pioneer 10, which maintained an almost constant view relative to Jupiter for several hours during closest approach (because its direction of travel was the same as the direction of rotation of Jupiter), Pioneer 11 traveled in a direction opposite that of Jupiter's rotation and traversed a full circle of longitude during its close-in observations during the 4 hr in which periapsis was centered.

Approximately 1300 commands were transmitted to Pioneer 11 on each of 2 days at closest approach. Many of these commands were intended to ensure that the equipment carried by the spacecraft would continue to operate in a correct configuration despite radiation effects. Thus, the spacecraft was repeatedly commanded to the correct data format, to the correct data-bit rate, to keep its transmitter switched on, and to keep the scientific instruments operating. Also, the spin-scan imaging photopolarimeter, which lost several important images during the Pioneer 10 encounter because of false commands generated by radiation, was periodically reset (indexed) to the correct aspect angle for planetary imaging. This command technique, which had proved invaluable during the encounter of Pioneer 10, was expanded in scope for the more rigorous encounter of Pioneer 11.

A more serious problem than the radiation environment of Jupiter was a threatened strike of diesel operators in Australia which endangered the mission in the last few hours before the critical and unique periapsis passage. Fortunately, the strikers permitted technical personnel to operate the ground station for the encounter. Had this not been permitted, the mission would have lost 6 to 8 hr of scientific data each day. However, flight operations could not be certain that the Deep Space Network station at Canberra would indeed be available for the encounter — the strike situation was that serious. In the less than 30 min available, the encounter sequence was reprogrammed to enable the Goldstone Deep Space Network station to maintain communications with the spacecraft for a longer period than normally, almost until the spacecraft set on the Goldstone horizon. This also required that the rate at which data were transmitted to Earth be dropped from 2048 to 1024 bits/sec. So the mission was more seriously endangered by social problems on Earth than by the harsh, alien environment half a billion miles away.

Although the spacecraft went behind Jupiter at 9:02 p.m. PST on December 2, telemetered signals continued until 9:42 p.m. because of the time delay in the radio waves' propagation over the great distance to Earth. Everyone waited anxiously. It was during this occultation that the spacecraft hurtled through its closest approach to the giant planet, skimming 43,000 km (26,725 miles) above the cloudtops as it passed through the greatest intensity of the radiation belts.

Would the spacecraft survive? Pioneer 11 was scheduled to emerge from behind Jupiter at 9:44 p.m. PST, 22 min after closest approach. But the signals, if they were still being transmitted from the spacecraft, would not arrive at Earth until 10:24 p.m.

Eleven seconds after 10:24 p.m. PST, the Deep Space Network station at Canberra, Australia, picked up the whisper-faint signal from the space-

craft and relayed it to the Pioneer Mission Operations Center at Ames Research Center. Engineers, scientists, and newsmen covering the event at the Center cheered. Ten seconds later the big antenna at Goldstone in the Mojave Desert picked up the signal, too. All was well. Pioneer 11 had survived its encounter with this giant of our Solar System. Again, the tail of the dragon had been given a mighty tug.

Although there were no serious problems during flyby, there were irregularities in the functioning of the plasma analyzer, the infrared radiometer, the meteoroid detector, and the spin-scan imaging system. Also there was a small decrease in output current of the spacecraft's power system; but this was less than that experienced by Pioneer 10 and caused no difficulties.

The most serious problem was again spurious commands that caused the infrared radiometer to miss observing the northern hemisphere of Jupiter despite the contingency commands. As soon as the signals reached Earth and the problem was detected, the Project Science Chief and the science advisor immediately prepared a 108-command sequence to correct the settings of the infrared radiometer's register, thereby saving 50% of the planned observations of the northern hemisphere.

In the next few hours, scientists were able to report the details of the radiation belts and to inspect the tremendously detailed spin-scan images of the northern hemisphere of Jupiter that were returned to Earth. Predictions of the high-energy electron intensity during close encounter proved to be correct, but, surprisingly, the measured proton flux was about 1/10 that predicted (based on extrapolations from Pioneer 10 data). Pioneer 11 showed that near the planet the radiation belt is intense but occupies a smaller volume than expected. Although Pioneers 10 and 11 found shells of extremely high-energy protons near Jupiter's magnetic equator, the shells were dangerous only at low latitudes and posed a relatively minor hazard to spacecraft flying through them at highly inclined trajectories. Also, the intensity of high-energy electrons was found to be only slightly higher than that found by Pioneer 10, even though Pioneer 11 went much closer to the planet. But Pioneer 11 also found a flux of high-energy electrons at higher latitudes that was greater than expected from the measurements made by Pioneer 10.

Again the picture emerged of an enormous spinning magnetic field buffeted by the solar wind and stirred by Amalthea and the Galilean satellites.

During this second encounter, Pioneer 11 determined very accurately the mass of Callisto (1.47 lunar masses). Also, the close approach provided information to determine more accurately the gravitational field of Jupiter itself.

In making the first observations of Jupiter's immense polar regions (Figure 5-21), Pioneer 11 found that the planet's cloudtops are substantially lower at the poles than at the equator, and they are covered by a thicker but transparent atmosphere. Although there is much less evidence of rapid atmospheric circulation at the poles than at the equator, the polar area unexpectedly showed many small convective cells, dwarfing similar thunderstorms that occur on Earth. Blue sky, visible at the poles, was attributed to the same cause as terrestrial blue skies — to multiple molecular scattering of light by gases of the transparent atmosphere at Jupiter's poles.

Many more flow features were revealed in the clouds around the Great Red Spot than were seen a year previously by Pioneer 10. And new details were revealed within the spot which suggested convection and circulation patterns. The center of the spot appeared brighter than its edges.

Immediately after the encounter with Jupiter, Pioneer 11 was officially renamed Pioneer Saturn as it headed to an exploration of the next outer giant planet of our Solar System. The spacecraft is, however, referred to as Pioneer 11 throughout this book.

Several weeks after the Jupiter encounter, problems again arose with spurious commands that this time could not be attributed to radiation. The problem continued for several months as Pio-

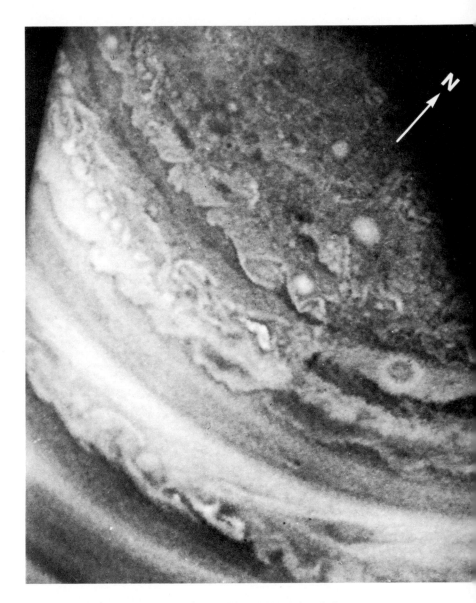

Figure 5-21. Pioneer 11 obtained these first photographs of the polar region of Jupiter which show that cloud patterns change dramatically between equatorial regions and the poles.

neer 11 headed toward Saturn. Analysis of special test results indicated that the asteroid-meteoroid detector had been damaged by radiation during the encounter with Jupiter and that it was the source of signals responsible for the spurious commands. The instrument was turned off and the spurious commands ended. But in the series of tests to isolate the cause of the spurious commands by turning off each piece of equipment in turn, the plasma analyzer had been switched off. When commanded on again, the instrument did not produce data even though its power came on. Because of its importance for the flyby of Saturn, this instrument was subjected to further, special command sequences in an effort to reestablish data output, but without success at this time.

After its encounter with Jupiter, Pioneer 11 looped high above the ecliptic plane and across the Solar System on its voyage to Saturn. By the end of May 1976, Pioneer 11 was halfway along its roughly 2.5-billion kilometer (1.5-billion-mile) flight between the two giant planets. And it was more than 1 AU above the ecliptic plane.

Some significant discoveries were made about the magnetic field of the Sun. At almost 160 million kilometers (100 million miles) above the ecliptic plane, the spacecraft was about 16° above the equatorial plane of the Sun. Measurements of the solar magnetic field by instruments onboard the Pioneer spacecraft showed that solar rotation produces a warped current sheet that separates the north and south magnetic fields of the Sun. As a consequence, the current sheet seems to move up and down as seen from Earth and from the other planets. Spacecraft close to the ecliptic plane, where all but Pioneer 11 had previously been confined, see a reversal of the solar field each time the current sheet passes through their paths (Figure 5-22). Instead of having a complex magnetic field broken into many sectors, as physicists had thought, the Sun was found to have a relatively simple north-pole/south-pole configuration, somewhat complex, but in many ways like the fields of Earth and Jupiter.

Two flyby trajectories were tentatively suggested for the encounter with Saturn: one would have penetrated the plane of the rings just outside the outer visible ring (A ring); the other would have penetrated inside the visible rings at about 1.15 Saturn radii.

The celestial mechanics objectives of the Saturn encounter might best be exploited by a flyby that carried the spacecraft inside the innermost visible ring and about 9000 km (5600 miles) above the cloudtops (Figure 5-23). Such a close approach to the planet would not only most accurately define

Saturn's gravitational field, but also provide data that, when combined with corresponding observations from a more distant Voyager flyby in 1981, would allow a good estimate of the mass of the ring system. The close approach would also provide information about the internal structure and shape of Saturn. Even if the spacecraft were damaged by its passage through the ring plane, valuable gravitational data would still be obtained before its penetration of the ring plane. In addition, the close approach would make it possible to distinguish an internal source from an external source of magnetospheric particles.

Scientists and mission planners were faced with a dilemma. Pioneer 11 offered the only chance for many years to explore the environment of Saturn near the planet. The two Voyager spacecraft that would follow the trail blazed by Pioneer 11 to Saturn were constrained to trajectories that carried them past Saturn at a much greater distance. As a result, they would not be able to provide information about the inner Saturnian particles and field environment. Moreover, no further missions to Saturn were planned by the United States. Eleven of the 12 principal investigators on the Pioneer program favored a trajectory for Pioneer 11 that would pass inside the bright rings and provide a very close approach to Saturn.

Either of the two trajectories could be chosen as late as 1977, when the spacecraft would be aligned in space so that it could be most accurately maneuvered to a selected course. During such a maneuver, the time of arrival at Saturn would be changed to ensure coverage by two stations of the Deep Space Network of the period of closest approach to the planet. In this way, there would be a better chance of obtaining all the data from this unique encounter with Saturn.

If Pioneer to Saturn survived its passage through the ring plane and through whatever radiation environment existed there, its subsequent close approach to the largest Saturnian satellite, Titan, could be expected to provide a more accurate measurement of Titan's mass. Also, spin-scan images of Titan might make it possible to search for surface

Figure 5-22. In its voyage across the Solar System high above the plane of the ecliptic, Pioneer to Saturn made important discoveries about the structure of the magnetic field of the Sun – the warped current sheet shown here.

markings. The photopolarimeter and the infrared radiometer could provide valuable information about the atmosphere of the huge satellite and about its temperature.

Titan orbits Saturn in just under 16 days, at a mean distance of 1,222,000 km (759,300 miles). Its diameter is about 4800 km (3000 miles). From Earth-based observations, Titan was known to have an atmosphere, the constituents of which were believed to be of a type that might have supported primitive life forms on Earth before the terrestrial atmosphere became oxygen-enriched. So the satel-

lite was regarded by some scientists as a prime candidate among bodies of the Solar System as one that might support life.

A complication in selecting the time of arrival of Pioneer at Saturn was the motion of Earth around the Sun. As Saturn moved relative to Earth to pass behind the Sun as seen from Earth, radio noise from the Sun would interfere with the faint radio signals from the spacecraft. So arrival at Saturn had to be timed in advance of Saturn's moving into conjunction with the Sun on September 11, 1979. The Sun-Earth-spacecraft angle was

101

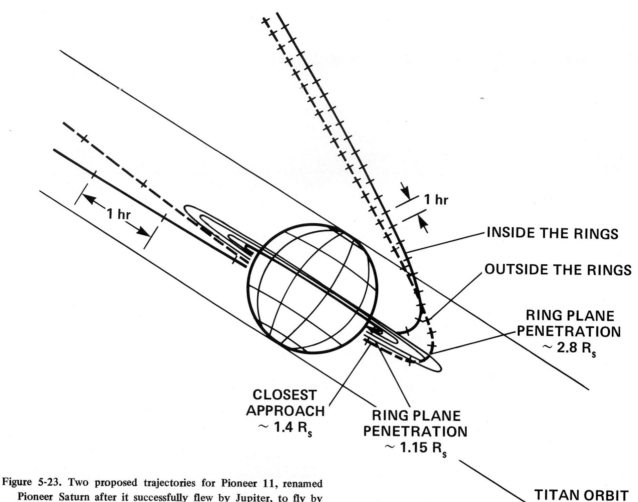

1 hr

1 hr

INSIDE THE RINGS

OUTSIDE THE RINGS

RING PLANE
PENETRATION
~ 2.8 R$_s$

CLOSEST
APPROACH
~ 1.4 R$_s$

RING PLANE
PENETRATION
~ 1.15 R$_s$

TITAN ORBIT

Figure 5-23. Two proposed trajectories for Pioneer 11, renamed Pioneer Saturn after it successfully flew by Jupiter, to fly by Saturn. One trajectory would carry the spacecraft outside the rings, the other inside the rings.

closing at about 1°/day around the time of encounter, so moving the encounter forward in time provided an opportunity for a subsequent encounter with Titan that would still allow radio signals to be received from the spacecraft. Unfortunately, there would be a period on the outward leg of the flight beyond Saturn during which some data about particles and fields would be lost because the radio signals from the spacecraft would be obscured by the radio noise of the Sun.

At the distance of Saturn, it was also necessary to accept a reduced rate at which data could be transmitted to Earth during the encounter. A rate of only 256 bits/sec (possibly 512 bits/sec) was anticipated, compared with 2048 bits/sec at the time of encounter with Jupiter. The lower bit rate primarily affected the data from imaging, which

102

required data to be sampled and transmitted rapidly. The effect was to reduce the image scans to smaller sectors of about one-half to one-quarter those possible at Jupiter. However, improvements to the Deep Space Network enabled a rate of 1024 bits/sec to be used for part of each station's pass.

Final course targeting for Pioneer 11 was completed during the first part of 1978. NASA Headquarters decided that the trajectory for the spacecraft's encounter with Saturn should pass outside the bright visible rings. The course correction needed to aim Pioneer toward this trajectory involved a series of timed rocket thrusts that locked the spacecraft onto a trajectory that would bring it to within 35,400 km (22,000 miles) of the edge of Saturn's outer bright visible ring (A ring).

The spacecraft would then swing under the plane of the rings to 21,400 km (13,300 miles) from the cloudtops. Later, this trajectory would carry Pioneer 11 within 355,600 km (221,000 miles) of Titan, the largest of Saturn's known satellites. The flyby chosen (Figure 5-24) was called a balanced flyby because the inbound descending and outbound ascending courses were the same distance from Saturn at the crossing of the ring plane, namely, 112,000 km (70,000 miles). The inclination of the spacecraft's trajectory to the ring plane would be 6.6°, with the trajectory's closest approach in the southern hemisphere of the planet. Earth and solar occultations would occur shortly after periapsis. During Earth occultation, the spacecraft would be out of communication; during solar occultation it would pass through the shadow of Saturn.

The most crucial moment of the Pioneer mission to Saturn would be on the morning of September 1, 1979, when Pioneer would first pass through the ring plane. An impact with a fragment orbiting in the E ring, believed to lie outside the A ring, could destroy the spacecraft. The spacecraft would pass through the ring plane in only 0.8 sec because of the high speed of the spacecraft and the thinness of the rings.

Meanwhile, by July 11, 1979, Pioneer 10 had crossed the orbit of the planet Uranus at a distance of 2.9 billion kilometers (1.8 billion miles) from the Sun. Pioneer 10 did not pass close to the planet, however, because Uranus was nearly halfway around its orbit on the other side of the Sun, 8.7 billion kilometers (5.4 billion miles) from Pioneer 10. The spacecraft, heading in the general direction of the star Aldebaran in the constellation Taurus, will reach the orbit of Pluto in 1990.

As the encounter period for Pioneer 11 approached, a precession maneuver was necessary to orient the spacecraft correctly. One of a pair of attitude thrusters malfunctioned. Controllers issued commands to switch to backup thrusters and the maneuver was completed successfully.

The 2-month Saturn encounter period started on August 2, 1979, when the Pioneer spacecraft was

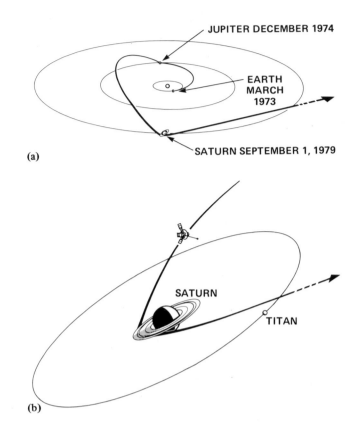

Figure 5-24. After its voyage across the Solar System (a), Pioneer 11 flew past Saturn along a balanced flyby trajectory (b). The spacecraft crossed the plane of the rings once inbound and once outbound, both at the same distance from Saturn. Closest approach to Saturn took place below the plane of the rings in the southern hemisphere of Saturn.

1.5 billion kilometers (932 million miles) from Earth. Ten-hour daily tracking began with two 64-m (210-ft) antennas in Spain and Australia. At the time, the spacecraft was hurtling toward Saturn at 30,600 km/hr (19,000 mph).

Four days later, tracking was increased to cover 18 hr each day and the large antenna at Goldstone in California joined the team of tracking stations. Then the various scientific instruments were exercised to ensure that they were functioning correctly for the encounter. They all were — after an epic journey of 6.5 years over a distance of 3.2 billion kilometers (2 billion miles).

Even the solar wind instrument, which had stopped providing data after the Jupiter encounter, had been revived — despite earlier attempts that were unsuccessful. Virtually every command possible was sent to the instrument but it did not respond. An analysis indicated that the malfunction was probably in the digital logic section of the instrument and had been caused by exposure to radiation at Jupiter followed by the low temperature reached when the instrument was turned off later during a power shutdown on the spacecraft to identify an intermittent fault. The instrument was left inoperable until late in October 1977. Then a series of power-on, power-off, and other commands was sent to the instrument. Success came when the instrument was thermally shocked by allowing it to cool down to a very low temperature, followed by a command to put maximum voltage on the instrument and to instruct it to operate in its fastest mode. This jolted the instrument. Nothing happened immediately, but by December 3, 1977, the instrument began to operate normally and continued to do so for the rest of the mission.

An improved PICS was developed to produce colored images of Saturn quickly during the encounter. During the earlier encounters with Jupiter, the colored photographs of the images had not been available until several hours after the data were received at Earth. During the Saturn encounter, as at Jupiter, the PICS converted the digital signal from the spacecraft to a picture, added a green image to produce acceptable color, and stored the video signal on a disk. However, during the Saturn encounter, the signal was then transferred from the disk to a color camera system designed and developed by Dunn Instruments, which transformed the video images into photographic color prints. This color camera reproduced the image of the planet on 8- by 10-in. Polaroid instant film and simultaneously recorded it on 35-mm and 120 size color transparency film. As with earlier encounters, the system displayed the colored pictures on TV screens within only a few minutes of their reception at Earth.

The first spin-scan test images successfully showed the disk of the planet with the rings visible as faint outlines around it. At a distance of

1.6 billion kilometers (1 billion miles) from Earth, Pioneer 11's spin axis had to be turned slightly on August 15. The spin axis had been kept pointing toward Earth so that the large antenna on the spacecraft would also point toward Earth. But to allow the UV photometer to view Saturn during the approach, the spin axis had to be moved. Controllers at Ames Research Center issued commands to fire two 1-sec burns of Pioneer's thrusters, moving the spacecraft's axis 1.2° to the left. This maneuver allowed the ultraviolet instrument to begin observing Saturn for 4 days, searching for evidence of the amounts of atmospheric hydrogen and helium, and gathering other data about the planet and its ring and satellite systems. On August 16, the coverage by the tracking stations was extended to 24 hr/day. Pioneer was 12.7 million kilometers (8 million miles) from Saturn.

Activity intensified on August 20. The thrusters were again fired to bring the antenna back to point within 0.5° of Earth. The spin-scan imaging photopolarimeter began taking its series of pictures of the planet. On August 25, simultaneous tracking by two Deep Space Network stations began so that information could be transferred at a higher bit rate from the spacecraft to Earth.

On August 27, the orbit of Phoebe, the most distant of Saturn's known satellites, was crossed. Pioneer 11 was then in the Saturnian system. But despite the spacecraft's tremendous speed of 33,100 km/hr (20,500 mph), which was increasing under the influence of Saturn's enormous gravity, it would take another 5 days to reach its point of closest approach. However, by this time, preliminary scientific findings were already being made.

Some of the most spectacular pictures from any space mission were returned to Earth when Pioneer obtained pictures of the side of Saturn's ring system on which sunlight was not shining directly. These pictures provided information that could never be obtained by observations from Earth. Those rings, which normally seem bright when observed from Earth, appeared dark in the Pioneer pictures, and the dark gaps in the rings seen from

Earth appeared as bright rings in the pictures from the spacecraft (Figure 5-25).

The images revealed roughly equal quantities of ring material in the region of Cassini's division between the two brightest rings and in the faint inner ring known as the crepe or C ring. This discovery was possible because Pioneer had a vantage point denied to Earth-based astronomers. The spacecraft was high above the plane of the rings and was looking at their shadowed side, unilluminated by the Sun. The spacecraft saw light through gaps in the rings scattered by particles there. The reverse images showed the normally bright rings as dark areas and the dark gaps between the rings as light areas. But there were some unexpected results. There was no immediate evidence from the Pioneer data for an inner D ring believed to be present between the C ring and the cloudtops, nor for a faint E ring that observers from Earth had claimed as being present outside the A ring.

The B ring appeared quite dark, but some light filtered through it in its inner regions. The outer region of the ring was, however, completely opaque even at the highest gain of the imaging system. Experimenters were surprised to find so much light scattered through Cassini's division, an effect that implied many more particles in the division than had been expected.

On August 30, there were still no signs in the telemetered data that Pioneer 11 had crossed through the bow shock of Saturn, an event that would have confirmed that Saturn had a magnetic

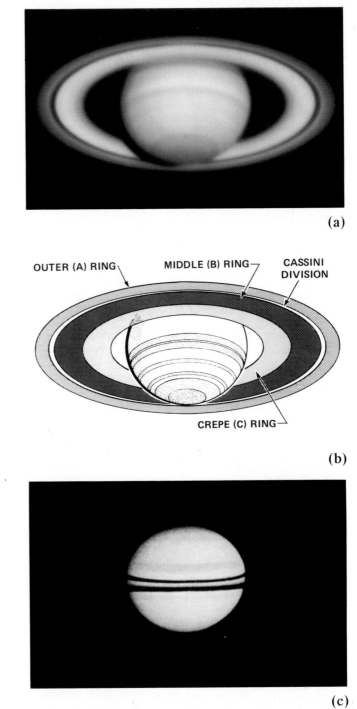

(a)

(b)

(c)

Figure 5-25. The faces of Saturn and its rings. (a) A high-quality contemporary Earth-based view of the planet photographed at the Catalina Observatory, University of Arizona. (b) A drawing identifying the main rings and Cassini's division. (c) A picture from Pioneer 11 from a distance of 2.5 million kilometers which shows the rings illuminated from behind to reveal completely new structural details.

105

field. But by this time the images showed dark polar regions and some faint markings on the disk. It was becoming quite clear, however, as suspected from Earth-based observations, that the features on the clouds of Saturn are much less clearly defined than those on Jupiter, perhaps because of the lower temperature of Saturn, which allows a high-altitude haze of ammonia to form and mask the details in the atmosphere at lower altitudes. Generally, the planet appeared free of red spots or white ovals of the type seen on Jupiter.

By the time the spacecraft was ready for its close encounter with Saturn, controllers had sent some 11,000 commands to it in a 1-month period. Six key retirees from the project returned for the encounter so that there would be a sufficient number of experienced CMOs (Chief of Mission Operations) for the 24-hr watches. These men, affectionately referred to as the "over-the-hill gang," were Joseph L. Frank, Robert U. Hofstetter, Ralph W. Holtzclaw, George C. James, Norman J. Martin, and J. Richard Spahr.

All was nearly ready for the big event. However, 25% of the telemetered data was being lost because of solar activity. In fact, three solar-related activities, in process when Pioneer 11 reached Saturn, were significant to the Pioneer mission. First, a strong interplanetary solar wind was buffeting the planet's magnetosphere and pushing it inward toward Saturn. Second, an energetic particle event on the Sun about a week before Pioneer arrived at Saturn was affecting the distribution of particles inside the planet's magnetosphere and masking any energetic particles that might be emanating from it. Third, signals from Pioneer had to pass near the Sun at a time of maximum solar activity. The interplanetary electron density and the degree to which magnetic fields were chaotic were both high at this time, thereby adversely affecting passage of data by radio from the spacecraft to Earth.

As a result of the third solar activity, project engineers decided to lower the telemetry rate from 1024 bits/sec to 512 bits/sec for the spacecraft's passage through the ring plane. Although this would not affect most of the data being

sampled by the spacecraft, it would limit the scanning fields of the imaging photopolarimeter and the infrared radiometer. No data were lost at the 512-bits/sec rate during the encounter. Scientists were actually obtaining more information from Saturn than had been expected when Pioneer left Jupiter. At that time it was expected that a maximum bit rate of only 256/sec could be obtained over the distance from Saturn to Earth. However, improvements to the Deep Space Network allowed a rate of 512 bits/sec and sometimes 1024 bits/sec during the encounter with Saturn.

The data from the spacecraft traveled at 300,000 km/sec (186,000 mps) — the speed of light — over the 1.6 billion kilometers (1 billion miles) to Earth. At a bit rate of 1024 bits/sec, this meant that at any given time there were 5.5 million bits of data strung through space like digital beads on an invisible thread between the spacecraft and Earth. Each bit was separated on either side by a distance of 293 km (182 miles).

At 6:00 a.m. PDT on August 31, Pioneer crossed Saturn's bow shock at a distance of 1.45 million kilometers (898,500 miles), much closer than the 4.7 million kilometers (3.5 million miles) that had been speculated, and showed that Saturn has a magnetic field — a major discovery by Pioneer. The magnetosphere of Saturn appeared to be about 1000 times stronger than Earth's, but only 1/20 that of Jupiter. The magnetic field was about 1/5 that predicted. The spacecraft stayed inside the shock for about a half hour and then the solar wind pushed the shock in beyond the spacecraft. Several passages through the shock were subsequently recorded.

Later, as the spacecraft penetrated closer to Saturn, several radiation belts were detected, with a complete cutoff of all energetic particles at the distance of the outermost ring. The rings appeared to absorb the charged particles from the radiation belts, thereby creating an environment that is one of the best shielded regions of our Solar System. Even in the radiation belts, the intensity of charged particles was much lower than in the belts of Jupiter. Pioneer had discovered that Saturn does not

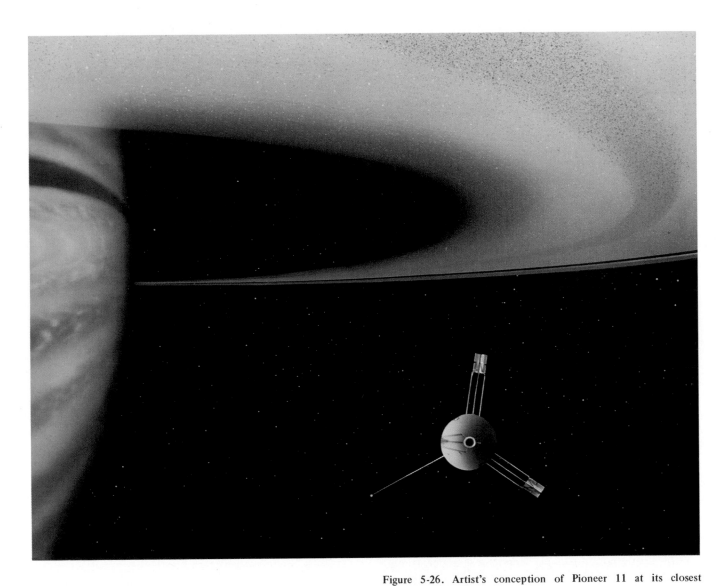

Figure 5-26. Artist's conception of Pioneer 11 at its closest approach to Saturn, speeding along beneath the magnificent ring system. Pictures could not be obtained at this time because of the high speed of the spacecraft and its closeness to both the planet and its ring system.

present a radiation hazard to close-flying spacecraft.

The spacecraft continued to plunge toward Saturn and, at 7:36 a.m. PDT on September 1, it crossed the plane of the rings for the first time, at a speed of 112,000 km/hr (70,000 mph). But scientists and project engineers had to wait 86 min, until 9:02 a.m. PDT, for the signals to reach Earth informing them that the crossing had been successful and the spacecraft was not damaged. Before the crossing there had been speculation that particles outside the A ring might have been sufficiently numerous to silence Pioneer. The meteoroid detector registered two hits on the way in, another close to periapsis, and two more when the spacecraft was flying below the rings behind the planet, thereby confirming the presence of some particles, with diameters of 10 μm or larger, near the ring plane. The survival of the spacecraft itself in its passage through the ring plane provided the most convincing evidence of the absence of a dangerous concentration of dust in this region.

Next, Pioneer skimmed along near the rings, below their illuminated side (Figure 5-26), moving too fast to obtain images of the rings. This was disappointing, but the geometry was unsuitable; in the time available, the spacecraft could not be commanded to roll the amount needed to obtain images during this close passage. At 9:31 a.m., Pioneer hurtled through its closest approach to Saturn at 114,150 km/hr (70,900 mph) at a distance of only 20,930 km (13,000 miles) above the cloud-tops. This was an incredible feat of navigation. After a 6.5-yr flight of some 3.2 billion kilometers (2 billion miles) across the Solar System, and after its close approach to Jupiter, the tiny spacecraft had reached a precise target in space and time some 1.6 billion kilometers (1 billion miles) from its launch site in Florida.

One minute after Pioneer's closest approach to Saturn, the telemetry was cut off as the spacecraft passed behind the planet. This radio blackout ended at 10:50 a.m. A short while later, at 11:35 a.m., the spacecraft again crossed the plane of the rings. Because these events could not be confirmed on Earth until the radio signals reached the Deep Space Network antennas some 86 min after leaving the spacecraft, project engineers did not know until 1:01 p.m. PDT that the Saturn flyby, with its second crossing of the ring plane, had been completely successful and that the spacecraft had survived for a flyby of Titan and an extended mission in search of the heliopause.

The close encounter had produced some exciting new results. Several additional satellites of Saturn were discovered from absorptions of charged particles — the first time the presence of previously unknown satellites had been inferred from experiments with particles and fields. It is probable that a new satellite discovered by the imaging experiment is the same satellite as one of those that produced the particle effects. The images also showed a narrow faint ring beyond the boundary of the bright A ring. An outer invisible ring was also inferred from the pattern of absorption of energetic particles. The magnetic field of Saturn was calculated and found to be 0.2 gauss at the

equator and about 0.6 gauss at the poles. Moreover, the Pioneer 11 data revealed that this field was almost exactly aligned with the axis of rotation of the planet, unlike the fields of Earth and Jupiter.

The temperature of Saturn established that the planet is still hot inside and that it emits more heat than it absorbs from the Sun. A tenuous cloud of particles was discovered above Saturn's atmosphere, possibly a halo of atomic hydrogen excited by interactions between charged particles, the rings, and the inner satellites.

A. Thomas Young, at that time Deputy Director of Ames Research Center, said: "We welcome Saturn into our books of knowledge with a lot of pride that we did it. We can report to Voyager: 'Come on through, the rings are clear.' "

At 11:04 a.m. September 2, Pioneer made its closest approach to the giant Saturnian satellite, Titan, at a distance of 353,948 km (219,950 miles). The telemetry bit rate had been increased to 1024 bits/sec for this encounter, even though interference from the Sun was increasing. There was some confusion about the time the infrared scientific data should be returned to Earth because tracking data had to be analyzed to ascertain how the encounter with Saturn had modified the outbound trajectory, and whether radio transmissions from a Soviet satellite in Earth orbit had interfered with the telemetry from the distant Pioneer. The Soviets had cooperated to avoid such interference at critical times of the Pioneer mission and had ceased transmissions from three of their satellites during requested periods. Fortunately, the data had not been lost but came back slightly later and were recovered from the telemetry record when a more precise trajectory had been determined for the spacecraft during its encounter with Titan. The data showed that Titan behaves as a body in equilibrium with the solar radiation and as one without internal heat sources.

Five pictures of Titan, which is larger than Mercury and perhaps the largest satellite in the Solar System, showed a fuzzy ball with a slightly orange tint and with a suggestion of blue around its edge caused by its thick atmosphere. Before computer processing and enhancement, the images showed little detail but were expected to make it possible to determine the diameter of the satellite to an accuracy better than 50 km (30 miles).

By September 3, Pioneer was rapidly moving away from the ringed planet at a speed of 36,210 km/hr (22,500 mph), and was then 2 million kilometers (1.3 million miles) from Saturn. The spacecraft passed from the magnetosphere into the magnetosheath at 2:00 a.m. PDT and stayed there for 5 hr before moving back into the magnetosphere as solar wind pressure changed. Again, many passages were recorded. The imaging photopolarimeter team obtained measurements of the light of Saturn, Titan, Dione, and Tethys, and the instrument continued to obtain pictures of Saturn as a half-illuminated disk with the rings still backlighted as on the approach trajectory.

The spacecraft continued to operate quite well as it approached the Sun line where it would pass behind the Sun as viewed from Earth. At that point, solar radio noise was increasing rapidly. Even at 512 bits/sec, 25% of the data was being lost. It was expected that the data rate would have to be reduced to 256 bits/sec soon. The following day, the bit rate was decreased to 128, then to 64, and finally to 32 bits/sec on September 6 when Pioneer moved into a grazing passage over the top of the Sun as seen from Earth. The spacecraft was still crossing the bow shock of Saturn intermittently out to a distance of 102 Saturn radii. During the encounter, the spacecraft had responded to some 15,000 commands from Earth. Commented Charles F. Hall, as the encounter officially ended: "This is another first encounter in which the country can take pride. It epitomizes the pioneering spirit of our nation."

The U.S. Postal Service had issued a commemorative stamp (Figure 5-27) depicting the initial flyby of Jupiter.

Truly, Pioneer had "blazed the trail" to the outer giants of our Solar System, opening these distant regions of space to exploration by larger spacecraft in following years.

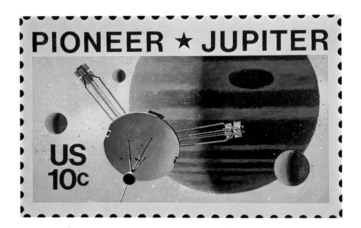

Figure 5-27. A commemorative stamp was issued by the U.S. Postal Service after Pioneer's successful flyby of Jupiter.

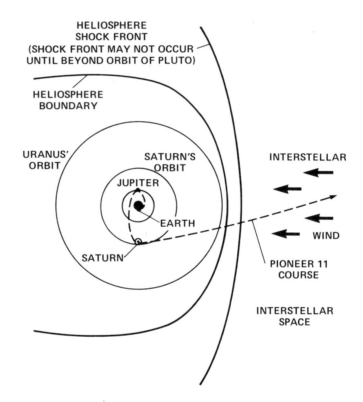

Figure 5-28. After their planetary encounters, the two Pioneers had a further mission. An important task was to seek the heliopause, the region where the solar wind holds the interstellar wind away from the Solar System. Pioneer 11 has the better opportunity to reach this region because it is traveling toward the bow shock of the Solar System.

Following their encounters with Jupiter and Saturn, the two Pioneer spacecraft still had further missions to complete (Figure 5-28). Each headed out from the Solar System in approximately opposite directions. Each continued to gather information about the environment of space and the solar wind. Scientists hoped that one or the other would reach the heliopause (the boundary of the heliosphere), where the influence of the solar wind ends and interstellar space begins, while we are still able to receive spacecraft telemetry data. Both spacecraft had a reserve of gas for maneuvering so that their dish antennas could be pointed toward Earth. And both had electrical power to operate instruments and transmit data. Pioneer 10 had an inefficient star sensor because of radiation damage at Jupiter and was expected to experience difficulties in achieving a correct alignment. It had to rely on its Sun sensor, but as the spacecraft moves farther from the Sun, the intensity of sunlight falls below the sensitivity threshold of the Sun's sensor. Pioneer 11, with a better star sensor, did not have this problem.

The capabilities of the Deep Space Network stations to receive faint radio signals had been improved at a rate that exceeded the diminution of the signals from the Pioneers with increasing distance. Consequently, the possible communication distance of the spacecraft was very much greater than had been anticipated when they were launched. The radioisotope thermoelectric generators also were better than expected, and their rate of degradation had lessened. At the conclusion of the Saturn encounter, scientists were optimistic that both Pioneers would continue to return data from much greater distances, out toward the boundary of the Solar System, to more than 40 AU (~6 billion kilometers or 3.7 billion miles). At such distances, signals from the spacecraft will take 5.5 hr to reach Earth.

The two Pioneer spacecraft will continue toward the beckoning stars, mankind's first emissaries into interstellar space.

6
Results at the New Frontiers

On its way to the first encounter of a space-craft with Jupiter, Pioneer 10 made several scientific investigations in the previously unexplored space beyond the orbit of Mars. After the encounter, Pioneer 10 continued its observations beyond the orbit of Uranus; it is expected to make interplanetary observations until at least the late 1980s when it will approach the orbit of Pluto. Moreover, the information returned by Pioneer 10 will be supplemented by Pioneer 11, the second spacecraft to reach Jupiter and the first to reach Saturn. Pioneer 11 also became the first spacecraft to explore interplanetary space high above the plane of the ecliptic during its voyage from Jupiter to Saturn. It, too, continues to transmit information from far beyond the orbit of Saturn.

By contrast with exploration of the inner Solar System, these new scientific frontiers were probed more slowly because of the vast distances involved. Decades may pass before all the scientific information is fully evaluated. But already our understanding of the Solar System beyond Mars has increased greatly from the data gathered by these pioneering spacecraft. This new information describes the interplanetary medium far beyond the orbit of Mars and to a height of 160 million kilometers (100 million miles) above the plane of the ecliptic (the plane of Earth's orbit); the asteroid belt; the magnetospheres of Jupiter and Saturn; the ring system of Saturn; and, with greater accuracy than previously known, the physical details of Jupiter and Saturn and their large satellites.

Interplanetary Medium Beyond the Orbit of Mars

Theoretically, the solar wind, streaming through the interplanetary medium, is expected to expand radially from the Sun in a symmetrical fashion so as to expand and cool adiabatically, that is, without exchanging heat with its surroundings. In such a theoretical model, the temperature of the solar wind would decrease with distance according to a 4/3 power law. At the distance of Earth from the Sun, observations showed that this law is not quite valid. The solar wind behaves somewhat differently, and it seems that nonuniformities in the solar wind arise from hot spots in the solar corona. Since the temperature of the solar corona determines the speed of the solar wind, such hot spots are expected to give rise to solar-wind streams of different speeds. Moreover, because the Sun rotates on its axis, a fast-moving stream of the solar wind can catch up with a slow-moving stream that begins earlier from a cooler part of the corona.

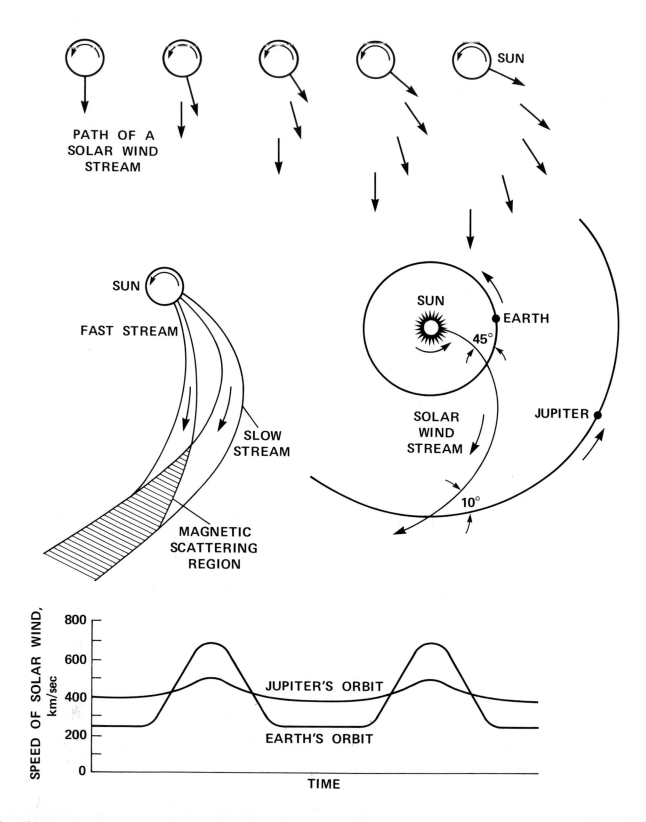

Figure 6-1. Fast streams of solar wind catch slow streams and produce scattering regions that prevent low-energy cosmic rays from penetrating the Solar System. The average velocity of the solar wind changes imperceptibly out to the Jovian orbit but, as shown in the lower diagram, the range of fluctuations is remarkably diminished at this distance. Pioneers 10 and 11 might reach the boundary of this scattering, where galactic cosmic rays are expected to increase in number.

When a fast stream catches up with a slow stream, it tries to penetrate it, but is prevented from doing so by magnetic fields carried by these streams. These fields are carried along because the energy density of the solar wind is many times greater than that of the interplanetary field.

The solar wind streams produce steep magnetic gradients when they collide. This magnetic interface becomes a scattering region for cosmic rays coming into the Solar System from the Galaxy (Figure 6-1).

Because of these scattering centers, no low-energy cosmic rays are able to penetrate into the inner Solar System. The question is: How far into the Solar System do the low-energy galactic cosmic rays penetrate? This is an important question because this radiation carries information about the composition of the stars.

It is predicted from the Pioneer observations that the scattering regions will not damp down until perhaps 40 to 50 times Earth's distance from the Sun. (The average distance between Earth and the Sun is 150 million kilometers, or 93 million miles − an astronomical unit, AU.) Pioneer 10 will reach this distance in the 1980s, and Pioneer 11 will reach such distances about a decade later. Pioneer 11 is moving in the same direction as our Solar System with respect to the local stars − in the direction of a hypothetical bow shock of the heliosphere and the interstellar medium. Pioneer 10 is traveling in almost the opposite direction. The heliopause, or boundary of the heliosphere, is expected to be nearer the Sun along the trajectory of Pioneer 11.

The question is: Will the spacecraft be able to return information from so far away? The ability of the Deep Space Network to receive data from the spacecraft has been improved year by year to keep pace with the vast distances traveled by the Pioneers. The other basic question is whether or not the spacecraft will continue to gather and transmit data. Until now, the spacecraft have experienced no major problems. The survival of the two Pioneers to the vast distances

beyond Jupiter and Saturn is very important in checking on the changes to the solar wind in the outer Solar System. Even as the output of power from the radioisotope thermoelectric generators falls due to an expected decreased output from the power-converting thermocouples, alternate experiments can be cycled − shut off and then later turned on again − to reduce the average power required, thereby making it possible to gather data to the limits of communications distance, possibly out to 6 billion kilometers (3.8 billion miles) from Earth.

Cosmic Ray Intensity Gradients

One of the continuing analyses of the Pioneer data concerns the measurement of the radial and latitudinal intensity gradients of cosmic ray protons, helium, and heavier elements entering the Solar System from the interstellar medium of the Galaxy. Measurements of such gradients enable scientists to test directly the predictions of models of the solar modulation (the solar control of the cosmic ray intensity observed within the Solar System). Small positive gradients continue to be found (intensity increasing with increasing distance from the Sun) for all nuclear species, although the gradients vary from time to time. The data show that the boundary between the region of solar modulation and the interstellar medium is far beyond 20 AU, at a much greater distance than was thought before the two Pioneers explored these regions of the outer Solar System (Figure 6-2). A search for this boundary requires that the Pioneers be tracked outward as far as possible.

The analysis of cosmic ray gradients continues as data are received. Since it now appears that data will be received from the Pioneer spacecraft at radial distances up to at least 40 AU, scientists hope, with continued tracking of the two spacecraft, to explore a major part of the modulation region.

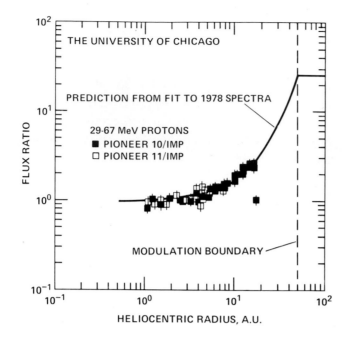

Figure 6-2. The data on cosmic rays entering the Solar System suggest that the boundary between the region where solar events modulate the cosmic rays and the interstellar region is well beyond 20 AU.

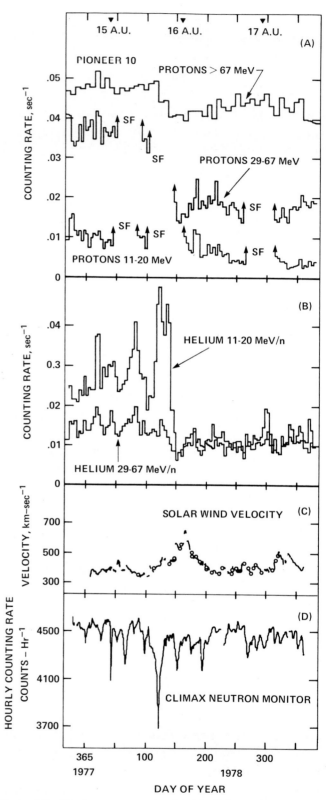

Modulation of Cosmic Rays

The two Pioneer spacecraft in the outer heliosphere have provided an opportunity to observe how increasing levels of solar activity affect the propagation of galactic cosmic rays into the inner heliosphere. As an example, during 1978, several large solar wind blasts were observed at Pioneer 11 and Pioneer 10, where the blasts had formed a single high-speed stream, continuous for at least two solar rotations. Shock waves associated with those streams produced a large decrease in the cosmic ray intensity, beginning at about Earth's orbit and extending progressively outward to about 16 AU; at about 16 AU, a stepwise intensity decrease occurred for the low-energy helium (Figure 6-3) as well as for the galactic cosmic rays. At low energies, this decrease persisted for at least 2 yr and radically changed the helium spectra.

Many cases of local acceleration of particles by the outward-moving blast waves were seen by

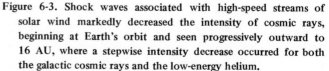

Figure 6-3. Shock waves associated with high-speed streams of solar wind markedly decreased the intensity of cosmic rays, beginning at Earth's orbit and seen progressively outward to 16 AU, where a stepwise intensity decrease occurred for both the galactic cosmic rays and the low-energy helium.

114

both Pioneers 10 and 11 — the first evidence for such accelerations in the outer heliosphere.

In addition to the large-scale modulation effects, strong 27-day variations in the intensities of both galactic cosmic rays and the anomalous helium persisted for many months and were associated with recurrent high-speed solar wind streams. These variations, often by a factor of 2 in amplitude, were most pronounced in the anomalous helium. They may serve to help man unravel the physical processes that control the solar modulation of cosmic rays.

The period from March 1, 1977, to June 15, 1977, was marked by the almost complete absence of either solar or corotating particle events in the data reported from the two Pioneers. The flux of protons and alpha particles for this period at average distances from the Sun of 12.8, 5.1, and 1.0 AU had peaks of alpha particles between 15 and 20 MeV per nucleon. The proton spectra for Pioneer 11 displayed a broad plateau between 15 and 30 MeV.

The rate of change of cosmic ray intensity with radial distance (about 2%/AU) was much less than had been predicted. In addition, the very large increase observed in low-energy helium (alpha particles) is not understood. Pioneer 10 also observed large increases in low-energy oxygen and nitrogen nuclei.

The presence of the anomalous components of cosmic rays poses significant difficulties for the conventional cosmic-ray modulation theory. One suggestion is that the low-energy portions of the helium and oxygen spectra result from the flow of neutral interstellar atoms into the heliosphere. In the heliosphere these particles are ionized by both solar ultraviolet radiation and by solar wind particles through charge exchange, and it is postulated that a certain fraction of the particles is accelerated in the interplanetary medium. The resulting singly ionized nuclei have much higher rigidities at a given kinetic energy per nucleon than do protons, and hence can more readily penetrate back into the inner heliosphere.

Interplanetary Acceleration Processes

Corotating streams of protons, helium nuclei, and possibly heavier ions are the dominant type of low-energy events observed at Earth's distance from the Sun. They occur in association with high-speed streams in the solar wind and show little correlation with solar flares or radio emission. They typically last for 4 to 10 days, thereby suggesting widths of 60° to 120° at Earth's orbit. Originally, scientists expected that these corotating streams would diminish rapidly with radial distance from the Sun as a result of both adiabatic energy loss and spatial effects. However, Pioneer 10 and 11 studies show that the intensity of these events increases by a factor of 10 or 20 out to distances of 3 or 4 AU. As observed at large distances away from Earth's orbit, there are two main characteristics of this class of energetic particles. First, although there is a positive radial gradient of some 220% each 100 million kilometers (62 million miles) between 0.3 and 1.0 AU, and an average gradient of 62% between 1 and 4 AU, there is a negative gradient of 25 to 62% per 100 million kilometers (62 million miles) from 4 to 6 AU. The second characteristic is a close association of energetic particles events with corotating interactive regions formed between high- and low-speed solar wind streams.

The discovery of the positive radial gradient between 1 and 4 AU led to the suggestion that interplanetary acceleration was the most plausible explanation for the events, and that the suprathermal component of the solar wind was a possible source of the particles. Detailed studies of the association between corotating particle streams and corotating interactive regions (which develop forward shocks and reverse shocks beyond about 1.5 AU) have concluded that the corotating interactive regions and their shocks can also accelerate particles. The possibility that there may be two types of acceleration processes superimposed on each other — one associated with shocks and the other associated with turbulent regions — has been suggested. However, the question of whether or not the two processes do occur, as well as the crucial question of the origin of the preaccelerated particles, remains unresolved, even though new light has been thrown on the subject by the findings from the two Pioneers.

Propagation of Particles from Solar Flares

The propagation of energetic particles accelerated by solar flares from the Sun to the outer regions of the heliosphere has been studied in detail. The variation of the radial diffusion coefficient with distance from the Sun has been obtained. At large heliocentric distances, very long times from onset to maximum are observed, often of several weeks' duration.

One surprising aspect of solar flare propagation was observed on Pioneer beyond 15 AU: The proton flux rose very slowly to a maximum and then often remained there for several solar rotations. Since Earth-based data show that there is no continual high flux of protons from the Sun, it appears that the entire heliosphere, near the ecliptic plane at least, is filled with this elevated proton flux. Analysis of flare events in the region beyond the orbit of Saturn is expected to yield important new results over the next few years.

Solar Magnetic Field

Pioneer experiments have shown that, as far as 3 billion kilometers (1.8 billion miles) from the Sun, the strength of the solar magnetic field declines as the inverse first power of distance from the Sun, and the density of the solar wind declines as the inverse second power — both as expected. As it moves outward, the solar wind stream becomes less variable and its gases cool less rapidly; the high-speed streams are converted into random thermal motions of particles, as shown in the lower diagram in Figure 6-1.

Experimenters also found that beyond Saturn the Sun's magnetic field, which guides high-energy particles out from the Sun, was wound tightly, almost like the groove of a phonograph record. However, even beyond Saturn, the solar wind still showed the effects of events on the Sun.

As noted in chapter 5, Pioneer 11 on its voyage from Jupiter to Saturn made a significant discovery about the magnetic field of the Sun: At the time of the spacecraft's passage above the ecliptic plane, it was found that the rotation of the Sun produced a warped current sheet separating the north and south solar magnetic fields. Consequently, this current sheet appears to move up and down as seen from Earth and other planets.

Interstellar Material

The experimenters also found that the uncharged hydrogen atoms of an interstellar wind — the gas between the stars — stream into the Solar System along the plane of Earth's orbit. Mysteriously, this direction is 60° from the direction of travel of the Solar System through interstellar space and hence 60° away from the direction from which the particles would be expected to come. The Pioneer spacecraft also found helium atoms in space for the first time. Experimenters believe that these, too, are from interstellar space.

The Pioneer spacecraft also measured changes in the ratios of helium, oxygen, and nitrogen to carbon among the low-energy cosmic ray particles. These changes were attributed to differences in the ionization potential of these elements by solar ultraviolet radiation. As neutral atoms of oxygen, carbon, and nitrogen enter the heliosphere from interstellar space, they lose electrons at different rates. Atoms of helium, oxygen, and nitrogen penetrate most deeply and, after an atom loses an electron, the atom is accelerated by solar-wind turbulence to become a low-energy cosmic ray.

Zodiacal Light and Gegenschein

Pioneer 10 provided new information about the zodiacal light, the faint glowing band of light along the zodiac, believed to be sunlight reflected from particles in interplanetary space. The slight enhancement of the glow exactly opposite the Sun in the sky — the Gegenschein, or counterglow — could be caused by distant particles illuminated like miniature full moons opposite the Sun, or by a stream of particles extending like a comet's tail from Earth.

The imaging photopolarimeter was turned on March 10, 1972, 7 days after Pioneer 10's launch. During the first few weeks of the mission, when the Sun was about 26° from the spin axis of the spacecraft, only that part of the sky more than 60° from the Sun line could be inspected by the imaging photopolarimeter. So observations concentrated on the counterglow. It quickly became apparent that the counterglow could not be associated with Earth — even though the spacecraft had not moved much farther from the Sun, it had moved ahead of Earth (Figure 6-4). Although the direction of the counterglow was directly away from the Sun as seen from the spacecraft, this direction was by this time different from the direction to the counterglow seen from Earth. So the antisolar glow was confirmed as being associated with light reflected from particles spread around the Solar System, not from particles associated with Earth itself. Experimenters later measured the faint glow of the Gegenschein to near the Martian orbit, again confirming its interplanetary nature.

A few weeks after leaving Earth, Pioneer 10 began to map the entire sky in observing the zodiacal light. Scientists found that zodiacal light decreases in brightness as the square of distance from the Sun. The rate of decrease slowed within the asteroid belt, thereby indicating that particles responsible for zodiacal light, although concentrated in the inner Solar System, also increase in number within the asteroid belt itself. But beyond 3.5 AU, the zodiacal light is

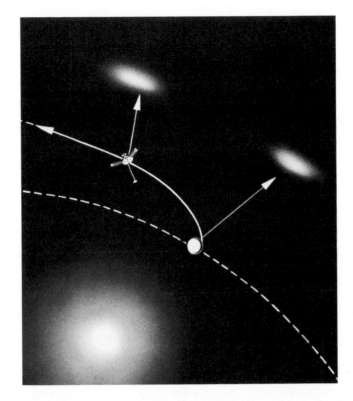

Figure 6-4. The Gegenschein, or counterglow, cannot be associated with Earth because, when seen from Pioneer, it was in a different direction in space than when seen from Earth at the same time. That is, it is always seen 180° from the solar direction, regardless of from where in space it is viewed.

negligible, and experimenters were able to record for the first time the integrated starlight from our Galaxy, free of zodiacal light. Since the brightness of zodiacal light at 2.41 AU is less than 1/10 that at Earth's orbit, experimenters concluded that the asteroid belt beyond that distance does not contribute significantly to the zodiacal light seen from Earth. The brightness of zodiacal light fades almost completely at a distance of 3.3 AU, where particles would have to circle the Sun in orbits having a period half that of Jupiter. Jupiter's gravity appears to sweep the Solar System clear of such particles beyond this resonance orbit. Thus, there is virtually no zodiacal light nor counterglow beyond the asteroid belt.

Meteoroids and the Asteroid Belt

Pioneer 10 provided some surprising data even before it reached the orbit of Mars. At one time it had been speculated that the reason Soviet and American spacecraft had encountered trouble on their way to Mars when the spacecraft were about 175 million kilometers (110 million miles) from the Sun was a band of dust or a concentration of asteroids inside the orbit of Mars. Pioneer 10 showed the speculation to be unfounded and provided data to suggest that Mars might even be sweeping its orbit clean of particles.

The 280-million-kilometer (175-million-mile) wide asteroid belt did not prove as hazardous as some speculation had suggested before Pioneer 10's epic voyage. Astronomers, who had observed the large number of minor planets in the asteroid belt, had postulated that these small bodies might be colliding with each other. Consequently, over the billions of years since our Solar System was formed, these collisions might have populated the zone of the asteroids with innumerable particles, ranging in size from the major asteroids to grains of dust. A myriad of such particles could present a serious hazard to spacecraft.

By June of 1972, just before the Pioneer 10 spacecraft entered the asteroid belt, its detector cells (which counted particles by the number of cells penetrated) had recorded 41 cell-puncturing impacts. These occurred at a fairly steady rate from launch in March of that year. By October, when Pioneer was halfway through the belt, the counting rate remained much the same and another 42 impacts had been recorded. This rate continued relatively unchanged all the way through the belt.

By mid-February 1973, Pioneer 10 had cleared the asteroid belt safely. There was no indication of swarms of tiny bodies capable of damaging spacecraft in these regions of space. The increase in the mass concentration of larger particles measured by the asteroid-meteoroid detector was less than a factor of 4. Thus, from a hazardous particle point of view, there was no asteroid belt. Fine particles seemed to be fairly evenly distributed between the

planets. These results were consistent with observations of the zodiacal light and counterglow and showed that the asteroid belt is not a serious hazard to spacecraft traversing it. Pioneer 11 confirmed these results when it, too, passed safely through the asteroid belt.

Also, very small particles of interplanetary dust seem to be swept from space by Mars and Earth to produce a gap at distances from 1.14 to 1.34 AU. The indications are that Earth and Mars sweep millimeter-sized particles out of their orbits. Small particles appeared to be concentrated near Jupiter by Jupiter's gravity, as indicated by a Pioneer 10 detection rate of tiny dust particles that was 300 times greater than it had measured in any region of interplanetary space since leaving Earth. However, such a concentration around Jupiter is not a significant hazard to spacecraft flying by the planet.

The increase in the number of meteoroid-sized particles hitting Pioneer 10's detectors as it flew by Jupiter suggested a hundredfold increase in dust density over that in interplanetary space. The number of particle hits recorded depends, of course, on the density of particles and on the relative velocity between the particles and the spacecraft. The difference between the increase in density (a factor of 100) and the increase in impacts (factor of 300) mentioned previously was caused by the difference in the relative velocity. The relative velocity increased over the interplanetary value when the spacecraft was near Jupiter.

The Pioneer 11 detector — because its design was less sensitive to small particles — detected fewer particles during its flyby. But the number of particles detected in the steeply inclined and retrograde trajectory of Pioneer 11 appeared to be consistent with the gravitational collection of particles from interplanetary space by the mass of Jupiter.

During the long flight of Pioneer 11 between Jupiter and Saturn, which carried the spacecraft high above the plane of the ecliptic, further impacts were recorded. Data obtained by Pioneer

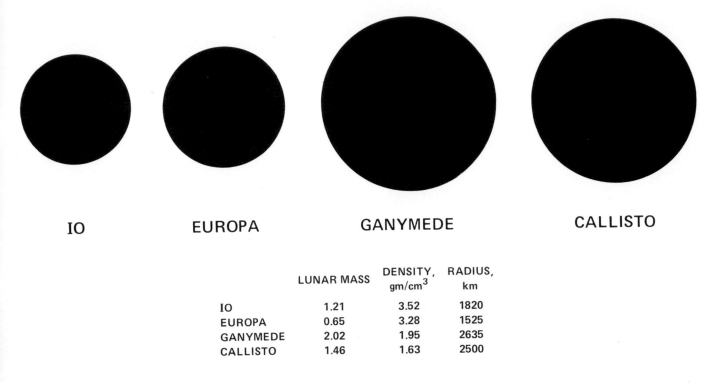

	LUNAR MASS	DENSITY, gm/cm^3	RADIUS, km
IO	1.21	3.52	1820
EUROPA	0.65	3.28	1525
GANYMEDE	2.02	1.95	2635
CALLISTO	1.46	1.63	2500

Figure 6-5. Pioneer 10 provided specific information on the physical characteristics of the Jovian satellites.

11 during about 14 months after encounter with Jupiter, when the spacecraft was traveling from about 5 to 3.7 AU, showed that the meteoroids in that region of space cannot be moving primarily in ecliptic planar orbits. Instead, they must have random inclinations to the plane of the ecliptic and may be in highly eccentric orbits. Because of the orientation of the spacecraft relative to its trajectory, it was impossible for meteoroids in direct circular orbits near the plane of the ecliptic to strike the meteoroid detectors during most of that part of the mission, yet the penetration flux remained essentially constant at the value observed throughout interplanetary space.

At Saturn, Pioneer 11 measured an increase in particle flux (described later). This increase was attributed to particles associated with the rings of Saturn and not to interplanetary meteoroids concentrated near Saturn by its gravitational force.

Encounter with Jupiter

The paths of the two Pioneer spacecraft through the Jovian system, observed by tracking them from Earth, revealed that the system — Jupiter plus its satellites — is heavier, by about half the mass of Earth's Moon (which is 1/81 of Earth's mass), than had been previously calculated. Jupiter itself is about one-quarter of a Moon mass heavier than previously calculated; its mass is 317.83 times that of Earth.

The close approach by Pioneer 11 to approximately 1.6 Jovian radii from the center of the planet (the radius of Jupiter being about 71,400 km) provided additional details of the gravitational field and confirmed the results derived from the Pioneer 10 flyby. Analysis of its gravity field shows that Jupiter is internally a very symmetrical planet with much weaker gravitational anomalies than the terrestrial planets (Mercury,

Figure 6-6. This close-in spin-scan image of Ganymede shows tantalizing markings on this huge satellite's surface. Earlier observations from Earth of the change in temperature during passages of Ganymede in and out of Jupiter's shadow indicated that Ganymede has a highly porous surface, the upper layer of which might be composed of loose, fine-grained rock.

Figure 6-7. Europa was too far away for the Pioneer spacecraft to obtain detailed images, although some surface markings were apparent (see chapter 9).

Venus, Earth, and Mars). This situation is best modeled by a planet almost entirely liquid.

A new measurement of the diameter of Jupiter and of the planet's polar flattening was made. The flattening of Jupiter was revealed by Pioneer to be slightly greater than that derived from the best Earth-based measurements. The diameter of the planet was measured at a pressure of 800 mbar near the cloudtops (a bar is roughly equal to the pressure of 1 atm of Earth). Its polar diameter is 133,540 km (82,980 miles) and its equatorial diameter is 142,796 kilometers (88,732 miles). These new values were established by the timing of the occultation of the spacecraft by Jupiter. Thus, Jupiter is nearly 20 times more flattened than Earth, principally because of its fluid state and its higher rate of rotation. The average density of Jupiter, calculated from its mass and volume, was confirmed as 1.33 gm/cm³ (the density of water is 1).

Jupiter's Galilean Satellites

The Pioneer spacecraft provided new information about the physical characteristics of the large Jovian satellites (Figure 6-5). In terms of the mass of Earth's Moon, the masses of the Galilean satellites in order of distance from Jupiter were found to be: Io, 1.21; Europa, 0.65; Ganymede, 2.02; and Callisto, 1.46. The mass of Io was 23% greater than that estimated before the Pioneer odyssey. The density of the satellites decreases with increasing distance from Jupiter and was refined as a result of Pioneer's observations. Io's density is 3.52; Europa's, 3.28; Ganymede's, 1.95; and Callisto's, 1.63 gm/cm³. The two inner Galilean satellites thus seem to be rocky bodies, for Io's density is indeed greater than that of the Moon. The outer satellites, because of their low density, could consist largely of water ice. All four satellites were found to have average daylight surface temperatures of about −140° C (−220° F).

These satellites were probably formed in such a way that lighter elements were depleted near Jupiter, or that water did not condense on Io and Europa because, being nearer to Jupiter, their higher temperatures, either during the time they condensed from the original nebula or as a result of subsequent heating of Jupiter, prevented the condensation of water.

Although a spurious command prevented Pioneer 10 from obtaining a spin-scan image of Io, the spacecraft did obtain images of Europa and Ganymede. The Ganymede picture, with features resolved to about 400 km (250 miles), showed a south polar dark circular region and a central dark region, each about 800 km (500 miles) in diameter, and a bright north polar region (Figure 6-6). Five years later, more detailed pictures from the Voyager spacecraft confirmed the presence of large dark circular patterns and showed that they are of ancient cratered terrain; bright areas appear to be regions in which fresh ice has been exposed by more recent meteoric impacts.

A less detailed spin-scan image by Pioneer 10 of the smallest Galilean satellite, Europa, presented an appearance somewhat similar to that of Ganymede. The satellite, however, was too far away from the spacecraft for a satisfactory picture (Figure 6-7), although bright and dark regions are distinguishable on the image. Later imaging by Voyager showed that Europa, when seen at high resolution, has quite a different detailed surface from that of Ganymede.

Pioneer 11 also obtained spin-scan images of several of the Galilean satellites (see chapter 9) which revealed gross surface markings that are very difficult to observe from Earth.

The satellite Io appeared to be quite different from the other Jovian satellites. Io is almost as large as Mercury, orange in color, and one of the most reflective objects in our Solar System. Dark polar areas were also seen. The phenomenal brilliance of Io was thought to result from an extensive crystalline layer, possibly like the salt flats in the American West. Sodium vapor emissions from Io, detected by observations from Earth, were shown to be from a sodium vapor cloud extending 16,000 km (10,000 miles) from Io's surface. It was thought that the sodium was being removed from sodium salts on Io's surface by the action of high-energy particles trapped in the magnetosphere of Jupiter and intercepted by Io in its orbit around the giant planet. Again it was necessary to await detailed pictures from the Voyager spacecraft to show that Io is a world of active volcanoes and that the orange, black, and white regions are probably the result of this volcanic activity spreading sulfur-rich materials over the surface.

The timing of the encounter with Jupiter was arranged so that Pioneer 10 was occulted by Io; as a result, the spacecraft's radio signals passed through the satellite's atmosphere on their way to Earth. During this occultation, the radio waves underwent minute amounts of refraction, showing that Io has an ionosphere. At the time of the Pioneer 10 flyby, the ionosphere extended 700 km (435 miles) above the day side of the small satellite. Io was thus revealed as a unique satellite in that it possesses an ionosphere while immersed in the magnetic field of its planet.

The density of the ionosphere varied from 60,000 electrons/cm^3 on the day side to 9,000 on the night side. Although the density of Io's atmosphere was too low to produce a measurable effect on the radio signals, the observed ionosphere suggests that Io has a very tenuous atmosphere with a pressure at the surface some 100 million times less than that at Earth's surface. This atmosphere is now thought to consist of sulfur dioxide gas released from Io's volcanic vents.

Pioneer 10 also found that Io was embedded in a cloud of hydrogen extending a third of the way around its orbit. This finding was quite unexpected. About 161,000 km (100,000 miles) wide and high, the cloud was 805,000 km (500,000 miles) long. Its shape resembled that of a third of a doughnut moving in orbit around Jupiter 402,000 km (250,000 miles) from the planet. Possible atomic oxygen and hydrogen clouds for Europa, of smaller size (about 110,000 km), were also detected. These atomic clouds were produced through the dissociation of water ice on the surface of Europa, probably by impact of particles.

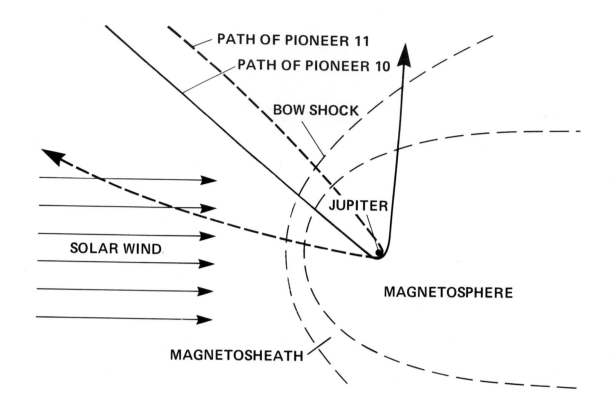

Figure 6-8. The bow shock and the magnetosphere of Jupiter were mapped by Pioneers 10 and 11; the magnetosphere was shown to be vastly more extensive than that of Earth. The bow shock and the magnetosphere also vary in distance from Jupiter under the influence of the solar wind to an extent much greater proportionately than do those of Earth.

Jupiter's Magnetosphere

Like Earth, Jupiter has a bow shock that is produced when the high-speed solar wind, carrying a magnetic field, interacts with the magnetic field of Jupiter (Figure 6-8). The solar wind is abruptly slowed so that its effective temperature is increased tenfold. The magnetic field surrounding Jupiter, as with the Earth, protects the planet from the solar wind; the solar wind cannot penetrate the magnetosphere. Between the magnetosphere and the bow shock is a turbulent region,

the magnetosheath, in which the solar wind is deflected around the magnetosphere. These phenomena are experienced around Jupiter on a scale vastly greater than around Earth.

The diameter of Jupiter's magnetosphere is such that, if it could be seen visually from Earth, it would be more than twice the angular diameter of the Moon or the Sun as they appear in Earth's sky. Pioneer 10's crossings of Jupiter's bow shock showed that the bow shock was over 26 million km (16 million miles) "wide" in the ecliptic plane, or about 80% of the distance between the

122

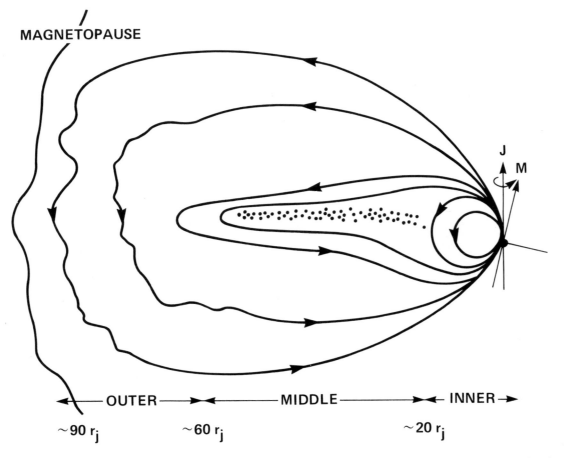

MAGNETOPAUSE

J

M

OUTER → ← MIDDLE → ← INNER →

~90 r$_j$ ~60 r$_j$ ~20 r$_j$

Figure 6-9. Jupiter's magnetosphere was found to be differently from that of Earth and to have three clearly defined regions.

orbits of Earth and Venus. The Jovian system was shown to be on a truly gigantic scale by earthly standards.

Pioneer 11 discovered that the magnetosphere is blunt on the sunward side and, vertically above and below the planet, it extends at least 80 Jupiter radii. Jupiter's magnetosphere was found to be rotating at several hundred thousand miles per hour at its periphery and to consist of several distinct regions. An inner region is shaped like a doughnut with Jupiter in the hole. Outside the doughnut is a disk-like region caused by ionized gas

probably from the planet's atmosphere and satellites. An extremely unstable outermost region is very much affected by the changing pressures of the solar wind.

The magnetosphere might also be described as spongy since it responds elastically to the varying pressure of the solar wind and is often compressed by a factor as great as 2. Pioneer 10 crossed the sharply defined boundary of the magnetosphere at 6.8 million kilometers (4.2 million miles) from Jupiter. Then, as the magnetosphere changed size, Pioneer's instruments again sensed

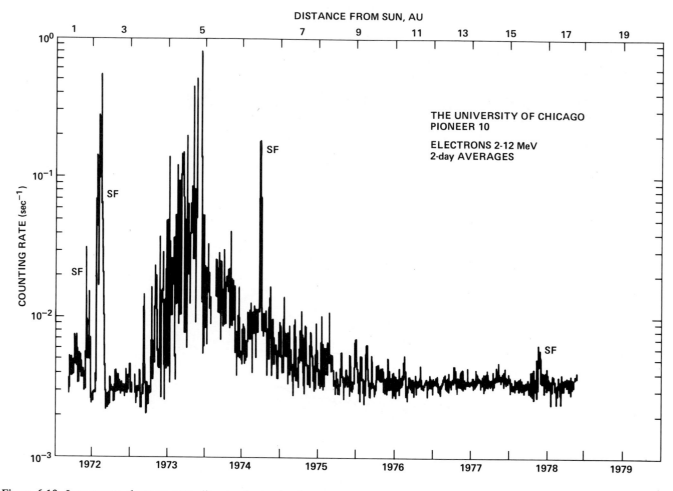

DISTANCE FROM SUN, AU

THE UNIVERSITY OF CHICAGO
PIONEER 10

ELECTRONS 2-12 MeV
2-day AVERAGES

Figure 6-10. Low-energy electrons were discovered escaping from
Jupiter. The flux decreased with distance from Jupiter.

leaving the magnetosphere and entering it again later, all this happening while the spacecraft continued its journey toward the planet. Pioneer 10 crossed the constantly moving bow shock 17 times on the post-encounter trajectory from Jupiter. Pioneer 11 recorded three crossings of the bow shock on the inward trajectory and three more outbound. Again, the multiple crossings of the bow shock and the magnetopause during the Pioneer 11 flyby implied that there is a very dynamic interaction between the solar wind and the Jovian magnetosphere.

The three distinct regions of the Jovian magnetosphere revealed by the Pioneers are illustrated in Figure 6-9. Under average conditions, representative dimensions are: an inner magnetosphere within about 20 Jupiter radii where the magnetic field of the planet dominates; a middle magnetosphere from 20 to 60 Jupiter radii where the magnetic field of the planet is severely distorted by trapped plasma; and an outer magnetosphere, beyond 60 Jupiter radii, which exhibits significant irregularities in both the magnitude and direction of the planetary magnetic field.

In the middle magnetosphere, ionized particles form a sheet of electric current around Jupiter. In turn, the current flowing in this sheet produces a magnetic field which, at large distances from Jupiter, is stronger than the magnetic field of the planet. In the inner magnetosphere, the planetary magnetic field is similar to that of a magnetic dipole or a short bar magnet; in the middle magnetosphere, the magnetic field is much distorted.

Several days before Pioneer 10's encounter with Jupiter, bursts of low-energy electrons were observed to have escaped from the planet. Further analysis of data from Pioneer and other spacecraft showed that these electrons have been detected far from Jupiter, both inward to the orbit of Mercury and outward to distances of at least 11 AU. The flux of these electrons was shown to fall off with increasing distance from Jupiter (Figure 6-10).

The propagation of these electrons from Jupiter has been shown to follow a diffusion equation in interplanetary space; however, whenever a region of interaction between solar wind streams is located between the observer and Jupiter, the electron flux is cut off; these regions act as barriers. Puzzling variations in the electron flux observed by the Pioneer spacecraft can be explained by this cutoff. For many years an effect has been observed at Earth of low electron fluxes, called "quiet time electron events." These events are now understood as being of Jovian origin. As a result of the Pioneer observations, scientists have shown that Jovian electrons are the dominant electron component in the inner Solar System, except during periods of large solar flares.

When Pioneer 11 was at high solar latitudes on its way from Jupiter to Saturn, it passed through a region well connected to Jupiter along the spiral magnetic field. This provided an opportunity to examine Jovian electron propagation not only along and perpendicular to the average magnetic field direction — both in the solar equatorial plane — but also in a direction perpendicular to the equatorial plane; observations in the latter direction had not been possible before. Analysis of the profile of the electron events recorded during 1976 and 1977 showed that the diffusion coefficient perpendicular to the equatorial plane is about 5 times less than the coefficient perpendicular to the field but *in* the equatorial plane, and 500 times less than the coefficient parallel to the field.

Jupiter's magnetic field at the cloudtops was found to be more than 10 times stronger than Earth's field at its surface, with the total energy of the field external to the planet being some 260,000 times that in Earth's external field. (The magnetic moment is 19,000 times that of Earth.)

The closer and more highly inclined trajectory of Pioneer 11 produced a more precise and detailed definition of the magnetic field of Jupiter. It was found to be 5% greater than that estimated from the Pioneer 10 measurements. The estimated strength of the magnetic field at the visible cloudtops is 4.2 gauss on the planet's equator.

Jupiter's equivalent dipole is tilted about 11° to the planet's axis of rotation, and the center of the field does not coincide with the center of Jupiter. Instead, it is offset from the spin axis proportionately twice as much as Earth's field is offset. Because of this offset the strength of the field emerging from the Jovian cloudtops was quite variable, from 14 to 11 gauss in the north and south polar regions, respectively, compared with Earth's polar field of 0.6 gauss. The polarity of Jupiter's field is reversed relative to that of Earth; a north-seeking compass would point south on Jupiter.

The field was found to be distorted by the external ring current and by the influence of the solar wind. Experimenters suggested that this distortion affects the motion of trapped particles forming the radiation belts and may be the cause of the periodic release of relativistic electrons from Jupiter into interplanetary space. The primary source of decametric radiation from Jupiter might be sporadic precipitation of particles into the northern hemisphere along the flux tube through Io.

Closer to the planet than about 3 Jupiter radii, the magnetic field is more complex than a simple dipole field. The magnetometer results fitted a model in which the quadrupole and octupole moments were at least 20% of the dipole moment compared with only about 11% for Earth. The somewhat larger quadrupole and octupole moments discovered in the magnetic field of

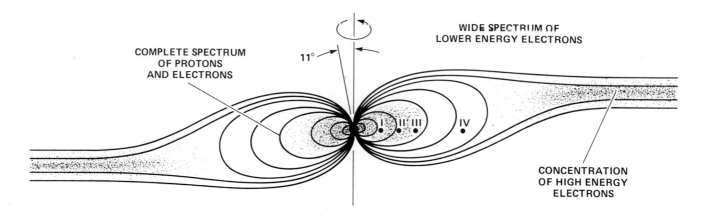

COMPLETE SPECTRUM
OF PROTONS
AND ELECTRONS

11°

WIDE SPECTRUM OF
LOWER ENERGY ELECTRONS

CONCENTRATION
OF HIGH ENERGY
ELECTRONS

Figure 6-11. Radiation belts consist of particles trapped in the Jovian magnetic field; the satellites sweep up many of these charged particles.

Jupiter have significant implications for models of the interior of the planet, assuming that the field is generated by an internal dynamo, a model generally accepted today for the generation of planetary magnetic fields. The complexities are thought to arise from complex circulation patterns within the metallic hydrogen bulk of the planet. The higher field strength relative to that of Earth would imply that the large, dynamo-producing core of Jupiter, that is, the metallic hydrogen, must be responsible for the field, rather than a small core of metals and silicates. To produce the measured quadrupole and octupole effects, the internal core would have to be proportionately larger for Jupiter than for Earth.

Energetic particles trapped in the magnetosphere of Jupiter constitute radiation belts (Figure 6-11) just as they do at Earth. The presence of these radiation belts had been known since 1959 because of the decimetric radio waves generated by trapped electrons and received at Earth. Such radiation belts require that a planet have a magnetic field to constrain them. In fact, their presence led scientists to estimate the strength of Jupiter's magnetic field — an estimate that proved to be in order-of-magnitude agreement with the direct measurements of Pioneers 10 and 11.

Because of Jupiter's tilted magnetic field, the radiation belts are also tilted and they wobble up and down in the surrounding space as Jupiter rotates on its axis. Consequently, a spacecraft passing the planet moves in and out of the belts. The inner belt, consisting of electrons and protons having a wide spectrum of energies, forms the doughnut-shaped region of energetic particles around the planet, corresponding generally with the classical dipole magnetic field shape and extending to about 10 Jupiter radii. Before the Pioneer observations, these trapped particles were generally assumed to be captured from the solar wind. However, from data collected by Pioneer 11, scientists concluded that the particles throughout the magnetosphere may originate from Jupiter's atmosphere and its satellites rather than from the solar wind.

Peak intensities of electrons in the belts, as measured by Pioneer 10, were 10,000 times greater than Earth's maximum; protons were several thousand times more intense than in Earth's belts. The inner radiation belts of Jupiter, as measured by Pioneer 10, had the highest natural radiation intensity so far measured, comparable to the intensities following the explosion of a large nuclear bomb in Earth's upper atmosphere.

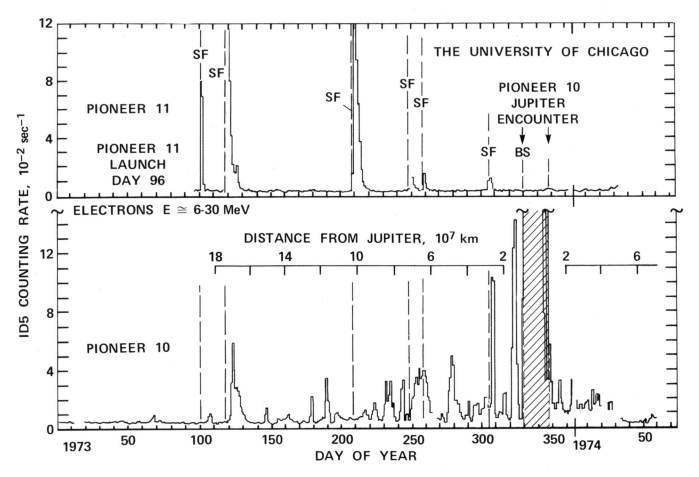

Figure 6-12. Comparison of the number of energetic electron events observed by Pioneers 10 and 11 during Pioneer 10's encounter with Jupiter.

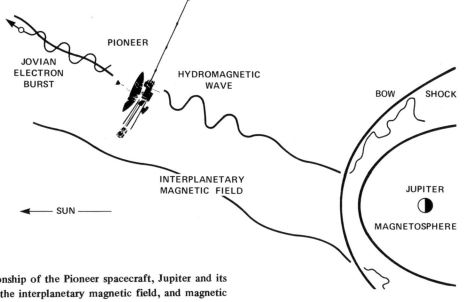

Figure 6-13. Relationship of the Pioneer spacecraft, Jupiter and its magnetosphere, the interplanetary magnetic field, and magnetic waves during a Jovian interplanetary electron event.

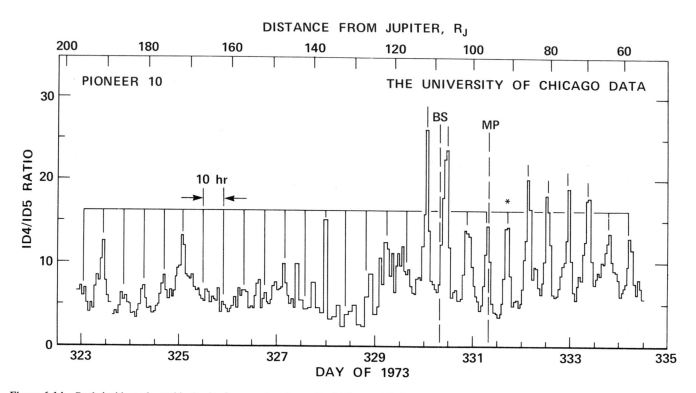

Figure 6-14. Both inside and outside Jupiter's magnetosphere, the 10-hr modulation of electron intensity appeared to be in phase, as shown in these data from the University of Chicago experiment (BS refers to bow shock and MP refers to magnetopause).

Pioneer 11 confirmed these high intensities and also found that there is a greater flux of energetic particles at high Jovian latitudes than would have been expected from the measurements made by Pioneer 10.

As mentioned earlier, an important discovery by Pioneer 10 was that Jupiter releases bursts of energetic electrons into interplanetary space. Pioneer 11 also detected these electrons and discovered that the bursts were in phase, relative to the rotation of the planet, with those observed previously by Pioneer 10. Two days before Pioneer 11 entered the magnetosphere of Jupiter, the spacecraft's instruments began to detect bursts of low-energy protons.

Jupiter was thus found to be an additional source of energetic particles which scientists can use to study the propagation of particles and magnetic fields in interplanetary space. Figure 6-12 shows the increasing rate of energetic electron events derived from the charged particle instrument's results as Pioneer 10 approached

Jupiter; Pioneer 11, still far from the planet, saw many fewer electron events. These events were observed when the interplanetary magnetic field provided a good connection between Jupiter and the spacecraft. Large-amplitude waves in the magnetic field were found associated with the electrons in interplanetary space. They were probably generated by the electrons. Figure 6-13 shows diagrammatically the relation of the spacecraft, Jupiter, the interplanetary magnetic field, and the magnetic waves during a Jovian interplanetary electron event. Since cosmic rays are probably confined to the Galaxy by similar self-generated waves, this observation by the Pioneer spacecraft has significance for galactic physics as well as planetary physics.

In addition to 10-hr variations in the electron intensity and spectrum observed inside Jupiter's magnetosphere, similar variations were observed as far as 150 million kilometers (93 million miles) from the planet. These external variations were in phase with those inside Jupiter's magnetosphere

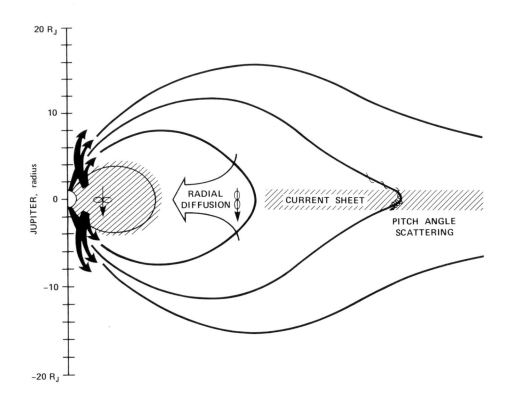

20 R_J

10

JUPITER, radius

0

RADIAL
DIFFUSION

CURRENT SHEET

PITCH ANGLE
SCATTERING

-10

-20 R_J

Figure 6-15. Energetic particles appeared to circulate in the magnetosphere, from which they were ultimately ejected from high latitudes into interplanetary space, thereby making Jupiter a second source of energetic particles that spray across the Solar System.

(Figure 6-14). Both inside and outside the magnetosphere, the variations appeared to be locked in phase; that is, they occurred regularly every 10 hr at about the same time, irrespective of distance from the planet.

The timing of the 10-hr intensity and spectral variations observed in the energetic electron flux in Jupiter's magnetosphere and in interplanetary space caused scientists to reexamine the idea that the variations might be caused by the flapping of the outer magnetosphere and the equatorial current sheet during Jupiter's rotation. Instead, the data suggested that the variations took place simultaneously in the whole outer magnetosphere, so that Jupiter resembled a blinking beacon more than a twirling floppy hat, as had been originally suggested when the Pioneer 10

data were interpreted. The full resolution of these alternative interpretations has not yet been achieved.

The results from Pioneer 11 suggest that the model of Jupiter's trapped radiation in the middle and outer magnetospheres is best represented by a disk with the magnetic field lines near the magnetic equator being much distended but closed and hence capable of trapping charged particles out to a distance of 100 Jupiter radii.

It also became clear that the magnetosphere was quite blunted on the sunward side of the planet. No information was available from either Pioneer 10 or 11 on the shape of the magnetosphere at large distances on the side of Jupiter opposite the Sun. This will require a Jupiter orbiter mission, such as Project Galileo.

129

A significant finding from the Pioneer 11 observations was that both electrons and protons stream toward and away from the planet along high-latitude field lines. The energies of these electrons were greater than 40 keV and less than 560 keV; proton energies were between 0.61 and 3.41 MeV.

A recirculation of energetic particles within the Jovian magnetosphere thus emerged as a possible feature of this giant planet. This hypothesis also suggests the emission of energetic particles into interplanetary space, as observed by Pioneers 10 and 11, from the poles and other high latitudes rather than exclusively from the equatorial regions of the magnetosphere.

Particles in the outer magnetosphere, which were diffusing inward toward Jupiter, appeared to be eventually squeezed into a pancake-shaped magnetodisk in the magnetosphere nearer the planet. Apparently, the particles interact with plasma waves generated inside the magnetosphere, which causes them to escape from the magnetodisk and to reach even lower altitudes. At these lower altitudes, they can be transported to high latitudes without significant energy changes. The particles are thereby injected onto high-latitude field lines and provide the outward streaming high-latitude flux of particles observed by Pioneer 11 (Figure 6-15). This dynamic recirculation may explain the otherwise baffling problem of the presence of particles with megavolt energies in the region of the outer magnetosphere, including its boundary.

Also, this process may explain why the 10-hr periodicity occurs rather than the 5-hr periodicity that would be expected if the energetic particles from Jupiter observed in interplanetary space were squirted from equatorial regions. The interplanetary magnetic field at a particular point in space would be expected to connect to either the north or south polar regions of Jupiter at any given time. Energetic particles originating from these regions by the circulation process would be modulated by planetary rotation so as to show a 10-hr periodicity. Thus, a process of crossfield

diffusion and escape of particles from the polar regions could account for the 10-hr period observed by the Pioneer spacecraft in interplanetary space. There is also a 10-hr period, or flapping effect, in the equatorial zone of the magnetosphere as well as the 10-hr variation observed in interplanetary space.

The dynamics of the Jovian magnetosphere with its charged particles appear to differ in at least four important ways from those of Earth. First, the presence of substantial intensities of electrons with energies greater than 20 MeV in the outer magnetosphere cannot be explained by a trapping of particles from the solar wind. Such solar wind particles could only reach energies of about 1 keV. Second, the corotation of energetic particles with Jupiter persists out to the magnetopause, near the outer limits of the magnetosphere, whereas for Earth corotation terminates at the outer boundary of the plasmasphere, far inside the magnetosphere. Third, the inner four satellites of Jupiter — Amalthea, Io, Europa, and Ganymede — are deep within the planet's magnetosphere and produce a fluctuating and complex structure of energetic particles. By contrast, the Earth's Moon is far outside Earth's magnetosphere, although it traverses the distant magnetotail each month. Fourth, it seems likely that the capture of solar wind particles may be a relatively minor feature of the dynamics of the Jovian magnetosphere, whereas the acceleration of particles internally available within the magnetosphere may be the dominant process, again quite different from Earth. Nevertheless, whether or not some solar wind particles are captured within the Jovian system, the solar wind is essential to establishing the physical conditions under which transfer of rotational energy from Jupiter to the charged particles can take place. The flow of the solar wind past Jupiter generates the axially asymmetric and nonrotating situation essential to develop the Jovian magnetosphere.

The presence of major satellites within the Jovian magnetosphere leads to interesting effects. The satellites sweep particles from the belts and

130

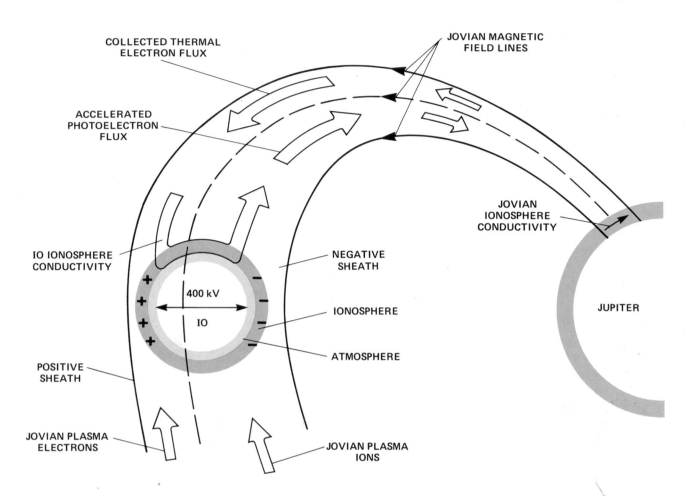

COLLECTED THERMAL
ELECTRON FLUX

JOVIAN MAGNETIC
FIELD LINES

ACCELERATED
PHOTOELECTRON
FLUX

JOVIAN
IONOSPHERE
CONDUCTIVITY

IO IONOSPHERE
CONDUCTIVITY

NEGATIVE
SHEATH

400 kV

IO

IONOSPHERE

ATMOSPHERE

JUPITER

POSITIVE
SHEATH

JOVIAN PLASMA
ELECTRONS

JOVIAN PLASMA
IONS

Figure 6-16. After the Sun, Jupiter is the strongest radio source in the sky. Enormous radio bursts come from the electric current that flows along the flux tube to Jupiter when Io, in effect, closes the switch. By its motion through the Jovian magnetic field, Io generates an electrical potential of 400 kV across the satellite. When Io reaches the right position, current flows along magnetic field lines down to Jupiter's electrically conductive ionosphere and back to Io. The circuit is completed through the ionosphere of the satellite. Pioneer 11 measured the current flow along the flux tube.

remove high-energy particles, thereby reducing the total radiation near Jupiter by as much as 100 times. This was an important Pioneer discovery, for if the satellites did not absorb so many of the damaging particles spacecraft could not be flown safely close to Jupiter. That would mean that the slingshot effect of Jupiter's gravity and orbital motion could not be used to propel spacecraft to the planets beyond Jupiter.

By far the largest number of particles is removed by the satellite Io. Additionally, Io is known to accelerate particles and to induce the emission of decametric radio waves. Radio bursts occur every 21 hr, half the period of Io's orbit. Pioneer measured a flow of electrons along magnetic field lines linking Io to Jupiter — lines referred to as the Io flux tube (Figure 6-16). As mentioned earlier, the spacecraft also found that Io has an ionosphere. These two facts point to a theory that may explain the modulation by Io of decametric radio waves from the Jovian system. Io's conductive ionosphere could complete an electrical circuit up and down the flux tube and through Jupiter's ionosphere. The movement of Io through Jupiter's magnetic field could induce an electric potential of hundreds of kilovolts across the satellite. This could drive a current around the circuit of the flux tube and the ionosphere of Jupiter, completing it through the ionosphere of Io. It has been calculated that there may be a flow of

10,000 billion watts through this circuit, thereby generating the radio bursts that have been observed at Earth for many years.

As Pioneer 11 crossed the orbit of Io, it measured large reductions in electron flux for energies below 560 keV and a marked reduction in proton flux for energies of about 1 MeV. Smaller effects were observed at the orbit of Amalthea, and only a slight effect was seen at the orbit of Europa. However, near the orbit of Ganymede, Pioneer 11 detected strong transient anisotropic bursts of 1-MeV protons. One sequence of 1-min bursts continued for several hours. These particles appeared to be locally accelerated.

Within Amalthea's orbit, Pioneer 11 detected an extremely complex radiation environment with varying particle fluxes around Jupiter. Several theories were put forward in an effort to explain this puzzling observation. It was generally thought that the magnetic field models developed from the Pioneer 11 observations were somewhat incomplete due to limitations imposed by the spacecraft's trajectory, and that a more detailed model would eventually explain the data. The remote possibility that the observed radiation belt features could have resulted from absorption effects caused by an undiscovered satellite or possibly by a ring of particles, or both, was also suggested. This suggestion was based on detailed simulations conducted with existing magnetic field models to map the trajectories of charged particles. It was found that, by placing a hypothetical absorber at 1.83 Jupiter radii, the observed features could be matched almost exactly. This position was suggested for the possible location of a satellite, a ring, or both. The Voyager results have shown that both a ring and a satellite exist at this radial distance, although most theories predict that such objects would have been destroyed long ago by tidal forces generated by Jupiter's powerful gravity and would have been precipitated into the Jovian atmosphere. Thus, Pioneer 11 may be credited with providing evidence for Jupiter's ring and its newly discovered satellite, although the interpretation of this evidence did not appear altogether persuasive until the Voyager images were obtained.

The Pioneer 11 spacecraft discovered a high electron current flow at the orbit of Ganymede. Such an increase in electron flow had not been observed during the other passages of Pioneer through satellite orbits, except near the Io flux tube where Pioneer 11 detected an increase of about 10 times in the flux of electrons with energies above 0.46 MeV.

Although the configuration of the outer Jovian magnetosphere is still not completely understood, especially how the 10-hr modulation originates, the picture of the Jovian system emerged as an enormous spinning magnetosphere continually stirred and mixed by the Galilean satellites and by Amalthea (i.e., the five inner satellites), a magnetosphere in which processes are at work very different from those in Earth's magnetosphere. During the Pioneer 11 encounter, the total electron dosage was less than that experienced by Pioneer 10 even though Pioneer 11 approached closer to Jupiter. This was because the trajectory of Pioneer 11 was highly inclined relative to that of Pioneer 10. As a result, the Pioneer 11 mission established that spacecraft trajectories could be planned so that the spacecraft would pass quickly and safely through the plane of intense radiation. The practicality of an orbital mission to Jupiter and the need for such a mission have thus been demonstrated. Also, the practicality of the gravity-assist slingshot technique to explore the outermost reaches of the Solar System was demonstrated. Pioneer 11, renamed Pioneer Saturn after its encounter with Jupiter, was on its way to the next outer gas giant with virtually no damage to its electronics or scientific instruments.

The Planet Jupiter

The Pioneer spacecraft permitted close looks at Jupiter as well as the environment surrounding it. These close looks were made possible by the spin-scan imaging technique, infrared and ultraviolet experiments, and the radio occultation

132

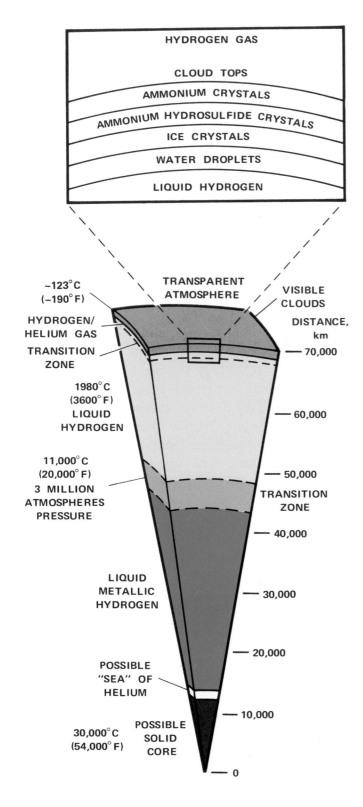

HYDROGEN GAS

CLOUD TOPS

AMMONIUM CRYSTALS

AMMONIUM HYDROSULFIDE CRYSTALS

ICE CRYSTALS

WATER DROPLETS

LIQUID HYDROGEN

TRANSPARENT ATMOSPHERE

VISIBLE CLOUDS

−123°C (−190°F)

HYDROGEN/ HELIUM GAS

TRANSITION ZONE

DISTANCE, km

— 70,000

1980°C (3600°F) LIQUID HYDROGEN

— 60,000

11,000°C (20,000°F) 3 MILLION ATMOSPHERES PRESSURE

— 50,000

TRANSITION ZONE

— 40,000

LIQUID METALLIC HYDROGEN

— 30,000

— 20,000

POSSIBLE "SEA" OF HELIUM

— 10,000

30,000°C (54,000°F)

POSSIBLE SOLID CORE

— 0

Figure 6-17. The Pioneer data confirmed models of Jupiter's interior that suggest the planet is mostly liquid with a small rocky core and a deep hydrogen-rich atmosphere.

and celestial mechanics experiments. As a result, astronomers were able to refine theories about the internal composition and the meteorology and atmosphere of Jupiter. Although the spin-scan images are discussed in detail in chapters 8 and 9, it is appropriate here to summarize the current theories about Jupiter, which were strengthened by or were evolved from the Pioneer results.

Jupiter appears to be almost entirely fluid, with possibly only a very small core of silicates and metals (Figure 6-17). Jupiter's center may have a temperature of 30,000° C (54,000° F), a result of heat from continued gravitational contraction and a reserve of residual primordial heat. Since the temperature of the Jovian cloud-tops is about −148° C (−234° F), there is a wide range of temperatures within the planet so that millions of cubic miles of the atmosphere could be at room temperature.

Atop the bulk of the planet is a turbulent region of atmosphere, possibly 970 km (600 miles) thick. The top regions of this atmosphere produce clouds that are the visible surface of Jupiter as seen from Earth. A transparent atmosphere extends above the visible clouds and ultimately leads to a multi-layered ionosphere of highly rarefied, electrically charged gas.

Jupiter exhibits convective circulation patterns, but the rapid rotation of the planet and outward flow of internal energy makes the weather patterns very different from those of Earth.

From changes to the paths of the Pioneers determined from their radio signals, the density distributions within Jupiter imply that the planet must be largely liquid, with no concentrations of mass and no detectable crust or solid surface. But Jupiter could still possess a small, liquid, rocky core of a few Earth masses consisting of iron and silicates. The composition of Jupiter is not precisely like that of the Sun since there is a fivefold enhancement of heavy materials on Jupiter, probably in the form of silicates and ices of ammonia, methane, and water. Scientists cannot yet define how these heavier materials are distributed throughout the planet.

133

Jupiter is probably 85 to 90% hydrogen; despite the high internal pressures, the hydrogen is most likely liquid because of Jupiter's high internal temperatures. However, the pressure within Jupiter at about 24,000 km (15,000 miles) below the visible cloudtops is sufficient to convert liquid hydrogen into a metallic form that more readily conducts heat and electricity.

Temperatures and pressures are enormously high in the interior of Jupiter. At 970 km (600 miles) below the cloudtops, the temperature is probably about 2,000° C (3,600° F). At 2,900 km (1,800 miles), the temperature is believed to be 6,000° C (11,000° F). At 24,000 km (15,000 miles), the temperature may reach 11,000° C (20,000° F), and the pressure may be 3 million Earth atmospheres.

Jupiter also contains 10 to 15% helium which might, theoretically, be soluble in liquid hydrogen. It is speculated that, if conditions are not just right, the helium might be insoluble within the hydrogen and form a shell around the central core of Jupiter on top of which the liquid metallic hydrogen would float. There is no adequate theory yet on the miscibility of metallic hydrogen and helium within a planet such as Jupiter. There might be precipitation of helium in the molecular hydrogen, which would be important to layering and to convective processes within the planet. In turn, these could affect the magnetic field. Additionally, there is the question whether rocks might dissolve in a hydrogen-helium mixture at high temperature. This could prevent the formation of a discrete rocky core or could have dissolved such a core that had already formed earlier in the history of the planet.

The seething internal activity in the metallic hydrogen of Jupiter is thought to be evidenced by the complex magnetic field of the planet. Hydrogen moving up from the center of Jupiter, like water coming to a boil in a saucepan, would produce eddy currents that give rise to the magnetic field through rotation of the planet.

Somewhere around 970 km (600 miles) below the cloudtops, where the pressure is low enough for liquid hydrogen to become a gas, the atmosphere of Jupiter begins. It is unlikely, however, that there is a sharp transition surface similar to the surface of an ocean. Rather, there is probably a gradual change through a mixture of gas and liquid. But the top 970 km (600 miles) of the planet, where hydrogen no longer exists in liquid form, is defined as the Jovian atmosphere.

Jupiter's atmosphere accounts for about 1% of the mass of the planet. It is predominantly hydrogen (about 85 to 90%) with 10 to 15% helium and less than 1% of other gases. These elements are found in the same proportions on the Sun. Although helium was believed present in Jupiter, the gas was not positively identified until the Pioneer 10 flyby.

Jupiter's atmosphere also contains small amounts of ammonia and methane, and traces of deuterium, acetylene, ethane, and phosphine. In recent years, water vapor has been detected in small quantities as have carbon monoxide and hydrogen cyanide. Several trace gases have been discovered, and more are being discovered, through the use of telescopes mounted on high-altitude aircraft that surmount some of the masking absorptions of Earth's atmosphere. In the atmosphere extending 32 km (20 miles) or more above and below the visible cloudtops, solar heat and internal heat from the planet affect circulation and modify the weather patterns. Jupiter's clouds form in the atmosphere by condensation, as on Earth. But Jupiter's clouds appear to contain ammonia and ammonia compounds as well as water. The topmost clouds are thought to be of ammonia crystals with water clouds confined to the lower levels.

An inversion layer 35 km (22 miles) above the visible clouds is thought to be caused by a layer of aerosols and hydrocarbons such as ethane and acetylene. In this layer, sunlight is absorbed and adds heat to the cooling atmosphere. Methane, too, would absorb sunlight and contribute to this inversion layer.

Pioneer 10's occultation experiment at first produced results for the temperature structure of the Jovian atmosphere that were in conflict

134

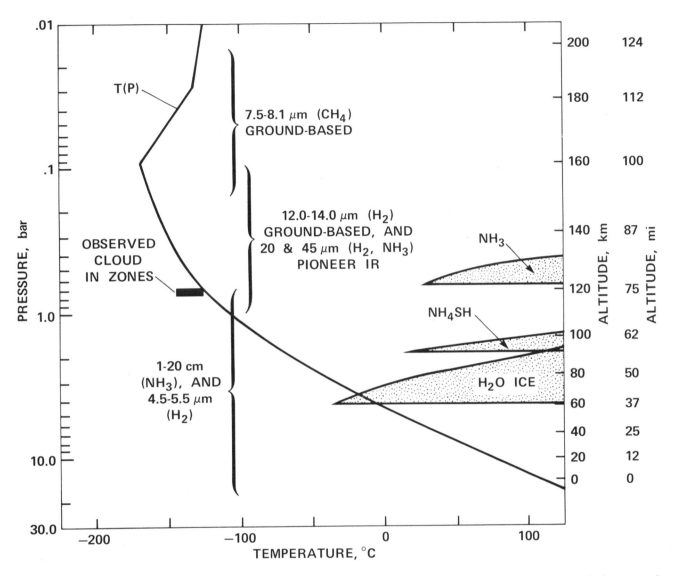

Figure 6-18. The temperature profile in the Jovian atmosphere and the locations of the various cloud layers shown are based on data from the infrared radiometer experiment.

with ground-based observations and with the data from the infrared radiometer. Moreover, the data from Pioneer 11 were consistent with those from Pioneer 10. They were finally matched with the ground-based observations by taking into account the great oblateness, or spin flattening, of Jupiter and its effects on the path of the radio waves through the Jovian atmosphere. For three measurements — entry and exit of Pioneer 10 and exit of Pioneer 11 — the occultation data were quite consistent. They showed a temperature inversion between the 10- and 100-mbar levels, with temperatures between $-133°$ and $-113°$ C ($-207°$ and $-171°$ F) at the 10-mbar level, and between $-183°$ and $-163°$ C ($-297°$ and $-261°$ F) at 100 mbar. At the 0.001-mbar level, the temperature of the Jovian atmosphere, determined from an occultation of the star Beta Scorpii as observed from Earth, was about $-103°$ C ($-153°$ F). At the cloudtops, however, the temperature as measured by Pioneer was about $-148°$ C ($-234°$ F) (Figure 6-18).

The Pioneer observations also showed that the poles and equatorial regions of Jupiter have effectively the same temperature; the temperature is also the same on the northern and southern hemispheres and on the day and night sides. Also, because the axis of Jupiter is inclined only a few degrees to the plane of its orbit, the planet does not have seasons like those on Earth.

Because the Sun's radiation is more concentrated per unit area in the equatorial regions than in the polar regions, the equator would be expected to be warmer than the poles, as on Earth and other planets; however, the temperatures do not differ. Two theories were proposed to account for the even distribution of temperature as measured by infrared radiation from Jupiter: The first holds that the circulation within the atmosphere should be very efficient in redistributing the solar heat; the second suggests that the heat flux from inside Jupiter is sufficiently greater at the poles to balance the lesser solar input there. Since no equator-to-pole atmospheric flow pattern is seen on Jupiter, the second theory seems more likely to fit conditions on the planet. It is believed that convection is so effective over the entire planet that it eliminates any temperature differences due to the solar input variations with latitude. Thus, at the poles, where the cloud temperatures would be expected to fall, convection brings heat from the interior and keeps the temperature constant. At the equator, where the clouds are warmed more by the Sun, convection is reduced accordingly. Thus, the planet acts as though controlled by a natural thermostat.

It has been speculated that the spots on Jupiter, including the Great Red Spot, are probably large, hurricane-type features consisting of groups of persistent air masses that rise like gigantic thunderstorms (Figure 6-19). For reasons mentioned above, it is no longer believed that the Great Red Spot is a column of gas anchored to some feature on a hypothetical surface of Jupiter. The core of Jupiter is now believed to be much too small to produce effects that would extend to the visible surface of the clouds. The Pioneer spacecraft revealed no noticeable density differences to suggest that the Great Red Spot extends toward the core.

Fundamental questions remain unanswered: What causes the Great Red Spot? Why has it lasted so long? Speculative theories are constantly being advanced as, for example, that the Great Red Spot is the Jovian equivalent of a hurricane — but the validity of these theories remains in doubt. Equations that describe the atmospheric flow on a rapidly rotating planet with an internal heat source can be solved by powerful computers. Several scientists have developed mathematical models to explain the Great Red Spot. Whether these new hydrodynamic solutions do, in fact, apply to the real Great Red Spot must await careful comparison of the predictions of the spot's behavior and characteristics. Time-lapse motion pictures obtained with the Voyager spacecraft later threw more light on the complex motions and their probable causes.

One of the most significant images from Pioneer 10 showed a similar red spot, though much smaller, in the northern hemisphere at the same latitude as the Great Red Spot (Figure 6-20). Its shape and structure confirmed that these red spots are meteorological features in the atmosphere. The Great Red Spot appeared to rotate counterclockwise as seen from above, a motion clearly defined in the Voyager pictures. It is thus anticyclonic and behaves as an ascending mass of gas flowing out at the level of its top which pokes several miles above the surrounding clouds.

By looking at sunlight reflected off a cloud, it is not possible to tell, even on Earth, what is under the cloud. But the nature of this reflected light reveals much about the size, distribution, and refractive index of the droplets comprising the cloud. There was no haze over the Great Red Spot as observed by the Pioneer near the limb. At the terminator, the Great Red Spot showed a bluish tint where the sunlight was scattered into space. Scientists speculated that the red color of the spot may result from phosphine being carried to great heights where it is broken down by solar ultraviolet to produce red phosphorus.

136

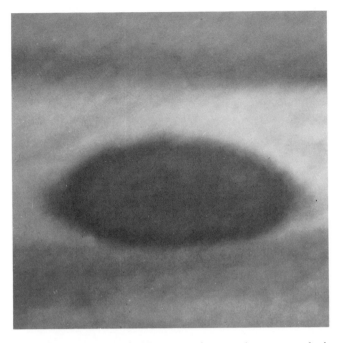

Figure 6-19. The Great Red Spot was shown to be an atmospheric feature resembling a great system of thunderstorms rising several kilometers above the topmost clouds of Jupiter.

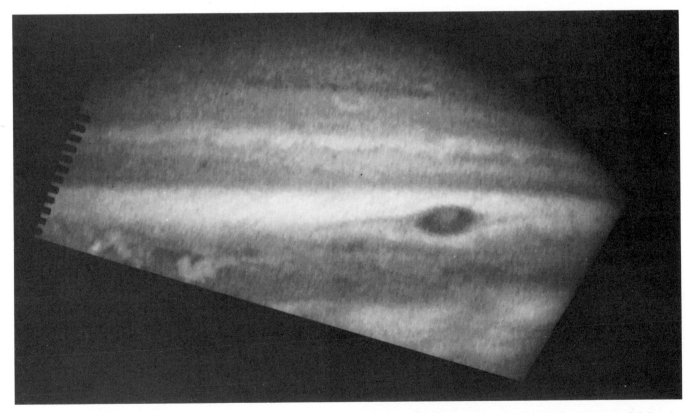

Figure 6-20. A northern red spot on Jupiter, recorded in new detail by Pioneer, supported the view that these red spots are hurricane-like phenomena.

 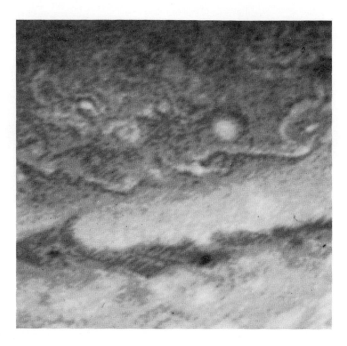

Figure 6-21. Pioneer 11 obtained unique views of the polar regions of Jupiter, views impossible to obtain from Earth. These polar atmospheric patterns are very different from those in the equatorial and temperate regions.

The views of the north polar regions of Jupiter (Figure 6-21) were unique in that such views are not possible from Earth. Pioneer's pictures showed that north of the North Temperate Belt, the dark belts and light zones characteristic of regions closer to the equator became successively less organized. The band structure changed into oval and circular patterns within 30° of the pole. The details were greater in the red images of the polar regions, thereby suggesting that the atmosphere is thicker over the polar clouds than over the temperate and equatorial regions of the planet.

Photopolarimetry was also used to estimate the optical depth of the atmosphere above the cloudtops. It appeared to be three times greater at latitudes above 60° than in the equatorial zone. But the effects may have been caused by a thin, high cloud layer or an unknown absorber in the upper atmosphere.

The Pioneer observations of Jupiter added considerably to our basic knowledge of the atmospheric dynamics of cloudy planets by providing information on very deep atmospheres in rapid rotation without any solid surface interactions with the atmosphere. They also provided information about atmospheres driven mainly by heat from below rather than from the Sun.

Pioneer results seemed to confirm earlier theoretical deductions that the Great Red Spot and the light-colored zones are regions of well-developed clouds, swirling anticyclones, and rising air masses. The darker belts, by contrast, are cyclonic, sinking masses of air leading to depressed clouds. The belts and zones of Jupiter reflect sunlight in very different ways. It is speculated that the belts may appear dark because of dark aerosols suspended in the gaseous atmosphere there. On Jupiter, the familiar cyclones and anticyclones of Earth are stretched into linear or hook-shaped features on this rapidly rotating planet, with extremely turbulent areas separating adjacent bands of different velocities, areas in which there are many examples of classical von Kármán vortices.

Whereas a storm system such as a hurricane on Earth may last for several days or weeks, storm systems on Jupiter last much longer. The Great Red Spot has been observed for nearly three centuries, although at least twice it has virtually disappeared. On Earth there are strong interactions between atmospheric systems and the land masses over which the systems travel. These masses tend to break up an atmospheric system passing over them. In addition, Earth systems are powered by solar heat concentrated in the tropics during daylight. Thus, they tend to break up when they move away from the tropics and into the night hemisphere of Earth. However, Jupiter's storms are powered mainly by internal heat flow that is more evenly distributed planetwide and over the day and night hemispheres. It is not known why Jovian weather systems can last so long,

(b)

(a)

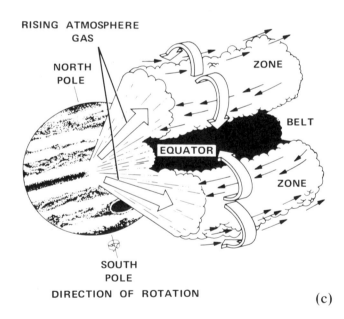

(c)

Figure 6-22. Some of the bright zones of Jupiter (a). Some may be analogous to tropical convergences of Earth (b). Jupiter's zones appear to contain warm, moist, rising atmosphere and the belts, cool, dry, falling Jovian air (c). Masses of atmosphere from the tops of the zones spread toward the equator and poles, but Coriolis forces cause the flow to turn 90°. Flow toward the poles is forced east and flow toward the equator is turned west. Thus, the atmosphere in Jupiter's banded regions flows around the planet, somewhat like Earth's trade winds.

139

although it is clear that the huge mass of a swirling body of gas has immense rotational inertia and consequently has a long lifetime.

Some of the bright zones on Jupiter (Figure 6-22(a)) may be analogous to tropical convergences on Earth, which show up plainly on satellite photographs (Figure 6-22(b)) as bands of thunderstorms, a few degrees north and south of the equator. On Earth they are caused by the trade winds, blowing toward the equator, and moist air rising in the tropics. The consequent thunderstorms spread their tops into cirrus clouds which then flow back toward the poles. Similarly, on Jupiter, rising air masses may produce great anvil-shaped masses of cumulus clouds, which appear as bright bands in the North Tropical and South Tropical Zones (Figure 6-22(c)).

A problem still not resolved is why, when ammonia and water are both colorless when condensed, Jupiter displays bands of colored clouds and red spots. Certain ammonia compounds, if sufficiently exposed to ultraviolet radiation, produce colors like those on Jupiter. Sufficient solar radiation does penetrate to the cloud levels. Perhaps carbon compounds or traces of sulfur and phosphorus — all believed to be present in primordial material — supply some of the color. Only traces would be needed to react in sunlight and produce the colors seen on Jupiter. It could very well be that, because the gas of the Great Red Spot rises so high, it is subjected to irradiation by solar ultraviolet which triggers a different set of photochemical reactions that deepen the color.

However, since solar ultraviolet radiation penetrates to lower cloud levels, that is, to the belts, the Great Red Spot may result from a different type of chemical reaction, from low temperature, or from longer exposure to the radiation because its gases are less mixed than those of the belts.

The presence of free radicals could also explain the colors on Jupiter. At very low temperatures, such as those experienced in the higher cloud layers, chemical compounds can exist with some of their normal complement of atoms missing and

still be relatively stable — these are called free radicals and they are generally highly colored.

Limb darkening on Jupiter shows that the clouds of the planet consist of a thin upper layer, which is semitransparent to red light, above a more dense lower layer. The particles of Jupiter's upper clouds are much smaller than particles in Earth's clouds.

A precise modeling of the Jovian cloud layers was still continuing at the time of the Voyager encounters in 1979. Generally, two cloud layers appeared to be present on the planet: a thick, low deck with a gaseous atmosphere above and a thin, high layer topped by aerosols. The Jovian cloud particles were not spherical (unlike the sulfuric acid droplets of the Venusian atmosphere). Instead, the Jovian particles seemed irregular and probably larger than the wavelength of light. Clouds seemed to be lower at the poles. But, alternatively, the upper cloud layers might have been diffuse with many aerosols suspended in the upper atmosphere.

The pictures of Jupiter revealed several surprises about the clouds. The detailed cloud structures in intermediate latitudes were unexpected. The billows and whirls near the edges of belts and zones confirmed that the direction and speed of the winds change rapidly there. Motions in latitude as well as in longitude seem to be evidenced by trends and slants in the North Tropical Zone, for example. The plume in the Equatorial Zone was revealed in remarkable detail, which provided structural information so important to understanding these common cloud forms of that zone.

Infrared observations of Jupiter have been made from the ground at wavelengths of 5 μm where there is a window of transparency in the atmospheres of both Earth and Jupiter. Maps of Jupiter at this wavelength, made at the Hale Observatories, reveal belts and zones very much the same as shown in photographs of Jupiter taken by visible light. But the dark visible belts are light (hotter) in the infrared pictures, and the light visible zones are dark (cooler) (Figure 6-23). The infrared radiation comes from deep within the atmosphere and

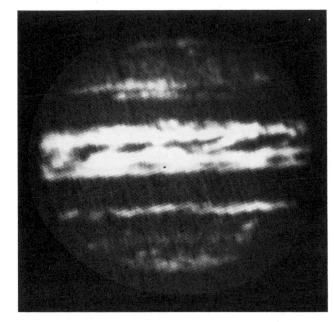

(a)

(b)

Figure 6-23. Ground-based infrared maps of Jupiter (a) show a correlation between infrared sources and the dark zones of the planet seen on the Pioneer images (b). (*Photograph: J. A. Westphal, Hale Observatories*)

shows that the dark visible belts are lower, or thinner, hotter clouds, while the bright visible features are higher, or thicker, cooler clouds. There is also a close correlation between infrared maps of the dark, bluish-gray regions, which are interpreted as dark holes in the clouds. These show as regions of increased infrared radiation. The 5-μm pictures also correlate well with the Pioneer pictures of visible features; the prominent plume and various cells and wave features are clearly the same.

The Pioneer 10 and 11 spacecraft also made infrared maps of Jupiter, but at 20 and 40 μm where, although there is less detail because of less penetration and less temperature contrast, the planet emits more infrared radiation than it does at 5 μm (Figure 6-24). These maps also confirm the high and low clouds and provide information on the general heat balance of the planet — namely, that Jupiter emits more heat than it absorbs from the Sun.

Figure 6-24. An infrared map of Jupiter from Pioneer 11 provides information about the heat balance which shows that Jupiter emits 1.7 times more heat than it receives from the Sun.

141

instruments showed that the shock was very turbulent; its precise position was difficult to determine. Across the shock, the solar wind speed was observed to change from 470 km/sec (292 miles/sec) to less than 140 km/sec (87 miles/sec). Its temperature increased from 30,000 K to nearly 470,000 K. As Pioneer passed inward through the magnetic field of Saturn, another important discovery was made — Saturn's magnetic field was unique in that its orientation corresponded almost exactly with the axis of rotation of the planet, the magnetic axis being tilted less than 1°. This contrasts markedly with the magnetic fields of Earth, Jupiter, and Mercury, which are tilted 10° to 20° with respect to their axes of rotation (Figure 6-27). The surprising lack of any appreciable tilt to Saturn's magnetic axis causes difficulties in explaining the field by some dynamo theories of the generation of planetary fields. It also prevents the accurate measurement of the period of rotation of Saturn's interior by use of magnetic field observations.

The magnetic moment of Saturn is 540 times stronger than Earth's, and 35 times weaker than Jupiter's. The strength of the field at the equatorial cloudtops of Saturn is about 0.20 gauss — Earth's field at the surface is 0.31 gauss. Polar fields of Saturn are 0.63 gauss (north) and 0.48 gauss (south). The center of Saturn's field is displaced northward some 2400 km (1490 miles) along the axis of the planet. Like the field of Jupiter, the polarity of Saturn's field is opposite to that of Earth.

Because there is only a relatively small quadrupole component in Saturn's magnetic field, scientists believe this means that the field must originate far below the visible surface and that Saturn must have a core of metallic hydrogen smaller than Jupiter's metallic hydrogen core.

Like Earth and Jupiter, Saturn has a detached, strong bow shock and a magnetopause. The magnetosphere of Saturn (Figure 6-28) is very responsive to changes in the solar wind, but on a smaller scale than that of Jupiter. The observed dimensions of the magnetosphere of Saturn were, however,

144

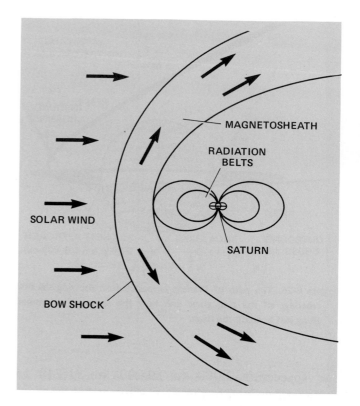

Figure 6-28. Interaction of the solar wind with the magnetosphere of Saturn showing how the wind is deflected by the bow shock and flows around the planet in the magnetosheath. The sizes of the magnetosphere and the radiation belts change in response to the external pressure of the solar wind.

perhaps half the average because of the markedly enhanced solar wind pressure when Pioneer encountered the planet. The blunt sunward side of the magnetosphere, where the bow shock is located, moves in and out as the pressure of the solar wind varies. The outbound leg of the trajectory, along the dawn meridian, carried Pioneer across the magnetopause five times between 30 and 40 Saturn radii, and nine times across the bow shock between 49 and 102 Saturn radii (see Table 6-1).

Boundary	Day of Year	Date (1979)	Distance from Saturn, Saturn radii
Inbound Leg			
Bow shock	243	August 31	24.1
Bow shock			23.1
Bow shock			20.0
Magnetopause			17.3
Outbound Leg			
Magnetopause	246	September 3	30.25
Magnetopause			33.24
Magnetopause			35.9
Magnetopause			39.0
Magnetopause	247	September 4	39.81
Bow shock		September 4	49.26
Bow shock	248	September 5	56.8
Bow shock			59.9
Bow shock			63
Bow shock			64.5
Bow shock	250	September 7	81.2
Bow shock	251	September 8	94.7
Bow shock			95
Bow shock			102

The magnetosphere has four distinct regions. An outer magnetosphere had, at Pioneer encounter, a corotating plasma in which the flux of charged particles varied considerably with time. From 15 to 6 Saturn radii, the observed direction of 1-MeV proton streaming is consistent with full corotation. On the outbound leg of its trajectory, Pioneer found that there may be a magnetotail or a magnetodisk generated in the outer magnetosphere. The magnetic field in this outer magnetosphere was compressed near noon and extended equatorially near dawn, probably because of the presence of a current sheet (Figure 6-29) in or near the magnetic equator and possibly associated with formation of a magnetotail. There was, however, no evidence for a magnetodisk in the planet's dayside magnetosphere. But near dawn in Saturn's magnetosphere, the field lines became equatorial instead of north-south, thereby showing the presence of a current sheet.

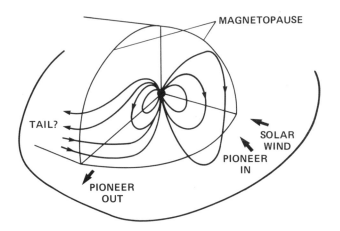

Figure 6-29. A schematic of the magnetic field of Saturn along the inbound and outbound trajectories. In the outer magnetosphere, the dipole magnetic field is compressed near noon. Near the dawn meridian, by contrast, it is swept back more or less parallel to the equator and the magnetopause.

Inside about 6 Saturn radii, the inner boundary of the first region, the numbers of low-energy protons dropped markedly. This effect is believed to result from the sweeping effect of the satellites Dione, Tethys, and Enceladus and by a thin ring of dust (E ring). This second region has been called the "slot" because of its reduced level of radiation.

Starting at 4 Saturn radii, the third region, the inner magnetosphere, has a complex spectrum of very energetic charged particles. Protons with energies greater than 80 MeV were measured to a maximum flux of 2.5×10^4 /cm^2/sec, and electrons with energies greater than 0.56 MeV, to a flux of 9×10^6 /cm^2/sec.

There was a distinct region (Figure 6-30) associated with the satellite Mimas where particles were depleted.

Analysis of particle fluxes, spectra, and distributions shows that: (a) The low-energy ($\sim$1-MeV) protons in the outer magnetosphere come either from the solar wind or from solar energetic particle beams. (b) The electrons from 40 keV to several MeV throughout the magnetosphere come from the solar wind. (c) The very high-energy ($\gtrsim$80-MeV) protons in the inner magnetosphere come from the decay of neutrons produced in the

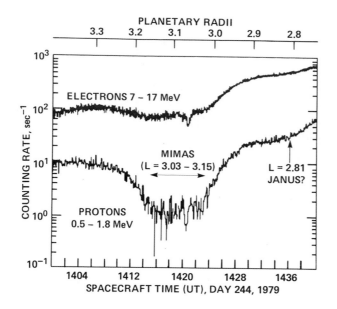

Figure 6-30. Absorption of charged particles by Mimas is shown by these data.

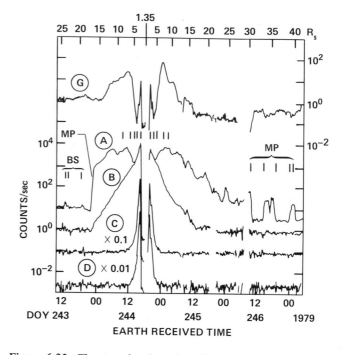

Figure 6-32. The trapping boundary for energetic particles was accurately coincident with the magnetopause as shown here for a general overview of 15-min counting rates (BS, bow shock; MP, magnetopause).

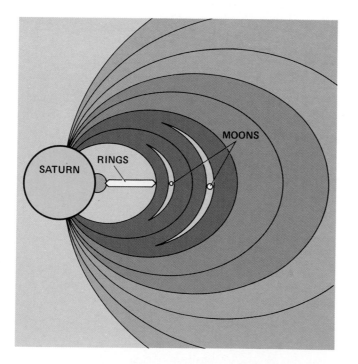

Figure 6-31. Diagram of Saturn's inner magnetosphere and the trapped radiation belts. Decreases in particle flux at the locations of the orbits of Saturn's satellites result from the sweeping effect of these satellites. The satellites absorb any particles that strike them. Also, the rings effectively block particle flux at their outer edge; thus the innermost region of the magnetosphere is radiation-free.

atmosphere and rings of the planet by cosmic ray bombardment.

In the fourth region of the magnetosphere, internal to the outer edge of ring A, the rings have swept up nearly all trapped radiation to create an environment almost free of radiation.

Thus, Pioneer discovered that Saturn, like Jupiter and Earth, has belts of trapped energetic particles, mainly protons and electrons (Figure 6-31). The trapping boundary for energetic particles was observed to be accurately coincident with the magnetopause on both inbound and outbound legs of the trajectory (Figure 6-32). The particles are present around Saturn in quantities comparable to but greater than those in Earth's radiation belts, but they extend over a much greater region because Saturn's magnetosphere is so much larger than that of Earth. Saturn's radiation belts are some 10 times larger in linear dimensions than Earth's radiation belts. Even so, the total radiation dosage of electrons of energy greater than 0.56 MeV experienced by Pioneer during its flyby

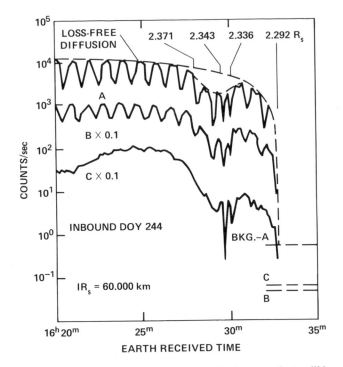

Figure 6-33. Any high-energy protons and electrons that collide with ring particles are absorbed completely, as shown in this plot along the inbound trajectory.

of Saturn was 7×10^{10} electrons/cm^2, which is about the same as that encountered during only 5 min of the spacecraft's passage through the most intense region of Jupiter's inner radiation belt.

The radiation environment of Saturn is made much less intense by the presence of the rings, which have a marked effect on the radiation belts of the planet. Particles in radiation belts oscillate up and down across the equatorial plane of the planet, first toward one pole and then, as though reflected by a mirror, back toward the other. As particles gradually diffuse inward toward the planet, they are absorbed by the rings. Any high-energy electrons and protons that collide with ring particles are wiped out completely (Figure 6-33). From these observations the outer edge of the A ring is found to be at a radial distance of 2.292 ±0.002 Saturn radii. Also, the general magnetic field of the planet reduces the level of high-energy cosmic radiation, thereby making the region inward of the outermost edge of the rings perhaps the most radiation-free space within the Solar

System. However, a weak flux of high-energy electrons was discovered under the rings. It had an intensity 4 to 5 times the interplanetary flux of such electrons during quiet periods of solar activity.

As Pioneer approached Saturn, the spacecraft's instruments measured a maximum intensity of very energetic protons at 2.67 Saturn radii. Anomalies in the rate of increase, and some decreases in the number of particles inward toward the planet, provided crucial information on the origin of these particles as summarized above.

Generally, the trapped radiation in the inner magnetosphere was spaced symmetrically around the planet, thereby showing that Saturn's magnetosphere is much more stable than Jupiter's. The effects of satellites in sweeping energetic particles from the radiation belts was more clearly defined at Saturn than at Jupiter because of the regular nature of Saturn's magnetosphere.

A speculative possibility is the effect of Jupiter on Saturn's magnetosphere. About every 20 yr, Jupiter may shield Saturn from the solar wind when Saturn becomes immersed transiently in an extended magnetotail of Jupiter. Then Saturn's magnetosphere might expand dramatically. Such a condition may be observed when Voyager 2 encounters Saturn in 1981.

Saturn's Satellites

Just after Pioneer passed through the plane of the rings on its inward passage, the number of energetic particles decreased abruptly — to about 2% of the prevailing value for 10 sec. The experimenters attributed the absorption of particles to a previously unknown satellite-sized body. The satellite, designated 1979 S2, had to be at least 170 km (106 miles) in diameter to account for the effects observed. It is the first satellite to be discovered from an analysis of energetic charged particles, apart from the Pioneer 11 evidence for a ring or inner satellite of Jupiter noted earlier. Its orbit was within that of Mimas, about 14,500 km (9,010 miles) from the outer edge of the visible

147

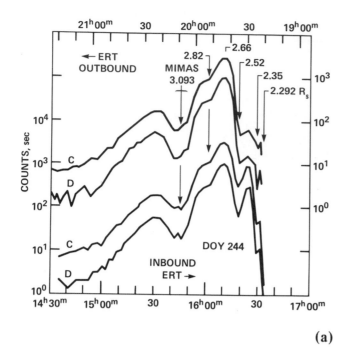

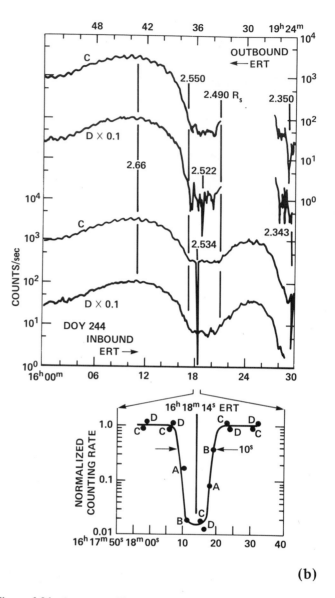

(a)

(b)

rings at 2.53 Saturn radii from the center of the planet (Figure 6-34).

On the previous day, the imaging photopolarimeter discovered a new satellite. It showed up on two of the computer-generated pictures of Saturn as a small dot of light, consisting of three pixels only, near the outer edge of the rings (Figure 6-35). The small satellite was designated 1979) − 1979 S1 and 1979 S2 could be the same object detected independently by two quite same object detected independently by two quite different techniques. Moreover, the satellite may be one of those detected by ground-based observations during the edge-on presentation of the ring system in 1966. Pioneer also found that there was absorption of high-energy electrons and protons by the satellites Enceladus and Tethys. As a result of this absorption, low-energy charged particles are sputtered from the satellites' surfaces and create an oxygen-ion rich plasma torus at the orbit of each satellite. Strong ultraviolet radiation from these oxygen ions was detected by Pioneer's ultraviolet photometer.

Figure 6-34. A new satellite of Saturn (1979 S1) was discovered by analysis of absorptions of charged particles, the first such discovery by this method. (a) Plots of average counting rates show the absorption by Mimas and several others nearer the planet, particularly one at about 2.52 Saturn radii. (b) More details of this absorption at 2.53 to 2.52 Saturn radii and at an enlarged scale (below).

There was no evidence of absorption of energetic particles by the suspected satellite Janus at or near a distance of 2.66 Saturn radii, although there were clear absorptions that might be associated with previously unknown satellites at 2.34 and 2.82 Saturn radii.

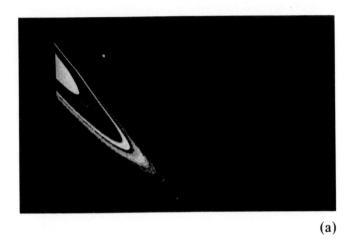

(a)

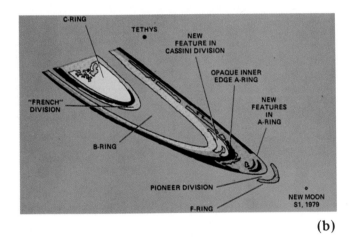

(b)

Figure 6-35. This picture by Pioneer shows great detail in the ring system, and the newly discovered satellite 1979 S1. (a) Computer-enhanced picture taken August 31, 1979, at a distance of 943,000 km (585,950 miles) from Saturn. (b) The satellite and some ring features; the satellite Tethys is also shown.

The Pioneer observations indicate that the F ring and the G ring contain small satellites and that there may be small satellites associated with the A and B rings. Formation of Saturn's rings by tidal breakup of a single satellite now seems unlikely. It is postulated that although near Jupiter the satellites Io and Europa formed, the lesser mass density of the solar nebula at the distance of Saturn's orbit resulted in the formation of a system of rings and small satellites.

The previously known large satellites did perturb Pioneer's path through the system. From these effects, the masses of Iapetus, Rhea, and Titan were determined more accurately; their mean densities were calculated as 1.8, 1.0, and 1.32 gm/cm^3, respectively. These satellites were confirmed as being low-density icy worlds. The particle absorption signature of Mimas appeared unexpected because it suggests that Mimas has a diameter less than 180 km (112 miles) compared with the generally accepted value of about 360 km (220 miles). If the smaller diameter is correct, the mean density of the satellite would be 5 gm/cm^3 — a surprisingly high value.

The photopolarimeter obtained polarization measurements of Titan's atmosphere over a wide range of phase angles. Light from Titan was found to be strongly polarized, and the data revealed the types of aerosols present in the Titan atmosphere. The data appear to be consistent with a haze of methane particles extending high into the atmosphere. Infrared radiation at 45 μm from the clouds revealed a cloudtop temperature of only −198° C (−324° F), about as expected for a body in equilibrium with solar radiation and one that generates no internal heat. There may be warmer regions below that are obscured by aerosols, but nevertheless it appears that Titan does not have a significant internal heat source. A greenhouse effect, which would trap solar radiation, was not ruled out; however, the results from Pioneer do not support the possibility that life or precursors of life exist on Titan. The images of Titan obtained by the Pioneer spacecraft do not show any revealing detail.

149

Data sets at red and blue wavelengths recorded by the imaging photopolarimeter provided information to determine the radius of Titan more precisely. These radii are 2845 ±25 km and 2880 ±22 km for red and blue wavelengths, respectively. The difference may result from there being a thin haze of submicrometer particles above the nominal haze layer.

The linear polarization of the integrated disk of Titan in red and blue light at phase angles between 15° and 97° provided information about the sizes of particles in the atmosphere of this large satellite. A polarization of 54% measured in blue light at 90° phase angle implies that the particles near the top of Titan's atmosphere must have radii smaller than about 0.09 μm if they have a refractive index of 2.0. A smaller polarization in red light (41%) implies that the optical thickness of the layers of small aerosols is about 0.6 above an effective depolarizing surface. The shape of the polarization/phase curve in blue light suggests increasing particle size with increasing depth in the atmosphere.

Pioneer's ultraviolet instrument discovered a cloud of hydrogen atoms around Titan, extending at least 300,000 km (186,400 miles) along the orbit and about 180,000 km (112,000 miles) thick. This discovery suggests that the methane in Titan's atmosphere is being broken down into hydrogen and carbon by solar radiation. Hydrogen atoms would possess sufficient energy to escape into space — hence the observed hydrogen cloud. Since the heavier carbon atoms do not travel fast enough to escape, they would be expected to remain in the atmosphere and possibly to produce aerosol clouds, the particles of which ultimately fall to Titan's surface.

The Rings of Saturn

The Pioneer missions provided valuable information on the magnificent ring system of Saturn. Discovered by Galileo in 1610, the true nature of this ring system — swarms of small orbiting bodies — was not understood until the speculations of Huygens in 1659. This ring system has divisions and gaps where the orbiting particles are fewer in number than in the visible rings. The most prominent of these is Cassini's division. Before the Pioneer encounter, the division was believed to be about 6400 km (4000 miles) wide, but Pioneer refined the dimension to 4200 km (2600 miles). The division separates the two main bright rings, A and B.

Some of the most spectacular pictures from any of the space missions were taken by Pioneer when it obtained images of Saturn's ring system illuminated from behind. These pictures provided valuable new information that could never be obtained from Earth. Those rings, which normally appear bright when viewed from Earth, appear dark in the Pioneer pictures, and the dark gaps in the rings as seen from Earth appear as bright rings in the Pioneer pictures (Figure 6-36). The gaps appear bright because they are not entirely free of material and the particles within the gaps scatter the sunlight. However, the particles within the bright rings are sufficient to intercept most of the

Figure 6-36. A general view of Saturn and its magnificent ring system during the approach of Pioneer — rings are illuminated from behind.

150

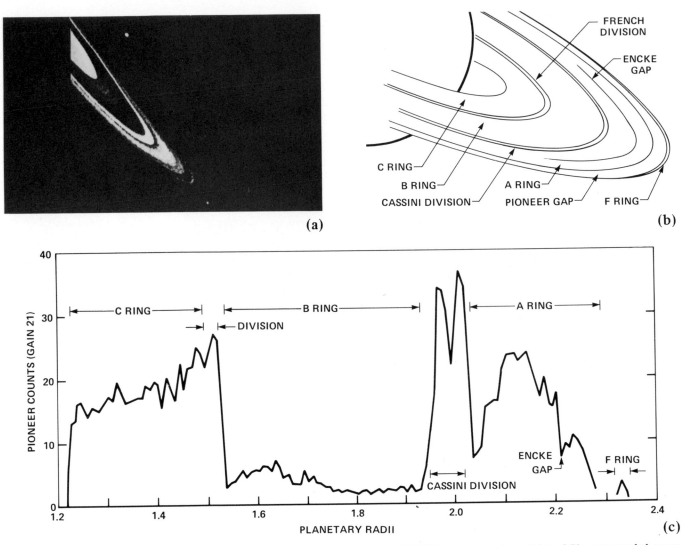

Figure 6-37. The unique vantage point of Pioneer revealed many new features in the rings. (a) One of the many images obtained by Pioneer. (b) Features in the ring system. (c) Brightness of the rings on the unilluminated side in red light plotted versus distance from Saturn in planetary radii.

sunlight and permit only a small amount of it to pass through. These new viewpoints based on light transmitted through the rings allow scientists to assess much more accurately the thickness of the ring material.

Several surprises came from Pioneer's observations of the ring system. No visual trace was found of an outermost E ring (sometimes referred to as the D′ ring), first referred to by Fournier when the rings were viewed edge-on in 1907. He wrote of a faint, transparent, and luminous ring outside the principal rings of Saturn. Other astronomers claimed they had seen the E ring when the rings were again edge-on in 1952 through 1954; it was photographed by W. A. Feibelman and G. P. Kuiper in the 1966 period. Some radar data appeared to support the presence of the E ring but in the imaging data from Pioneer there was no trace of the ring. Nonetheless, the energetic particle measurements suggest confirmatory evidence for a thin tenuous E ring. Also, the dust detector provided evidence for the E ring and suggested a thickness of 1800 km with an optical depth (opacity) greater than 10^{-8}.

151

The A ring, the bright outer ring seen from Earth, was found by Pioneer to transmit in part appreciable amounts of sunlight; it appeared bright in the Pioneer pictures. Considerable structural details could be seen in the ring (Figure 6-37); the outer 25% was substantially darker than the rest of the ring, thereby showing that it contains more material. The inner parts showed several regions that have a low particle density, but the innermost edge contains much material and is almost as opaque as the B ring. This B ring, the brightest ring seen from Earth, is almost completely opaque to sunlight striking it on the side away from the observer.

The composition and sizes of the particles comprising the rings have for many years been a matter of debate and speculation. The celestial mechanics experiment showed that the total mass of the rings is less than 3 millionths that of Saturn itself. Where the rings were illuminated by sunlight, Pioneer measured a temperature of $-208°$ C ($-342°$ F). Where the planet's shadow fell on the rings, the temperature was $-210°$ C ($-346°$ F). This small difference in temperature indicates that the rings receive energy from the dark hemisphere of Saturn. The temperature of the unilluminated face of the rings was about $-218°$ C ($-360°$ F). This temperature indicates that considerable infrared radiation is transmitted through the rings, but the rings are thick enough to insulate the dark side from the warmer sunlit side. The rings cannot be more than 4 km (2.5 miles) thick. The size of the ring particles appeared to be in the centimeter range. However, Pioneer observations of the unilluminated side of the rings indicate a distribution of much smaller particles also — $\sim$100 μm in diameter. These may result from collisions between larger particles.

The dark Cassini division between the A and B rings appeared quite bright when seen from Pioneer (Figure 6-38) because it contains particles, and these scatter light through the division. A less bright region near the middle of the division indicated a gap there.

152

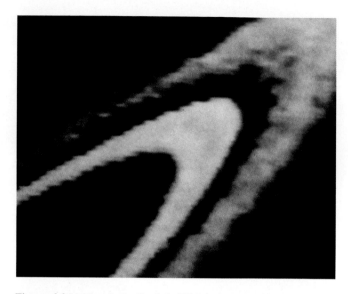

Figure 6-38. The dark Cassini division between rings A and B appeared quite bright from the Pioneer spacecraft. This closeup shows the effect of back-illumination in detailing the ring structure.

The C ring or Crepe ring, discovered by Bond in 1850, is a very faint dusky ring inside the B ring. The C ring was clearly identified on the Pioneer pictures as a bright ring (see Figure 6-38) since it also scatters light. Particles in this ring were apparently as diffuse as in Cassini's division.

Pioneer confirmed the existence of another ring division that had been suggested by several French astronomers. Pioneer pictures of the shadows of the rings on the clouds of Saturn (Figure 6-39) clearly revealed a division between the B and C rings. The division, about 3600 km (2200 miles) wide, was called the French or Dollfus division.

Although no optical trace was found of the E ring (apparently it is too faint to be detected by the imaging photopolarimeter), a narrow ring appeared outside the A ring on the Pioneer pictures (Figure 6-40). The Pioneer experimenters called the new ring the F ring. It is quite narrow, less than

Figure 6-39. The vantage point of Pioneer allowed pictures such as this, not only the back-illuminated rings but their shadows on the cloudtops of the planet.

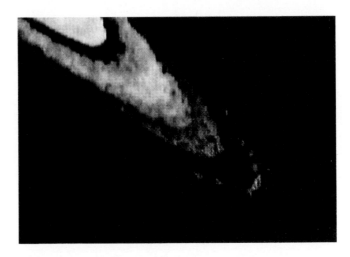

Figure 6-40. Closeup of the ring system showing the new ring discovered by Pioneer, the F ring.

800 km (500 miles) wide, and it is separated from the outer edge of the A ring by a gap of about 3600 km (2240 miles) — named the Pioneer division by the spacecraft team. Details of the measurements of the ring system from Pioneer data are given in Table 6-2.

TABLE 6-2. DIMENSIONS OF THE RING SYSTEM OF SATURN FROM PIONEER DATA

Ring feature	Distance from Saturn, Saturn radii[a]		
	Optical	Infrared	Particles
Guerin Division	1.215 to 1.284		
C Ring	1.284 to 1.5	1.25 to 1.53	
French Division	1.50 to 1.535		
B Ring	1.525 to 1.995	1.93 to 1.95	
B Ring Gap	1.66	1.635	
Cassini Division	1.955 to 2.030	to 2.02	
Cassini Division Gap	1.97 to 2.01		
Encke Gap	2.225		
A Ring	2.030 to 2.267		
Pioneer Division	2.293 to 2.336		2.29 to 2.34
F Ring	2.336 to 2.371		2.34 to 2.37
G Ring			2.49 to 2.55
E Ring			4.0 to 8.0

[a] Radius of Saturn taken as 60,000 km (37,280 miles).

Pioneer also discovered a substantial glow of atomic hydrogen around the ring system, which was enhanced at the B ring. The presence of hydrogen is attributed to the dissociation of water molecules sputtered off the rings by sunlight.

The Planet Saturn

Measurements of the trajectory of Pioneer past Saturn allowed the shape and gravity field of the planet to be determined more precisely than ever before. Because of the planet's rapid rotation, Saturn's polar diameter is about 10% less than its equatorial diameter. The polar flattening was determined more precisely from the spin-scan imaging data. By overlapping graphical predictions of geometric distortions of spin-scan images with raster scans of the raw data (both displayed on the same scale), the precise geometry of each data-seeking sequence was established. The predictions are quite sensitive to the dimensions assumed for Saturn and its rings. As a result, scientists concluded that the ratio of polar-to-equatorial radius is 0.912 ± 0.006 and that the Encke gap in the rings is 133,500 km (82,960 miles) from Saturn's center.

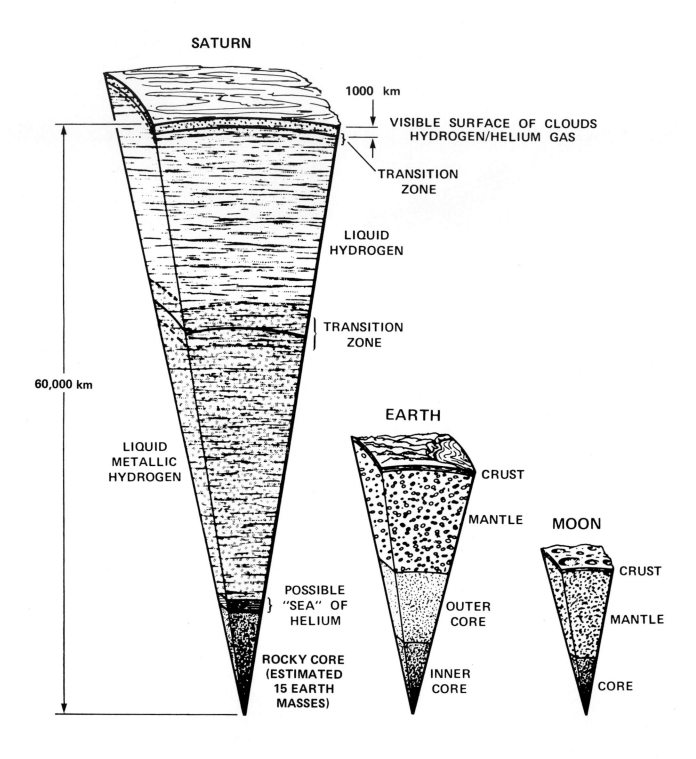

SATURN

1000 km

VISIBLE SURFACE OF CLOUDS
HYDROGEN/HELIUM GAS

TRANSITION
ZONE

LIQUID
HYDROGEN

TRANSITION
ZONE

60,000 km

EARTH

LIQUID
METALLIC
HYDROGEN

CRUST

MANTLE

MOON

CRUST

POSSIBLE
} "SEA" OF
HELIUM

OUTER
CORE

MANTLE

ROCKY CORE
(ESTIMATED
15 EARTH
MASSES)

INNER
CORE

CORE

Figure 6-41. The interior of Saturn compared with those of Earth
and our Moon: a small rocky core surrounded by a deep shell
of liquid metallic hydrogen, topped by a shell of liquid hydrogen
and an atmosphere of hydrogen-rich gas. The liquid metallic
hydrogen region is not as large proportionately in Saturn as in
Jupiter.

154

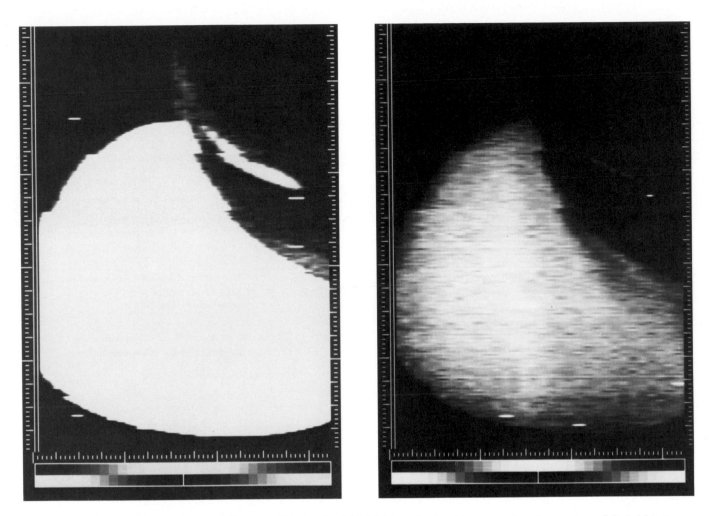

Figure 6-42. Infrared radiometer image of Saturn and its rings in which brightness is related to temperature; temperature of the brightest areas is about –173° C (–280° F). The left image shows contrast in the colder region of the rings. The right image shows contrast in the warmer region of the planet. The distortion in the images results from the high speed of the spacecraft and the time required to gather the data for them. On the left, the warm infrared radiation from the planet is seen through the Cassini division between the A and B rings. The brightness level on the right image implies that Saturn emits heat at a rate 2.8 times that at which it absorbs energy from the Sun.

Analysis of the gravity field, coupled with a calculated temperature profile based on the infrared measurements of heat emitted from the clouds in excess of that absorbed from the Sun, allowed the experimenters to develop a new view of the interior of the planet (Figure 6-41). The planet's core of about 18 Earth masses appears to have two distinct regions. An inner core, about the size of Earth but with a mass about 3 times that of Earth, is a mixture of iron-rich rocky materials. An outer core, of about 9 Earth masses, is thought to consist of ammonia, methane, and water. It probably extends from the center of the planet to about 23% of the radius, that is,

to about 13,800 km (8,575 miles). Above the core and extending to about 58% of Saturn's radius, there appears to be a region of liquid metallic hydrogen, a form of hydrogen at high temperature and under great pressure so that it readily conducts electricity. The presence of this material was also indicated by the characteristics of the planet's magnetic field. The nature of this field implied that the metallic hydrogen dynamo region of Saturn must be substantially smaller than that of Jupiter: 0.5 Saturn radii compared with 0.75 Jupiter radii, respectively.

The effective temperature of Saturn measured by the infrared experiment (Figure 6-42) was

−177° C (−287° F), some 30° C less than that of Jupiter. Saturn was found to radiate 2.8 ±0.9 times more heat than it absorbs from the Sun. Photometric data lead, however, to a greater number. Analysis of photometric observations at large phase angles in red and blue light led to an important conclusion. If Saturn scatters light similarly at other wavelengths, its bolometric geometric albedo together with the effective temperature of −177° C (reported by the infrared experimenters) imply that Saturn radiates three times as much energy as it receives from the Sun.

It is suggested that only about half the planet's heat is generated by leftover heat of formation and by a continuing compression of the planet's core by the enormous weight of all layers of material above it. Additional heat is probably being evolved by a separation of the planet's two major constituents, hydrogen and helium. At Saturn's temperature, which is lower than Jupiter's, helium does not remain mixed with hydrogen as it might be within Jupiter. The denser helium, gradually sinking to Saturn's core, is generating heat. Infrared and radio occultation data show that the outer atmosphere of Saturn is about 90% hydrogen and 10% helium.

Saturn's Atmosphere and Cloud Systems

The pictures of Saturn's clouds showed surprisingly little contrast. The infrared data suggest that these clouds are thicker than the Jovian clouds. The images showed some scalloping on the edges of belts and zones, as on Jupiter. Such scalloping is caused by differences in velocities between adjacent air masses. There were subtle colors in the clouds away from the poles, but at the poles there was a clearly blue-green color. This was believed to result from Rayleigh scattering of light in the atmosphere. Saturn's cloudtops appeared lower at the poles than at the equator. Hence the planet's gaseous atmosphere could be seen above the clouds, ranging in color from dark blue to slightly green.

156

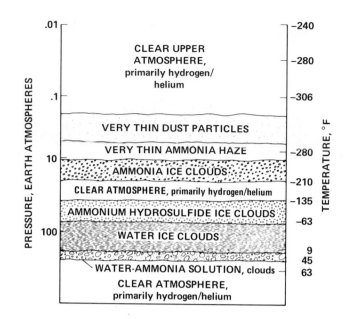

Figure 6-43. Possible arrangement of the clouds within the atmosphere of Saturn and temperatures at the various levels.

Saturn's pastel colors changed to brownish belts at about 55° latitude in both hemispheres. Near the terminator, the colors darkened, indicating that light was being scattered by the molecules of the atmospheric gases.

The polarization measurements of Saturn indicated an atmosphere (Figure 6-43) of clear gas to a pressure of 2 atm, then a region of small absorbing particles, then an ammonia haze, with a topmost ammonia cloud deck. The cloudtops appeared to be at a pressure of about 750 mbar. The colored clouds may be deeper in the atmosphere of Saturn than they are in the Jovian atmosphere, thereby accounting for the lack of strong coloring on Saturn. Generally, Saturn appeared to have more and narrower belts and zones than Jupiter. There appeared to be features like jet streams, one at about 70° north latitude and another near the equator. A plume in the northern hemisphere, similar to that seen on Jupiter by Pioneer, was also discovered. The jet stream is much faster than that of Jupiter: 350 km/hr (217 mph) compared with 150 km/hr (93 mph).

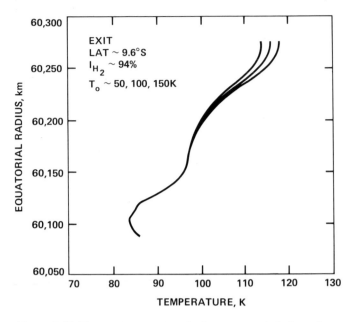

Figure 6-44. Temperature structure in the upper neutral atmosphere of Saturn as determined from the radio occultation experiment of Pioneer.

An ultraviolet glow, intensified at the polar regions, could be caused by aurorae or it might be a limb-brightening effect.

Infrared measurements of the globe of Saturn showed that temperature dropped within 8° of the equator — corresponding to the high clouds of the equatorial yellow band. Also, the temperature of the belts and zones differed by about 2.5° C (4.5° F). The temperature of the upper atmospheric layers was about 5° C (9° F) warmer than expected, thereby confirming suggestions that substantial heat moves from inside the planet outward, almost certainly by convective circulation.

Saturn's ionosphere, as measured by the occultation experiment near the terminator, extends much higher than that of Jupiter, but the inferred temperature is about the same, of the order of 1000° C (1830° F). Two peaks of electrons were identified. The highest, at about 1800 km (1100 miles) above the cloudtops, has about 1.1×10^4 electrons/cm³. The other, at 1200 km (745 miles) has a peak electron density of 9×10^3/cm³.

The S-band radio signal also penetrated the neutral atmosphere of Saturn to the level of about 150 mbar (19% of Earth's atmospheric pressure at sea level). The temperature structure derived from these data matches the temperatures derived from the infrared radiometer measurements for a compoposition of 90% hydrogen, 10% helium. The minimum temperature was about –185° C (–301° F) at a level of about 100 mbar (Figure 6-44).

The mission of the two Pioneer spacecraft to explore the giant planets of our Solar System was remarkably successful. Many questions had been answered and many discoveries made. Nonetheless, these giant planets, with their intriguing satellites, ring systems, and complex magnetospheres, posed many new questions. Some of these are being answered by the Voyager spacecraft, but others will remain for future missions to place orbiters around these giants and to dispatch probes deep into their atmospheres. The Pioneer trailblazers opened the outer Solar System to mankind, but a full exploration of the many planetary worlds there will take decades of human effort. This exploration will undoubtedly reveal surprises equally as great as those of the Pioneers.

158

7

Images from Jupiter and Saturn

The Pioneer 10 and 11 spacecraft used small instruments called imaging photopolarimeters (IPPs) to form images of Jupiter and Saturn. The IPPs measured the strength of sunlight scattered from the clouds of the planets and their satellites, and converted this light intensity data into digital representations of different shades of red and blue that made up each image. This digital information was then transmitted by radio to Earth where — with the aid of computers — scientists converted these signals into patterns of light and dark on a photographic film. This chapter describes the complexities of this process and discusses ways in which scientists overcame problems with this technique.

Bits and Pixels

Photographs in newspapers and magazines are reproduced by a technique known as the halftone process. If such pictures are enlarged many times, they are seen to consist of thousands of small, regularly spaced, black dots of varying sizes — large dots for dark areas and smaller dots for light areas. These dots are too small to be seen separately by the unaided eye; the viewer sees a continuous distribution of changing gray levels that make the picture. Small dots give the impression of light gray and large dots form the dark gray areas.

Instead of dots, a picture can consist of small contiguous areas called picture elements, or pixels, each with its own shade of gray. Pixels are usually square or rectangular, and if there are enough shades of gray and if the pixels are small enough, the eye fuses the array of little squares or rectangles into a continuous, smooth-looking picture. The shades of gray (or gray levels, as they are usually called) can also be divided into a limited number of different values — a number, say 64, of evenly spaced shades of gray is chosen, with black thus represented by 0, white by 63, and the intermediate shades by 1 through 62.

Figure 7-1. This scan photograph from an Earth Resources Technology Satellite (ERTS) covers the southern part of the San Francisco Bay area. (a) An overview of the area. (b) An enlarged view of part of the area, including a runway at San Francisco International Airport. The area covered is designated by the white square outlined on picture (a). The enlargement shows how the picture consists of discrete squares having different tones of gray. (c) A computer listing of numbers on the right identifies the value of the gray level of each square within the outlined portion of picture (b). The photographic-type image is generated from such numbers.

Figure 7-1(a) is a photograph originally consisting of pixels and gray levels instead of conventional dots, although it is reproduced here by a dot process. A small portion of the picture (shown magnified in Figure 7-1(b)) reveals the pixels and gray levels. The numbers on the right (Figure 7-1(c)) correspond to the gray levels seen in the enlarged portion of the picture.

To send pictures, or scenes, from one place to another, the original scene is scanned with an instrument that measures the intensity of light

(a)

160

gathered from each of many small areas in the scene. The intensity reading is converted, or coded, into a binary number (a string of zeros and ones, somewhat like the dot-dash nature of the Morse code) and sent by radio or over wires to a distant receiver. There the stream of impulses is converted back to appropriately positioned small gray areas on a film, thus creating a facsimile of the original scene. Similar processes, known as facsimile systems, have been in use for many decades to transmit newspaper photographs by wire.

Before the Pioneer missions to Jupiter and Saturn, however, such a system had not been used to obtain images of distant planets, even though it had been proposed for this purpose in 1953 for a Mars orbiter. Instead, all imaging of planets from spacecraft — except of Earth from Earth satellites — used television or conventional cameras. For reasons such as weight limitations and power requirements, it was decided not to use a television system for the Pioneer spacecraft, but rather to apply a well-established alternative method using a spin-scan telescope, a method already used by National Oceanic and Atmospheric Administration (NOAA) satellites to produce weather maps of Earth.

A more detailed technical description of the imaging photopolarimeter used on Pioneers 10 and 11 is given in appendix A; only a basic description is given here. A small telescope collected light from a 0.028° square (i.e., the equivalent of a 1-cm square seen at a distance of 20 m, or a 1-in. square at 55 yd) located along the direction the telescope was pointing — the line of sight. Color filters separated red and blue components of the light, and the strength of these components was then measured electronically.

As the spacecraft spun on its axis, the line of sight of the telescope swept out a large cone in space, which intersected the planet being encountered. The instrument recorded the brightness of

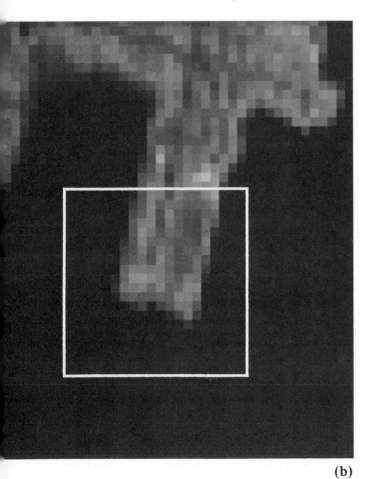

(b)

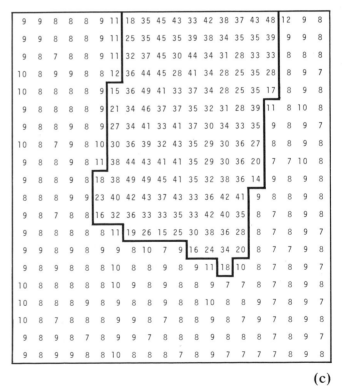

(c)

161

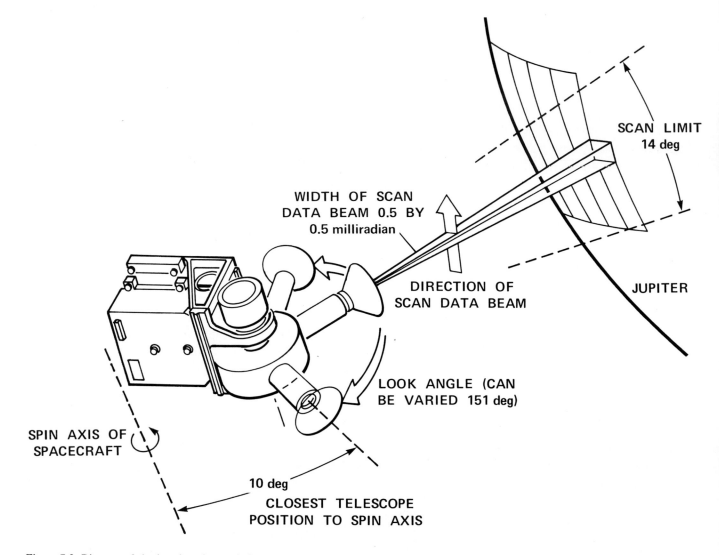

WIDTH OF SCAN
DATA BEAM 0.5 BY
0.5 milliradian

SCAN LIMIT
14 deg

DIRECTION OF
SCAN DATA BEAM

JUPITER

LOOK ANGLE (CAN
BE VARIED 151 deg)

SPIN AXIS OF
SPACECRAFT

10 deg

CLOSEST TELESCOPE
POSITION TO SPIN AXIS

Figure 7-2. Diagram of the imaging photopolarimetry system showing how it scanned across a planet, in this case, Jupiter.

the reflected light from each small contiguous area as it scanned the planet's surface in narrow strips, as shown in Figure 7-2. The intensity of the red and blue light reflected from each element of the scene was translated into a number from 0 to 63, and the number was telemetered to Earth. The sequential string of numbers provided information on the different strengths of the red and blue components of each pixel along the scan path of the photopolarimeter. On successive rolls of the spacecraft, the scan path was displaced sideways step by step, so that, over a period of time, the planet's disk was scanned and an image of it could be reconstructed.

The basic way to displace the scan path was to change the "look angle," the angle between the axis of the telescope and the spin axis of the spacecraft. The instrument could automatically change the telescope's look angle in commanded increments (steps) between each roll of the spacecraft, thereby allowing the required coverage of the planet.

The pixel scans in Figure 7-1 are straight, evenly spaced lines, but the Pioneer scans were quite different. Basically, the Pioneer scan lines were curved because of the way in which the line-of-sight cone intersected the ellipsoidally shaped planets. Addi-

162

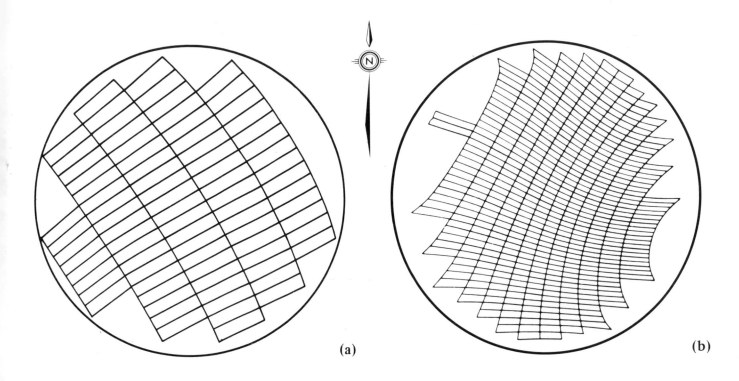

Figure 7-3. Two typical scan maps of Jupiter showing how the line of sight of the scan telescope swept across the planet and built a picture consisting of discrete areas of different shades of gray. (a) A distant picture produced a relatively undistorted grid. (b) As the spacecraft neared Jupiter, the trajectory curved more, the spacecraft accelerated, and the imaging photopolarimeter took longer to completely scan the larger disk of the planet; therefore, since Jupiter rotated more during the scanning process, the grid became considerably distorted (as shown).

tional distortions were caused by the spacecraft moving an appreciable distance along its curved path around the planet during the time required to gather the many scans of data for a complete picture. Also, the planet was spinning sufficiently fast to distort the geometry of the scan lines.

Since project scientists had to know precisely where each piece of data came from to reconstruct an image, scan maps were constructed (Figure 7-3). The intersections on the distorted grids are points that define the small areas from which the light intensities were measured. The figure shows only every 25th roll and every 25th sector (group of pixels); to show all rolls and sectors on the figure would require 625 times more lines and intersections.

The imaging photopolarimeter gathered data from only a small part of each 360° roll, either for 14° or for 28° as commanded. The remainder of the roll was used to transmit data back to Earth. To tell the instrument where on the roll to take data, controllers sent the spacecraft "spoke" commands that defined the part of the spacecraft's roll in the same way that numbered spokes might define part of the circumference of a wheel.

Many other commands were needed in these complex, preplanned sequences to obtain spin-scan images of Jupiter and Saturn and their major satellites. Figure 7-4 is one of many graphic aids used to formulate and assist the command process. Note how the look angle of the instrument had to be changed as a function of time to obtain certain images of Jupiter and its satellites during the Pioneer 10 encounter. The three lines in the shaded band labeled Jupiter represent the center and outer edges of the planet's disk viewed from the spacecraft. The curved lines labeled JI, JII, etc., show how the look angles of the Galilean satellites (Io, Europa, Ganymede, and Callisto) changed. The two lines labeled SLA1 are positions to which the instrument could be rapidly sent. These positions were used to direct the instrument to start a sequence of operations and to recover from any anomalous situation, such as a spurious command caused by radiation. The numbered irregular line shows the actual position of the telescope as it gathered data over a 24-hr period.

Commanding the Imaging Photopolarimeter

The basic command strategy was to take repeated scans of the disk of the planet being imaged, interrupted by rapid returns to the starting look angle (SLA) for polarimetry measurements whenever one of the satellites crossed a starting look angle. For example, from the left in Figure 7-4(a), the imaging photopolarimeter was operating in its photopolarimeter mode at a starting look angle on Jupiter's satellite Europa, JII. To reach position 1, 21 commands had been issued, 12 of which were to overcome unwanted gain changes that had begun early in the mission.

Between points 1 and 7 in the sequence, five additional gain control commands were sent at 30-min intervals. At point 7, the imaging photopolarimeter was commanded into its threshold mode (mode 3), where the instrument moved its telescope in small increments continuously until the limb (edge of the visible disk) of Jupiter was detected. This point in the sequence involved 17 contiguous commands.

At point 8, the instrument was commanded to the imaging mode (mode 4), and it changed its look angle a step at a time at the imaging rate of 0.5 mrad per revolution of the spacecraft. This point in the sequence involved six additional contiguous commands, four of which were gain control (sensitivity) commands and two "spoke" commands.

Point 9 involved a single command to reverse the stepping direction of the telescope. Point 10 then involved 17 contiguous commands, 16 of which were gain control commands. The sets of commands at points 9 and 10, consisting of 1 and then 17 commands, were repeated at every similar point in the sequence that followed. Step 14 involved 26 commands, 23 of which were for gain control, which placed the instrument in the polarimetry mode at the starting look angle for the crossing of Jupiter's third Galilean satellite, Ganymede (JIII).

The commanding at point 15 was identical to that at point 7, and the commanding at point 16 was identical to that at point 8. At point 19, three commands were sent, which resulted in switching back to mode 3 and stepping beyond SLA1.

The commanding at step 20 reversed the direction of the telescope's turn to approach SLA1 from the correct side to position the telescope so that it could observe Ganymede. It involved 32 contiguous commands. The rest of the sequence depicted on the chart was constructed by repeating, at the appropriate time, a command sequence already described.

Similar sequences were executed for 8 hr each day beginning 30 days before closest approach and continuing until 30 days after closest approach, but were extended to 24 hr each day during the period from 8 days before to 8 days after closest approach. Similar sequences were used in the encounters of Pioneer 11 with Jupiter and Saturn.

As the Pioneer spacecraft approached their target planets and satellites, the rapid relative motions between the spacecraft and each target resulted in rapidly changing look angles for the imaging photopolarimeter. Figure 7-4(b) shows a typical observation chart for Pioneer 10's closest

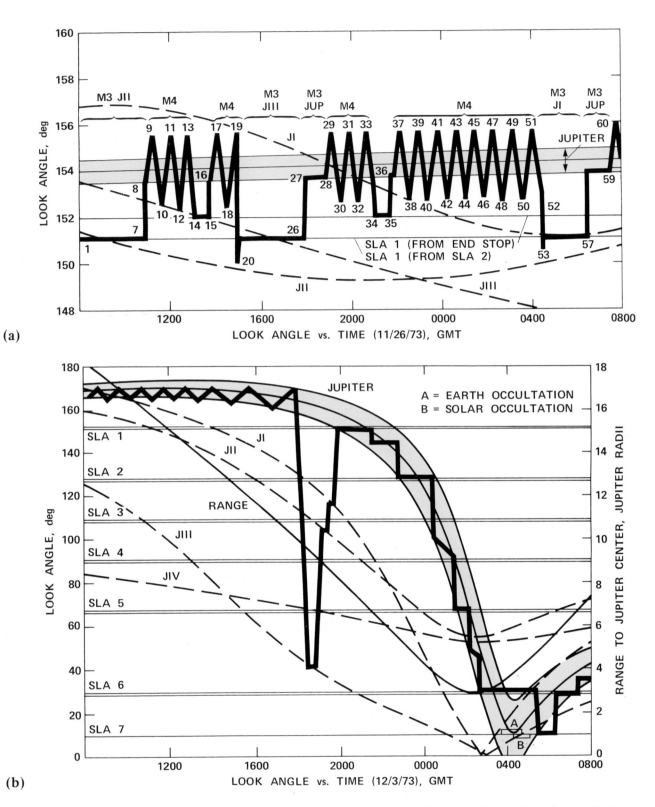

Figure 7-4. A typical 24-hr observation chart used to command the imaging photopolarimeter and later to determine how the instrument operated when pictures were taken. Such charts provided visual checks on the position of the look angle of the instrument at the spacecraft. (a) A chart when Pioneer 10 was distant from Jupiter. (b) A chart when Pioneer 10 was nearest Jupiter. (The main features of the charts are described in the accompanying text.)

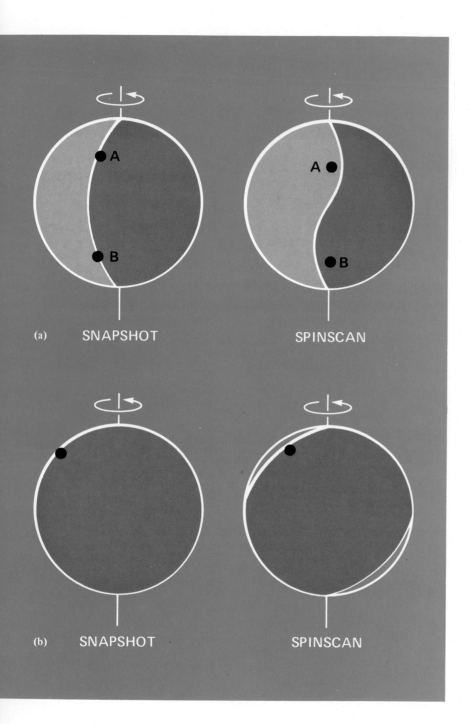

(a) SNAPSHOT   SPINSCAN

(b) SNAPSHOT   SPINSCAN

Figure 7-5. Distortion caused by the planet's rotation during a spin-scan image sequence. (a) Points A and B at the same longitude were scanned at different times so that A was in darkness when scanned and B was in daylight, although both should have been either in darkness or daylight. As a result, the terminator became distorted. (b) Similar effects occurred at the limb, with the result that the outline of the planet became distorted.

166

approach to Jupiter. To position the telescope properly, some 14 to 20 contiguous, time-critical commands were required at each point where the telescope look-angle curves changed abruptly.

Correcting Distortion in the Jovian Images

Gathering data for one of the larger spin-scan images of Jupiter and Saturn took about 30 min. This created a problem since, unlike taking a normal photograph in which all parts of the scene are viewed simultaneously and from a single point, the planetary images were made from image strips obtained from a moving viewpoint of a rotating object. The problem was how to display such an image.

One solution was to reposition the data so that it appeared as though the picture was taken at a particular instant in time, for example, at the mid-point of the data-taking sequence. The data were repositioned so that each pixel was placed where it was at the chosen "snapshot" time, not where it was on the planet when actually imaged. This process, called geometric rectification, creates a picture most nearly like one taken with a camera.

However, certain artifacts arise from this display method. They are a direct result of the method of picture-taking, that is, the picture is built up over a period of time during which parts of the object moved by different amounts. In Figure 7-5(a), points A and B have the same longitude on Jupiter. They rotate through the terminator (the shadow edge between day and night) at exactly the same time. A true snapshot, illustrated on the left, would show this. However, with spin-scan imagery, point A might be imaged a few minutes before sunrise, whereas point B, imaged later, might be in sunlight. When points A and B are positioned at their correct places in the reconstruction, that is, at the same longitude, the terminator appears bent (as shown) — an unreal situation.

A similar problem (Figure 7-5(b)) arises at the limb. In the spin-scan image, portions of the limb imaged before the equivalent "snapshot" time are displaced in the direction of rotation. There are no data to fill out the correct profile, and the shape of the planet is distorted (as shown). For close-in pictures, these problems are more serious, because it takes longer to scan the disk and the effects of relative motions are more pronounced.

Figure 7-6 compares several ways to display a spin-scan image of Jupiter. Figure 7-6(a) is a geometrically rectified image. But the image can be displayed in other ways that require less computing time. One way is simply to disregard the geometrical aspects and display the data exactly as received from the spacecraft, but this results in gross distortion such as that shown in Figure 7-6(b).

Another method, the correct-outline technique, is to display the data so as to preserve the correct outline of the planet while accepting some slight distortion of the area within the disk — appropriately called "rubber sheet" distortion. Details in any particular region are accurately portrayed, but larger regions may not be spatially related to each other as precisely as in the "snapshot" equivalent.

Normally, the difference between the two results is small. Figure 7-6(c) uses this correct-outline technique to display the same data as in (a) and (b). For technical reasons, it is easier to preserve the fine detail in the pictures with the correct-outline technique; all pictures of Jupiter reproduced in the following chapters were made by this technique.

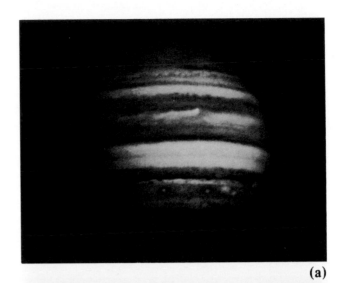

(a)

(b)

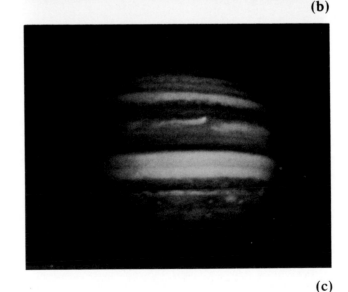

(c)

Figure 7-6. Three ways to display a spin-scan image of a planet, in this case, Jupiter. (a) A fully rectified image is almost equivalent to a snapshot. Every small area is repositioned to appear as it would had scans of all areas been made at the same time from a fixed point in space. The picture contains the types of distortions depicted in Figure 7-5. (b) No geometrical corrections were made and the planet is grossly distorted. (c) The shape of the planet is correct; there is little distortion of the individual features, but this third display mode requires only a small amount of computer processing compared with the more complicated processing required for the first display shown at (a).

167

Quality of Images

Apart from difficulties of presenting the pictures with the correct geometry, other factors also determine the quality of the images. For example, occasional data dropouts (loss of data) resulted in parts of the pictures being lost. Such losses ranged from a small section of one line of data, caused by a missing frame of telemetry, to one or more continuous lines of data. Replacing the missing parts with black fill, or simply skipping over the dropped lines, results in pictures with distracting features which, for scientific and esthetic reasons, should be reduced or eliminated. These corrections can be made by interpolating average values for the missing data from surrounding "good" data. Such "cosmetic" enhancement can be applied satisfactorily only when the amount of missing data is small. Figure 7-7 shows a severe case before and after "cosmetic" enhancement.

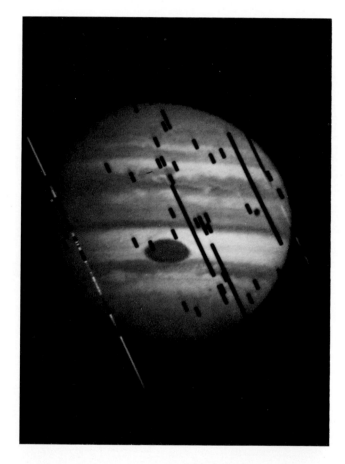 

Figure 7-7. Before and after correction of dropped-out frames of data from a spin-scan image. The cosmetic enhancement was achieved by computer processing to smooth over and insert areas of missing data.

As some images were acquired, the sensitivity of the imaging photopolarimeter would change, either intentionally by a command or because of a malfunction arising from radiation effects. The effect of this change was to darken or lighten bands within the picture. The compensation for such changes in sensitivity was straightforward; Figure 7-8 shows typical before and after images.

A minor problem arose with some of the imaging data from Pioneer 10 — the blue picture was too bright everywhere by a fixed amount. This fault was corrected in the data processing. Two other problems occurred with imaging data from Pioneer 10. Figure 7-9 shows a fine, ripplelike structure of low contrast over parts of the red image. It represents noise of unknown origin and,

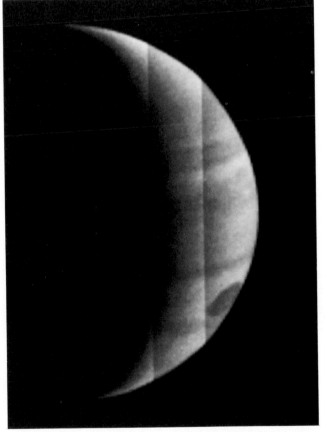

(a)

(b)

Figure 7-8. Before and after correction of sensitivity (gain) changes. The sensitivity of the imaging photopolarimeter was changed to compensate for variations in the brightness of the planet as the instrument scanned different areas of the disk, resulting in the bands on the spin-scan image (a). Computer processing corrected the bands to produce image (b).

169

because of its partially random nature, was difficult to eliminate from the images. This figure shows a particularly noticeable example, although the effect is also apparent in several pictures in chapter 8. The other defect, which also occurred in some Pioneer 11 images of Jupiter, is illustrated in Figure 7-10. The apparent flattening of portions of Jupiter's limb was caused by characteristics of the mechanism that changed the look angle of the telescope.

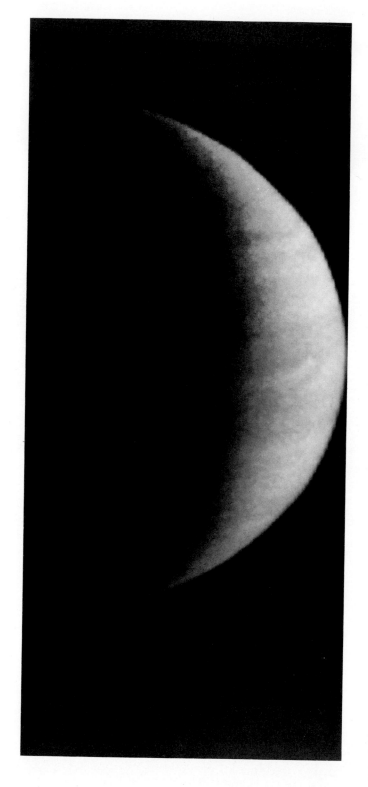

Figure 7-9. Noise of unknown origin affected the red-channel image of Pioneer 10; the resulting ripplelike effect was difficult to correct because of its semirandom nature.

Figure 7-10. A slight flattening of the limb in places was caused by a design characteristic of the imaging photopolarimeter which resulted in a slightly nonuniform stepping across the planet.

170

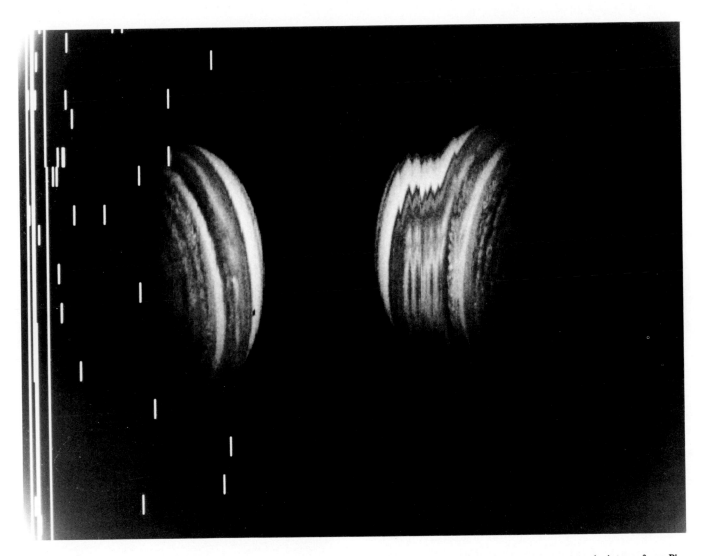

Figure 7-11. A raw data dump, or unprocessed picture, from Pioneer 11: On the right, an image severely distorted by a fault in the telescope drive system generated by intense radiation; on the left, the image suffers from a few dropped frames of data.

The intense radiation affected the imaging photopolarimeter of Pioneer 11 somewhat differently. After Pioneer passed through the most intense part of the radiation belts, the telescope drive mechanism became quite erratic. Instead of stepping uniformly across the planet, it would skip backward and forward in a somewhat random manner, sometimes not moving at all for several rolls of the spacecraft. The effect of this was to create severely distorted images. Figure 7-11 shows an example of the effects of this problem. Special computer programs had to be written before such data could be correctly assembled into pictures. The figure shows a raw data dump of blue-channel data for images D17 and D18 — image D17 is normal except for a few dropped frames, whereas D18 (on the right) is marred as a result of erratic stepping.

171

Making Color Pictures

The imaging photopolarimeter gathered data using the red and blue components of light reflected from the planets. To make color pictures, it was necessary, however, to have three colored components, such as red, green, and blue. Reconstructing with red and blue only would have presented a purplish image. Scientists were able to make three-color composite images by synthesizing a green image. This green image was derived from information contained in the blue and red channels and from knowledge of the color balance and color content of images of Jupiter and Saturn obtained from ground-based observations. The method worked well for Jupiter and Saturn since they have no known features observable only in green or purple light. A photograph of Jupiter, for example, taken through a green filter closely resembles a composite of photographs taken through red and blue filters. Figure 7-12 shows the real red and blue components, the synthetic green, and the color composite formed by a photographic superposition of the three; the effect without a synthetic green channel is also shown.

Color synthesis is often useful to scientists in their interpretation of clouds and features; however, too much emphasis should not be given to the exact hues and saturations of colors in the Pioneer pictures of Jupiter and Saturn because only two of the three color components are real. Nevertheless, the colors and contrasts are about the same as would be seen by an observer on the spacecraft, they are not exaggerated. Since Earth-based observations had not resolved color features on the satellites, there was no standard for comparing the colors of these bodies.

Processing Pictures from Saturn

The requirements for processing Pioneer 11's images of Saturn were different from those for the two earlier Pioneer encounters with Jupiter. Instead of raw data, edited images had to be sent quickly from the University of Arizona to Ames

Figure 7-12. Constructing colored pictures of Jupiter and Saturn from the red and blue data channels required that a green image be constructed first, then combined with red and blue. This process is used here for a Pioneer 10 image of Jupiter showing the Great Red Spot and the shadow of a Galilean satellite. The process produces a lifelike image on which the color balance has been adjusted to correspond with the best Earth-based observations of the planet. Mixing of only the red and blue images would give the planet an objectionable purplish appearance.

Research Center for display by the PICS. By contrast, the Jupiter PICS displays were of unedited data. After the Jupiter encounter, further editing had been a slow, card-oriented, batch-environment process that was satisfactory so long as the defects in the raw data images were not extensive and there was no need for corrected images to be quickly available. The Saturn encounter presented new problems that required a more powerful and versatile capability to correct the raw data and produce quality images quickly.

Three distinct sets of requirements defined the procedures and equipment for handling the image data during the Saturn encounter.

First, during the encounter, defects were introduced into the spin-scan images by irregularities in the instrument's performance. Data were also lost because of the great distance over which the data were transmitted. In addition, the sensitivity of the instrument was changed by command.

Second, scientists felt that the instrument would produce additional defects at Saturn encounter because of the radiation it had been subjected to at Jupiter. Also, by the time the spacecraft reached Saturn, the instrument had been operating in space for many years.

Third, there were constraints on the time available to process a picture before its display and release as hard copy for distribution.

When Pioneer 11 passed near Saturn, it was traveling at nearly 100,000 km/hr (62,000 mph). Because it could take as long as 1 hr to obtain a single image, the high speed of the spacecraft distorted the picture. So an image produced from raw data was shaped like a banana instead of a flattened sphere. Another distortion was produced by the differential rotation of the planet — its more rapid rotation at the equator than at the poles. Although similar problems had been experienced at Jupiter, Saturn was a special case because its highly visible rings made it impractical to use the methods appropriate for the Jupiter images. New techniques and hardware and software had to be developed.

A new set of constraints was introduced into the processing procedures, derived from an aroused interest by the public and the media in the outer planets as a result of the images of Jupiter returned by Voyager. Corrected images of Saturn were in great demand. More importantly, these quickly corrected images were needed to plan the Voyager encounters with Saturn after the Pioneer encounter.

Because stepping problems and other anomalies with the imaging photopolarimeter were anticipated, a more powerful and versatile system was needed to process the data from Saturn. The old system used at Jupiter could not process the data in the short times needed to display the results at Ames Research Center.

DIAL Image-Processing Facilities

Geometrical correction of the images was significantly enhanced by the DIAL facilities at the University of Arizona. The heart of these facilities for processing the images was a real-time image-processing computer. The computer had several powerful features, including three channels of random access refresh memory, three graphic overlay channels, three pipeline processing channels, and a red-green-blue CRT screen on which images could be monitored. A programmable cursor allowed individual pixels or subsections of an image to be located for selective processing.

Unprocessed images — typically with missing frames of data; shifted, repeated, or missing rolls; gain changes; and dropped pixels — were taken directly from magnetic tape and stored in two of the refresh memory channels, one for red image data and one for blue image data. The original 6-bit data were rescaled to 8 bits for processing. Parallel operations could be performed on the red and the blue channels to speed the processing.

Deliberate changes in the imaging photopolarimeter's gain produced blocks of rolls with quite different mean densities. Red and blue channels were

174

processed separately until, by repeated trial, no noticeable intensity step remained at the boundary between different areas of the picture.

Missing data were replaced by either linear interpolation or a process by which individual missing pixels could be literally "painted in" from surrounding good data. In the latter case, the cursor was used to select a matrix of 10 by 10 pixels centered in the region requiring data. Each pixel was magnified 10 times and the resulting 100 by 100 area was displayed on a blank corner of the cathode-ray-tube (CRT) display screen. The cursor was then used in a painting mode to transfer selected pixels to fill the gaps of missing data.

Stepping anomalies were corrected. During a first edit, the images were fine tuned by magnifying a section of the planet's limb or the ring edge to check the registration of adjacent rolls where errors were most critical. Data were also corrected for spoke changes during an image sequence. The crescent images include an example where the data acquisition window was shifted in space several times during a complete scan. The images were edited by imposing appropriate horizontal shifts to selected (cursor-delimited) rolls. Another requirement for image registration arose for semicomplete images. Red and blue were treated separately — one image was stored in refresh memory and one pipeline assigned to display it. The next image was stored in another refresh memory and another pipeline used to display it. Since shifting data horizontally and vertically in refresh memory was a relatively simple process, the two images could be mosaicked quite easily.

The first phase of rectifying an image consisted of carefully modeling how the spacecraft should have been viewing Saturn (Figure 7-13) — this required precise trajectory information. Then the method was to ascertain where, in a rectified picture, the selected points were located on the distorted spin-scan image — referred to as control-point determination. The coordinates of the control points in the two images defined the coefficients of two polynomial transformations, which

mapped any point in the rectified image to its location on the distorted image. In a more technical sense, geometrical rectification is a process by which the spatial distortion of the received image is described relative to the ideal or ground-truth image — an ideal image coordinate is mapped to an observed image coordinate by using a mapping function. Generally, the correct image is represented by a rectified, rectangular array of pixels. Similarly, the observed warped image is recorded as another rectangular array of pixels.

Corrective dewarping was done in two stages. First, for each pixel coordinate of the ground-truth image, the corresponding coordinate of the warped image was determined (Figure 7-14). The pixel amplitude of the warped image was then estimated by interpolating from the surrounding pixels. Next, a set of control points was defined by which the mapping functions could be determined by fitting

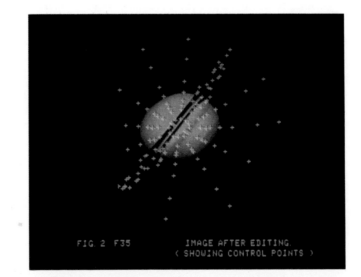

FIG. 2 F35   IMAGE AFTER EDITING.
                          (SHOWING CONTROL POINTS)

Figure 7-13. The pictures from Saturn were processed somewhat differently from the Jupiter images. Prototype control points (shown as crosses) were written into the graphics channel to overlay the "raw" observed data. The cursor was used as a roll-sector position locator to determine the degree to which control points and the image were offset.

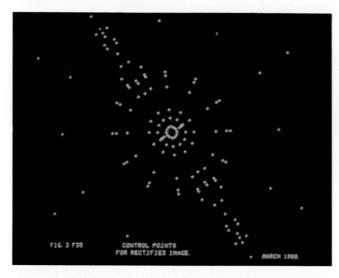

Figure 7-14. The distortion model was used to estimate the transformation required between "observed" and "rectified" spaces, given the control points of both spaces. A set of control points in rectified space is shown.

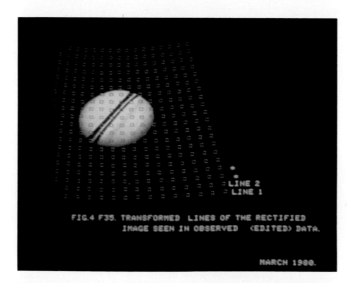

Figure 7-15. Overlay illustrating the progression of a straight scan line in rectified space as it searches for the appropriate data in the observed image, after transformation by the distortion polynomial. Each curved line in observed space represents a straight line in the corrected image.

176

optimized surfaces to the control points (Figure 7-15). A polynomial was used to model spatial distortion. Coefficients for the polynomial were chosen to minimize the mean-square error between the desired locations of the control points and the polynomial estimates of their locations.

The method for selecting control points has the following rationale. At any instant an observer or a camera onboard the Pioneer spacecraft would have an undistorted view of the Saturnian system. The planet's limb would describe an ellipse in space centered on Saturn. Other ellipses, centered on a line connecting the spacecraft with Saturn's center and congruent with the ellipse defining the limb, were used to describe points around Saturn's cloudtops, inside the limb. Similarly, the ring edges constituted a set of ellipses in space. The equations for these ellipses were determined for any instant, based on the spacecraft's trajectory and the dimensions and orientation of the Saturnian system. Then these ellipses were projected onto a rectified image plane perpendicular to the vector from the spacecraft to Saturn.

The locations of the control points in the rectified image were defined by selecting 12 points around each of 8 such ellipses. Typically, the limb ellipse was used with 3 congruent interior ellipses, along with 4 ring edges. From a judicious selection of coordinate systems in space, a very compact algebraic description of the loci of all points on these ellipses was effected in both planetary coordinates (pole along z axis) and spacecraft coordinates (spin axis along z axis).

If the very small changes in the spacecraft's latitude during a scan for one image were ignored, the eccentricity of these ellipses could be taken as constant; only their size changed. The task was to determine the precise time at which a given control point was in the 0.5-mrad field of view of the imaging photopolarimeter. The look and roll angles were computed for each control point at all trajectory time entries between and bounding the start and end times of a given image sequence. By linear interpolation, the locations were then predicted at all times during the picture-taking sequence. Similarly, from the fine encoder data, the approximate cone angle (look angle) of the telescope was known since (after editing) it was a simple linear function of time during each sequence. To determine the angle precisely, the spin-scan image was examined to find the specific scan line tangent to the limb. The point of tangency was a special control point which determined the precise look angle of the telescope and that sector number along the tangent roll closest to the tangent point. The tangent point also provided a time reference for all other rolls. The look and roll coordinates of all other control points were transformed to corresponding roll and sector coordinates with the tangent point as a reference.

The control point routines were used to measure the oblateness of Saturn by choosing 48 points on the limb ellipse and on the outer edge of the A ring and, from these points, smooth curves were generated that describe these loci in roll-sector space. A raster scan of the intensity data to the same scale as the plot was then overlaid to obtain a best fit.

The sequence of operations was as follows. The data entered the DIAL editor (where gain was equalized), missing data were replaced, stepping anomalies were corrected, and registration was obtained. Spacecraft trajectory data were used to generate control points, which were then used to compute a distortion model for image rectification. Rectification then took place so that the image could be made available for display (Figure 7-16). Afterward, the images could be enhanced further if required. The University of Arizona joined NASA's extensive data communications network (NASCOM) to allow a more rapid exchange of raw data and processed data.

Hardware Involved

The extensive computer power required for image rectification and enhancement was provided by an ECLIPSE S/230 computer, with 250,000

Figure 7-16. Rectified image with the relevant control points superimposed. The size of the final version was determined by the interpolation factor chosen. Since blue and red images were rectified in parallel, the image was ready to be displayed at this stage of processing.

words of central memory and over 1 trillion bits of on-line disk storage. A NOVA 3/12 computer was used to operate the NASCOM lines and to edit the data on a MEGATEK vector graphics terminal.

Image data could be displayed in several ways. Photographic negatives were produced by a pictorial output device (POD) controlled by the NOVA computer. Essentially, the POD consisted of a drum around which a sheet of film could be wrapped. An exposing light beam made a track around the drum. This light was modulated by the computer to reproduce the pixels of the image, thereby generating pictures for researchers and for press releases. To enable rapid display and release of images at Ames Research Center, the PICS was used as described earlier. An image processing facility at the University of Arizona supported the scientific interpretation of the images. This high-resolution system was used to enhance contrast, to study color balance, and to statistically analyze the imaging data.

Software Involved

The software for the image processing included NASCOMIN and NASCOMOUT, two programs developed to control communication of the data into and out of the system via the communication channels. Data lost during transmission, lines going down, repeated data, and abnormal transmission had to be handled automatically. Data were transmitted through NASCOM in blocks. When received at the University of Arizona, the imaging data were separated from data needed for communications and routing and were then reformatted into a form easily used by the processing system. Information gathered in different operating modes of the imaging photopolarimeter also had to be identified and separated by a program. A special file contained the data that was ready for editing; editing was handled by the NOVA editor, which consisted of several programs that did such things as look for dropped data and apply techniques to restore lost data.

The scheme for rectifying images was somewhat similar to those used for LANDSAT satellite image data, as explained earlier. After the image had been rectified, its immediate disposition was through a program called TRANSOUT to format it for communication, and then to NASCOMOUT to transmit it to Ames Research Center, where the data could be placed into PICS immediately or stored on tape for later display. The photographic transparencies were then produced on the pictorial output device with another program. The resultant negatives were used to produce black/white prints and to synthesize a color transparency from two colors. Later, data were transported to the processing facility at the University of Arizona for more extensive analysis.

8
First Encounter with the Giant

During November and December 1973, Pioneer 10, the first spacecraft to visit the giant Jupiter, sent back over 500 images of the planet. Most were taken far from Jupiter and showed very little detail compared to pictures taken earlier with telescopes from Earth. However, the pictures taken within 48 hr of Pioneer's closest approach (periapsis) to Jupiter were considerably better than any taken from Earth. Not only was the resolution greater, thereby revealing details of the complex cloud systems of Jupiter never before seen, but Jupiter was seen from vantage points not available to observers on Earth.

Because Jupiter is many times more distant from the Sun than is Earth, the angle between Earth and the Sun at Jupiter (the phase angle) never exceeds 11.5°. So astronomers on Earth can see Jupiter only as a fully illuminated disk; they cannot see Jupiter illuminated from the side or from behind, as the Moon can be seen in its crescent and half-moon shapes. Pioneer 10 viewed Jupiter for the first time under various conditions of illumination.

Figure 8-1 shows the Pioneer trajectory 20 hr before and after its closest approach to Jupiter. Pioneer 10 approached the planet below the Jovian equatorial plane, later crossing this plane again before departing from Jupiter north of the plane. The lower part of Figure 8-1 shows schematically the change in illumination of the Jovian disk, as seen from Pioneer 10 as it moved along its trajectory.

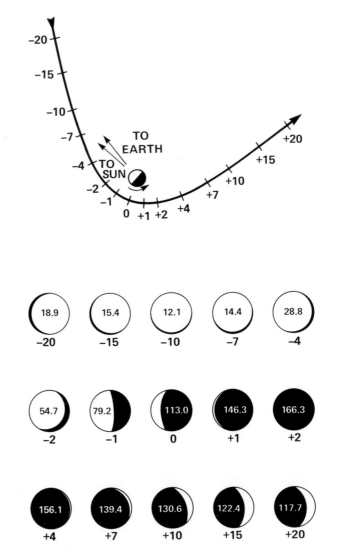

Figure 8-1. Phases of Jupiter as seen from Pioneer 10 from 20 hr before to 20 hr after its closest approach. The numbers on each disk represent the phase angle.

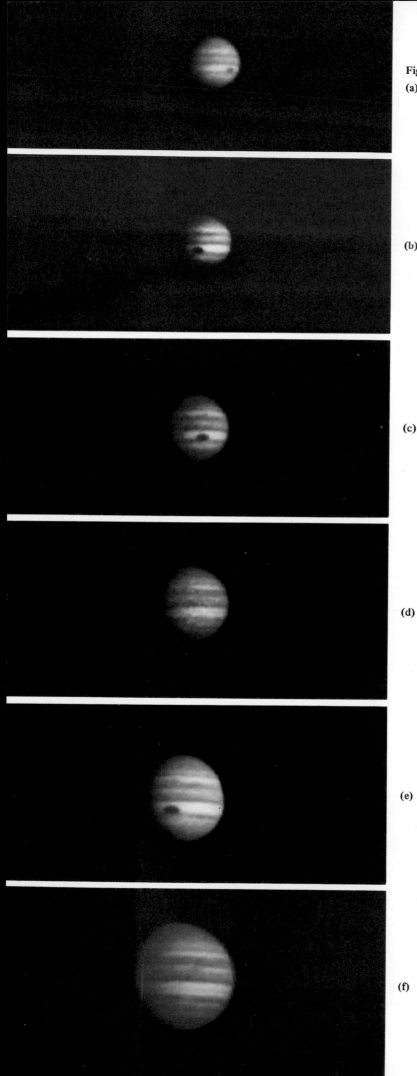

Figure 8-2

(a)

(b)

(c)

(d)

(e)

(f)

Twenty hours before closest approach, the dark limb was at the left of Jupiter. At 12 hr, it was under the planet as the spacecraft approached below the equatorial plane. Just before closest approach, the dark limb slipped around to the right side of the planet, after which the terminator swept rapidly across Pioneer's view of Jupiter, until the entire disk was dark as the spacecraft plunged into the planet's shadow. When Pioneer 10 emerged from the shadow, a crescent Jupiter was revealed, the beginning of a unique series of pictures.

On the following pages, the images taken within 4 days of closest approach are coded — such as A28 or B17 ("A" images were obtained before closest approach, "B" images, afterward). Appendix 2 gives a fuller explanation of the code and lists significant information about each image. All dates and times used here are Universal Time (UT), the same as Greenwich Mean Time (GMT). DOY stands for "day of year" — January 1 is DOY 1, and December 31 is DOY 365.

The series of blue-channel pictures (Figures 8-2 and 8-3) was taken at 2-day intervals, the first on DOY 321, 17 days before Pioneer 10's closest approach to Jupiter. The resolution of these pictures is not as good as could be obtained from Earth. The few scan lines on each picture are quite evident.

The Great Red Spot and the pattern of bands are clearly visible even at these great distances, from 16 to 7.5 million kilometers (10 to 4.7 million miles). The terminator is on the west side of the Jovian disk, displaced slightly toward the south.

The detail, as seen by the imaging photopolarimeter, is approximately the same as that which would have been seen by the unaided human eye at the same distance from Jupiter and, for Pioneer 11, from Saturn also. All the pictures of Jupiter and Saturn reproduced here and in following chapters show these giant planets as they might have been seen by an astronaut in a manned spacecraft flying by Jupiter and Saturn along the paths of the two Pioneers.

180

Figures 8-2 and 8-3 are reproduced to the same angular scale. The relative sizes are exactly as they would have appeared to an observer onboard the spacecraft as it approached Jupiter. These blue-channel images were selected to show Jupiter at intervals of approximately 1 day, starting 6 days before periapsis. The last image in the series has a resolution comparable with that obtainable from Earth when "seeing" conditions are good. Many of the pictures obtained over this period show satellites in the field of view. However, these satellites were too distant from the spacecraft to be resolved in detail, and were also nearly always too far from the planet's disk to be included in the cropped pictures reproduced here. One satellite appears in the last frame of the series, slightly below and to the left of the Jovian disk.

Figure 8-3
(a)

(b)

(c)

(d)

Figure	Mid time DOY:hr:min	Distance 10^6 km	10^6 mi.	Phase angle, deg
8-2 (a)	321:01:36	16.0	10.0	37.3
8-2 (b)	323:02:04	14.3	8.9	37.2
8-2 (c)	325:04:07	12.6	7.8	37.0
8-2 (d)	327:01:53	11.0	6.8	36.7
8-2 (e)	329:06:46	9.1	5.7	36.1
8-2 (f)	331:04:30	7.5	4.7	35.3

Figure	Mid time DOY:hr:min	Distance 10^6 km	10^6 mi.	Phase angle, deg
8-3 (a)	332:16:02	6.2	3.9	34.9
8-3 (b)	333:01:44	5.8	3.6	34.4
8-3 (c)	334:07:03	4.6	2.9	32.6
8-3 (d)	335:12:53	3.4	2.1	30.0

181

Figure 8-4

(a)

This spectacular series of consecutive pictures (Figures 8-4) was taken over a period of 4 hr, between 44.5 and 40.5 hr before periapsis. The Great Red Spot is prominent on each picture, and the shadow of the Galilean satellite, Io, traverses the disk of the planet. All these images were "cosmetically" enhanced (as described in chapter 7), especially A49 (shown in chapter 7 before and after enhancement).

(b)

(c)

Figure	Image no.	Mid time DOY:hr:min	Range 10⁵ km	10⁵ mi.	Phase angle, deg
8-4 (a)	A51	336:06:55	25.8	16.0	27.3
8-4 (b)	A50	336:07:31	25.6	15.9	27.2
8-4 (c)	A49	336:08:11	25.3	15.7	27.0
8-4 (d)	A48	336:08:48	25.0	15.5	26.9
8-4 (e)	A47	336:09:30	24.7	15.4	26.7
8-4 (f)	A46	336:10:07	24.4	15.2	26.6

182

The series of pictures A39, A35, A31, and A28 (Figure 8-5) on the following four pages shows one complete rotation of Jupiter. The final picture in the series was the last picture possible before the planet overfilled the field of view. Because part of the data used to create A35 is missing, the comb-like truncation appears on the northwest limb. This same effect occurs in several other pictures reproduced elsewhere in this book.

The gross morphology of belts and zones, with patterns of turbulence and convective cells in the middle latitudes of the planet, is clearly revealed in the pictures. The small white spots surrounded by dark rings, mainly in the southern hemisphere, indicate regions of intense, vertical convection similar to thunderclouds. Where the clouds are bluish and relatively featureless, the imaging photopolarimeter image provides a glimpse into the deepest, warmest parts of the atmosphere — called "blue festoons."

(d)

(e)

(f)

Figure	Image no.	Mid time DOY:hr:min	Range 10^5 km	10^5 mi.	Phase angle, deg
8-5 (a)	A39	336:14:33	22.3	13.8	25.5
8-5 (b)	A35	336:17:21	20.9	13.0	24.7
8-5 (c)	A31	336:20:18	19.5	12.1	23.8
8-5 (d)	A28	336:22:31	18.4	11.4	23.0

Figure 8-5 (a)

184

Figure 8-5 (b)

185

Figure 8-5 (c)

Figure 8-5 (d)

187

At the head of this bright plume, a cloud of warm particles rises from deep within the Jovian clouds. The tail extends to the left because the atmosphere moves more slowly in the upper regions than in the lower regions. The southerly deflection of the plume, and the scalloped edges of the belt above the plume, support the theory that a strong convective current circulates between the lower- and middle-latitude belts and zones. A color picture is shown together with the black/white images of the blue and red channels from which the color image was constructed (Figures 8-6).

Figure	Image no.	Mid time DOY:hr:min	Range 10^5 km	10^5 mi.	Phase angle, deg
8-6	A22	337:08:52	13.0	8.1	17.8

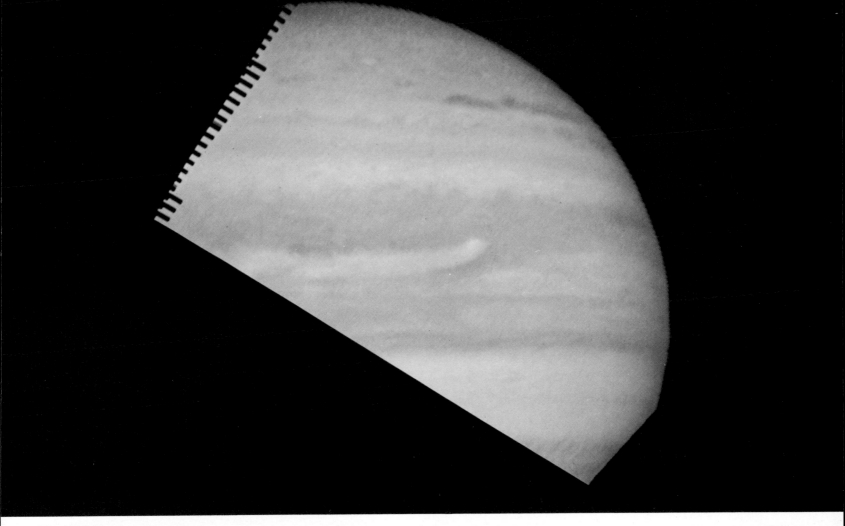

Figure 8-6 (a)

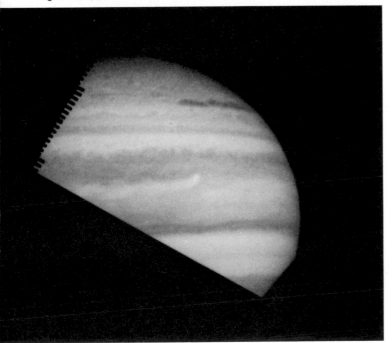

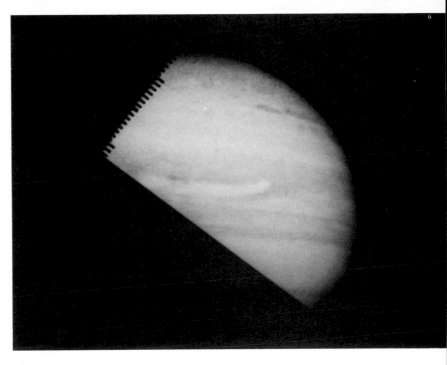

(b) Blue channel

(c) Red channel

189

Before the Pioneer mission to Jupiter, red spots, in addition to the Great Red Spot, had been observed from Earth. Pioneer 10 provided the first close look at one of these smaller red spots. This red spot in .the northern hemisphere is morphologically similar to the well-known and much studied Great Red Spot in the southern hemisphere (Figures 8-7). Ground-based observations indicated that this small red spot was quite young – probably not more than 18 months old at the time of the Pioneer 10 flyby. It was no longer visible a year later when Pioneer 11 flew by Jupiter.

Figure	Image no.	Mid time DOY:hr:min	Range 10^5 km	10^5 mi.	Phase angle, deg
8-7	A16	337:11:23	11.5	7.2	16.0

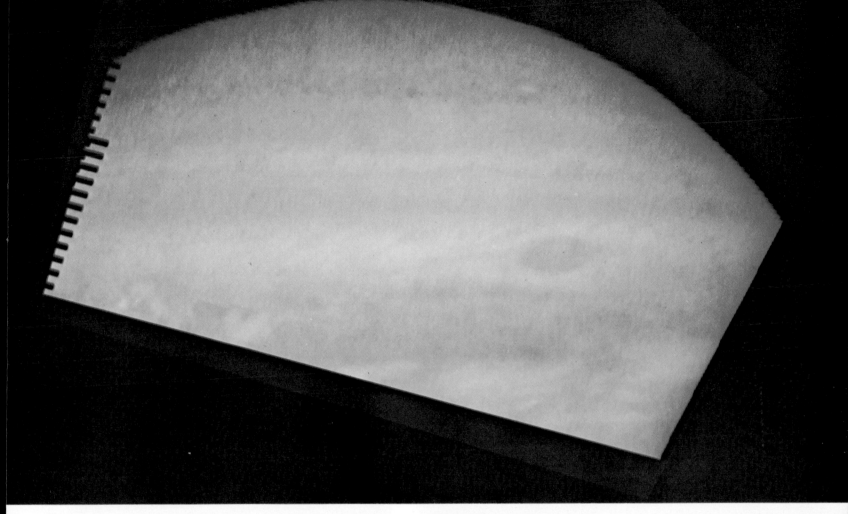

Figure 8-7 (a)

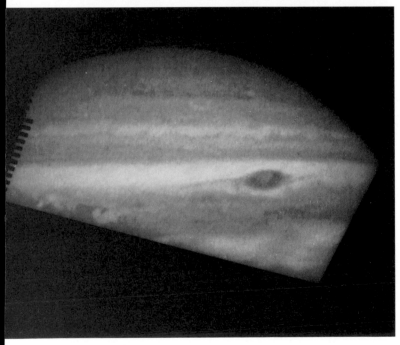

(b) Blue channel

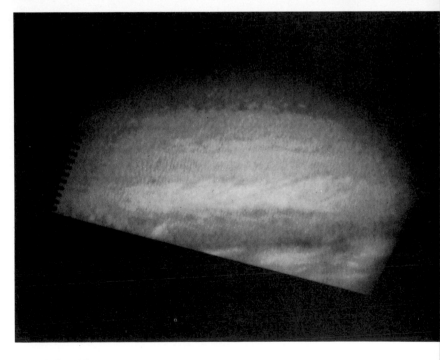

(c) Red channel

191

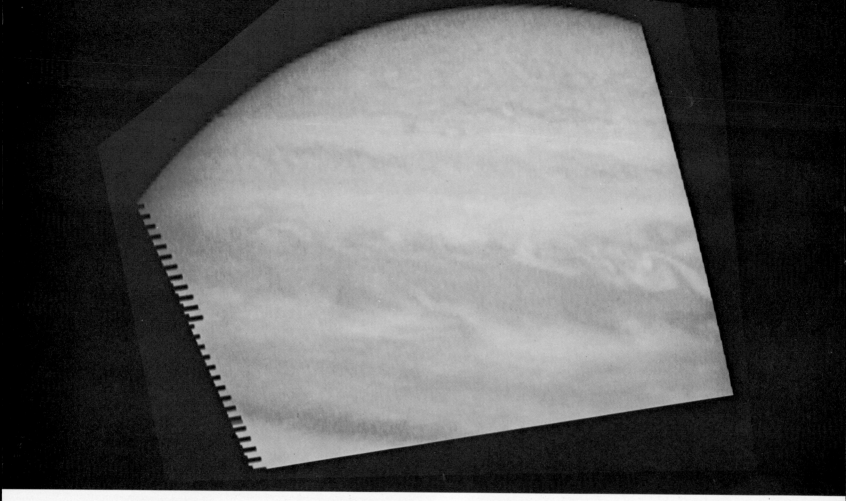

Figure 8-8 (a)

(b) Blue channel

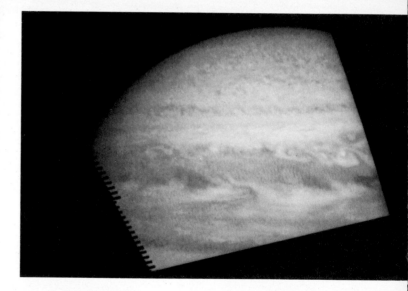

(c) Red channel

These views of Jupiter provide the best coverage of an enormously turbulent region (Figures 8-8 and 8-9). The "hooks" extend several thousands of kilometers. The belt structure is unstable at higher latitudes. At the top of the pictures, a belt frag-

ment, the darker elongated feature, appears in the transition zone between the belts and the relatively smooth-looking polar region more fully explored by Pioneer 11.

192

Figure 8-9 (a)

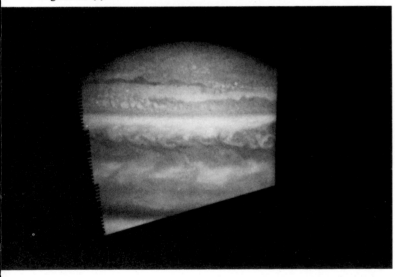

(b) Blue channel

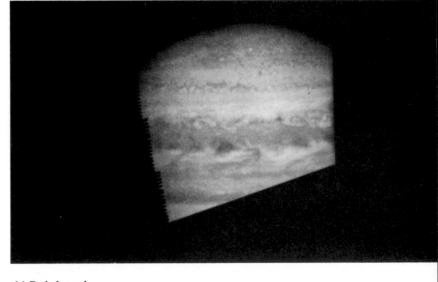

(c) Red channel

Figure	Image no.	Mid time DOY:hr:min	Range 10^4 km	10^4 mi.	Phase angle, deg
8-8	A9	337:14:47	95.4	59.3	13.4
8-9	A8	337:15:17	92.4	57.4	13.1

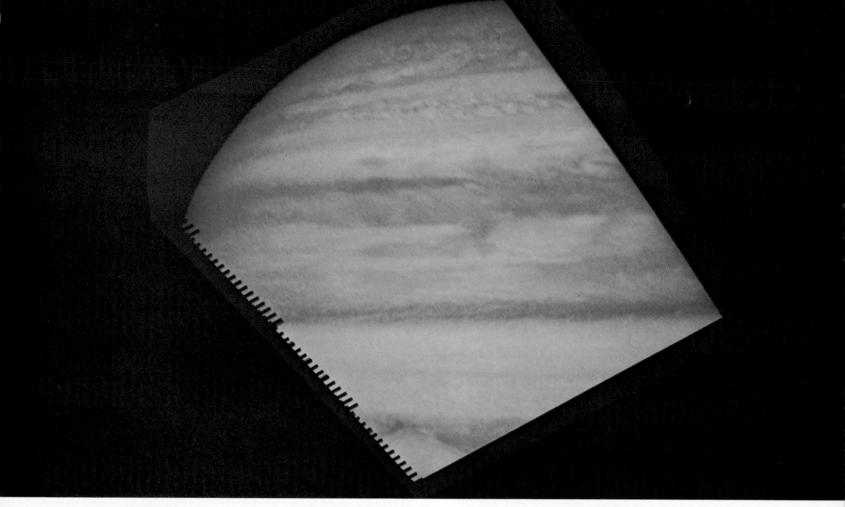

Figure 8-10 (a)

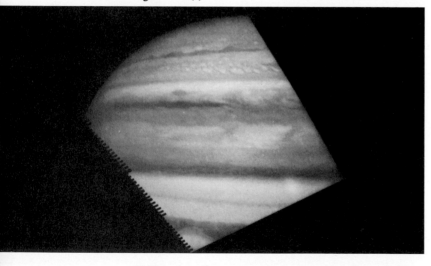

(b) Blue channel

(c) Red channel

The fine detail revealed in these cloud photographs (Figures 8-10 and 8-11) helped scientists unravel the complex behavior of the Jovian atmosphere. Gross differences between the red and blue images are apparent. The fine, repetitive, wavelike structure discernible in the red-channel image, which appears as a bluish ripple on the colored image, is not real and should be ignored.

194

Figure 8-11 (a)

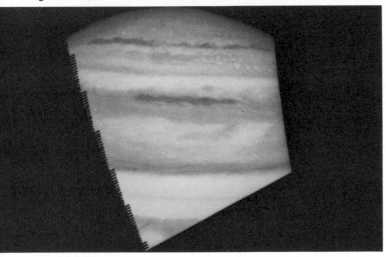

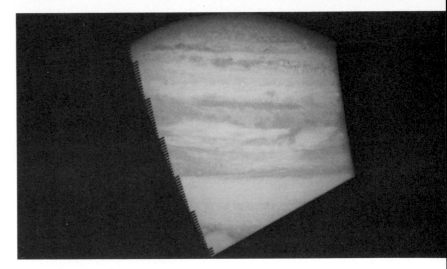

(b) Blue channel

(c) Red channel

Figure	Image no.	Mid time DOY:hr:min	Range		Phase angle, deg
			10^4 km	10^4 mi.	
8-10	A7	337:16:19	86.1	53.5	12.4
8-11	A6	337:17:05	81.4	50.6	12.2

Figure 8-12 (a)

The differences between images from the red and blue channels are not only intriguing but also important from the standpoint of scientific analysis. This image (Figure 8-12) again shows the plume conspicuous in Figure 8-6. But the detail is much improved in this picture, one of the best close encounter pictures from Pioneer 10. Features are seen in this picture that can only be glimpsed from Earth. Unfortunately, Pioneer 10 flew by so quickly that cloud movements cannot be discerned from one picture to another. Even so, the great detail enabled inferences to be drawn from these images concerning the dynamic properties of the Jovian atmosphere.

Figure	Image no.	Mid time DOY:hr:min	Range 10^4 km	10^4 mi.	Phase angle, deg
8-12	A5	337:18:28	72.6	45.1	12.2

(b) Blue channel

197

(c) Red channel

Figure 8-13
(a)

(b)

While moving away from Jupiter, Pioneer 10 viewed this giant planet as never before seen by man: sunrise on a crescent-shaped planet. This series of images (Figure 8-13) shows the red spot in the northern hemisphere, the Great Red Spot, and portions of the large plume shown in Figure 8-6. The contrast is less in the crescent phase — because of the way in which cloud particles scatter light. Irregularities in the profile of Jupiter resulted from a characteristic of the mechanism that drove the imaging photopolarimeter's telescope. The final picture is the last taken by Pioneer 10 — on New Year's Eve, 1973.

(c)

(d)

Figure	Image no.	Mid time DOY:hr:min	Range 10^5 km	10^5 mi.	Phase angle, deg
8-13 (a)	B11	339:00:50	14.7	9.1	116.4
8-13 (b)	B17	339:04:54	16.8	10.5	114.0
8-13 (c)	B23	339:08:09	18.5	11.5	112.4
8-13 (d)	B39	339:21:25	24.9	15.5	108.2
8-13 (e)	B69	341:14:08	43.7	27.2	102.5
8-13 (f)	–	365:18:08	160.0	99.5	97.0

(e)

199

(f)

9
Jupiter Revisited

Pioneer 11, the second spacecraft to fly by Jupiter, returned approximately 460 images of Jupiter and its Galilean satellites during November 18 through December 9, 1974. The trajectory of Pioneer 11 past Jupiter was quite different from that of Pioneer 10 — Pioneer 11 approached much closer to Jupiter's cloudtops (0.6 Jovian radii compared with 1.86 for Pioneer 10), inbound from south of Jupiter's equator and outbound toward the north (Figure 9-1). This trajectory allowed the spacecraft to obtain many unprecedented images of high latitudes of the planet. The views obtained on the incoming leg reached latitudes near the south polar region. Also,

because the plane of the trajectory was highly inclined (51.8°) to the Jovian equator (Figure 9-2), several good images were obtained of the planet's north pole.

To distinguish the Pioneer 11 images from those of Pioneer 10, the image numbers, sequentially arranged around periapsis, were given a "C" and "D" notation — "C" images were obtained before periapsis, "D" images after periapsis. (Full details of the images are given in Appendix 2.)

Two images (Figures 9-3 and 9-4) taken about a day before and after periapsis show the attitude of Jupiter during approach and departure. Unlike those of Pioneer 10, the series of Pioneer 11 images

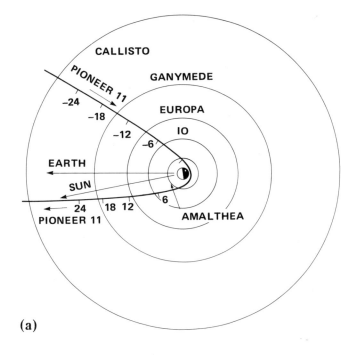

(a)

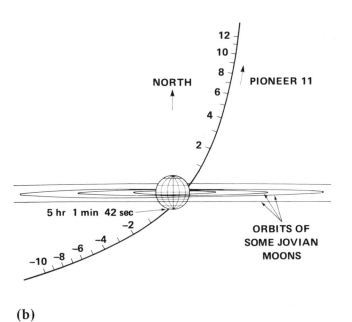

(b)

Figure 9-1. The path of Pioneer 11 past Jupiter shown (a) from above the north pole of the planet and (b) from its equatorial plane.

did not show a rapidly changing position of the terminator. In all "C" images, the terminator was positioned similar to Figure 9-2; in all "D" images it was positioned similar to Figure 9-4.

Because of the closeness of the approach and the high relative velocity of the spacecraft over the cloudtops, good images could not be obtained near periapsis; the data gathered would have been too sparse to be assembled later into a satisfactory image. Four pictures on each side of closest approach (images C4 through D4) were taken in the step-inhibit mode of operation of the imaging photopolarimeter, in which the motion of the spacecraft provided the sweep of side-by-side scans needed to build up the picture. At close range, only partial views of the planet could be obtained. Four pictures of this series are shown in Figures 9-11 through 9-14.

About one day before periapsis, a malfunction caused by radiation affected the stepping function of the telescope; because of this, a few images were partially lost before a workaround could be effected. Images C16 through C10 suffered from this problem. As soon as the problem became known, the observing team from the University of Arizona worked to correct the command sequences to ensure that no more images would be lost.

The resolution of the images increased as Pioneer 11 approached Jupiter (Figures 9-5 through 9-8). Figure 9-6 is one of the better pictures of the Great Red Spot; Figure 9-11 is an even closer view. When compared with Figure 8-5(b), these two pictures show graphically how the structure in the belt below the spot changed considerably between the two Pioneer encounters. Figure 9-7 shows the large plume prominent in Figures 8-5(d) and 8-6 from the Pioneer 10 encounter. An unusual view of the plume is also shown in Figure 9-16.

Figure 9-8 shows great detail in the belts and zones, including many light and dark cells which indicate convective activity in the south temperate zones. Note the small red spot in the northern hemisphere.

202

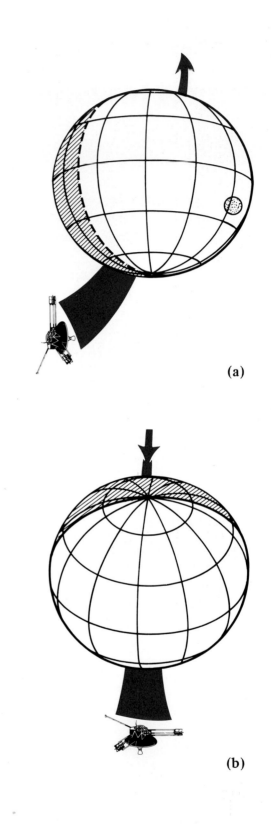

(a)

(b)

Figure 9-2. View of Jupiter from Pioneer 11 for (a) incoming and (b) outgoing paths.

Figures 9-3 and 9-4. Typical views of Jupiter as Pioneer 11 approached (top) and departed from (bottom) the planet.

Figure	Image no.	Mid time DOY:hr:min	Range 10^5 km	10^5 mi.	Phase angle, deg
9-3	C22	335:21:00	21.42	13.31	49.2
9-4	D17	338:13:57	20.85	12.96	36.1

	Image no.	Mid time DOY:hr:min	Range 10^5 km	10^5 mi.	Phase angle, deg
Figure 9-5	C9	336:13:57	12.35	7.67	55.1

Image no.	Mid time DOY:hr:min	Range 10⁵ km	10⁵ mi.	Phase angle, deg
C8	336:15:29	11.44	7.11	56.1

Figure 9-6

Image no.	Mid time DOY:hr:min	Range 10^5 km	10^5 mi.	Phase angle, deg
C7	336:17:14	10.38	6.45	57.5

Figure 9-7

206

Image no.	Mid time DOY:hr:min	Range		Phase angle, deg
		10^5 km	10^5 mi.	
C6	336:18:51	9.36	5.82	59.1

Figure 9-8

Figure 9-9. A computer-processed color image compared with an image produced from unprocessed raw data (as shown on facing page).

208

Figure 9-10 is an image derived from data as they were received at Ames Research Center, without computer processing of any kind. This is a blue-channel image, and the red-channel image contained similar problems. Four computer corrections were applied to the data (as described in chapter 7) to produce the corrected image seen opposite in Figure 9-9. The distorted shape of the planet was first corrected, the distortion from the motion of the spacecraft and the viewing geometry. Second, the three bands of varying image intensity, a consequence of maximizing the scientific value of the data for photometric analysis of the clouds, were eliminated. Third, the black areas of missing data caused by problems at the receiving station were filled in by interpolating neighboring values. Fourth, two rolls of unsynchronized data from the spacecraft, shown as diagonal streaks, were correctly repositioned.

Figure 9-10. A black/white picture made from the raw unprocessed data of C5 received at Ames Research Center, without computer processing.

Image no.	Mid time DOY:hr:min	Range 10^5 km	10^5 mi.	Phase angle, deg
C5	336:21:26	7.65	4.75	62.6

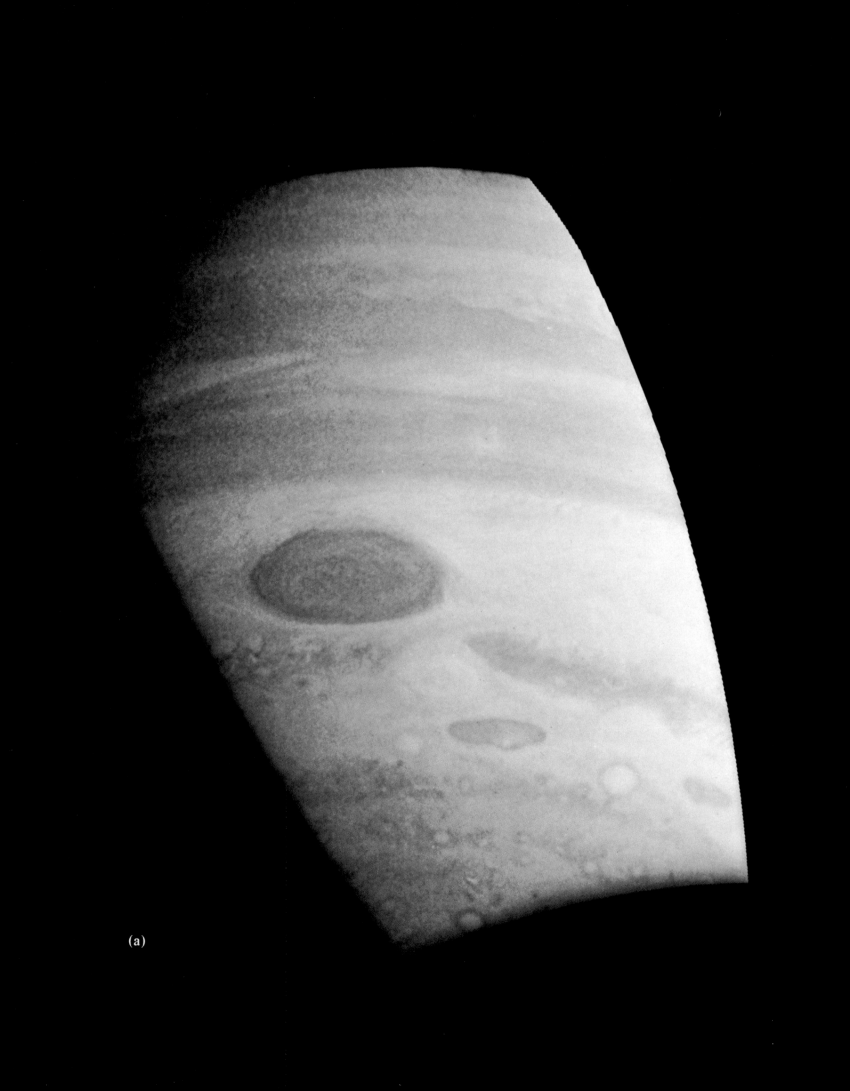

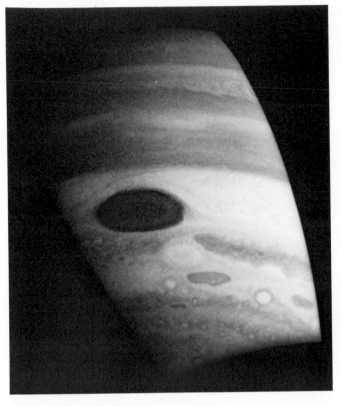

(b)

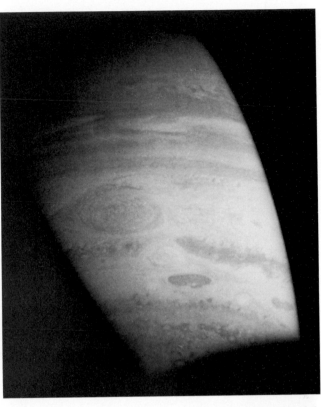

(c)

For planetary astronomers, this image of the Great Red Spot of Jupiter was one of Pioneer 11's most exciting results. From Pioneer 10, the highest resolution image of the spot had been degraded by radiation problems, but Pioneer 11 obtained this unique image (Figure 9-11(a)). The area covered by the image on the planet is shown in the line drawing insert (d) on this page.

The image, obtained 545,000 km (339,000 miles) above the cloudtops, contains more than 4,000 individual pixels (see chapter 7) of measurable data in the red area of the spot – a wealth of detailed markings since each pixel represents an area of approximately 237 km (147 miles) square. Scientists will be able to compare this image with those obtained by other spacecraft in later years to ascertain how the structure of the Spot changes with time.

Planetary scientists have derived new interpretations of the Great Red Spot from this image. Despite the relatively high resolution obtained, there is much less fine structure visible in the spot than in comparable areas at other latitudes (e.g., in Figure 9-12 and 9-14). The Great Red Spot appears to lie in the most quiescent zone of Jupiter, which may contribute to its stability.

The blue image has little internal detail (Figure 9-11(b)), the main feature being the dark border on the periphery of the spot. A break appears in the border in the northeast portion of the spot, where some of the red material appears to intermix with the South Tropical Zone.

The red image reveals much internal detail (Figure 9-11(c)), perhaps the most significant being two circular outlines that cross over near the center of the spot. This same feature also appeared in the Pioneer 10 images. This image does not show clear evidence of

motions within the spot. The image does not show direct evidence of flow lines from any single region inside the spot, which could be interpreted as a source or a sink of red material.

Figure 9-11. Close-up view of Jupiter's Great Red Spot. (a) Color composite, (b) blue-channel image, (c) red-channel image, and (d) drawing showing location of image on the Jovian disk.

Image no.	Mid time DOY:hr:min	Range 10^5 km	10^5 mi.	Phase angle, deg
C3	337:00:30	5.45	3.39	69.8

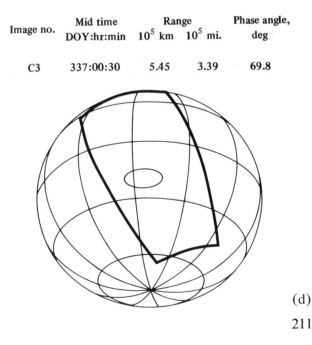

(d)

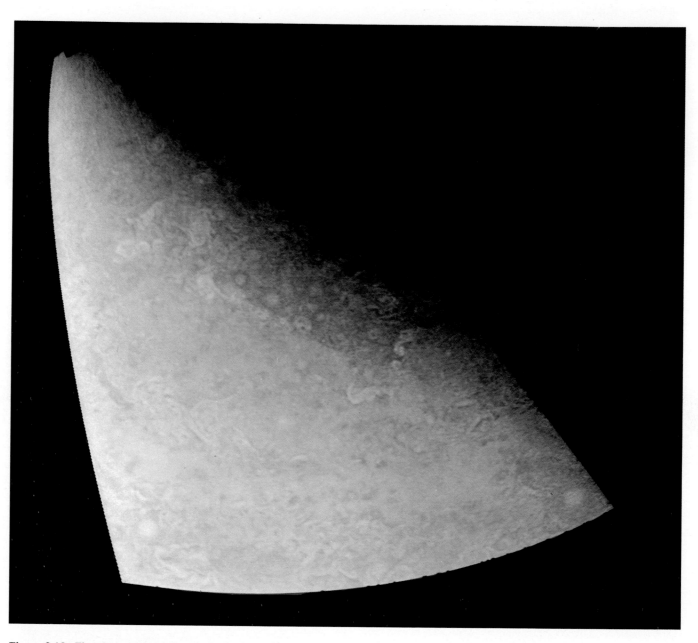

Figure 9-12. First image taken after periapsis showing the north pole of Jupiter (see line drawing).

Image no.	Mid time DOY:hr:min	Range 10^5 km	10^5 mi.	Phase angle, deg
D1	337:09:27	3.75	2.33	64.1

This first image (D1) of the outward leg of Pioneer 11, taken 3.5 hr after periapsis, shows the first view of the Jovian north pole. The location of the image boundaries on the planet is shown on the line drawing. The image shows evidence of great activity in the cloud forms at high latitudes, but the banded structure of the tropics has changed to a random pattern of cells and turbulence extending down to the limits of resolution.

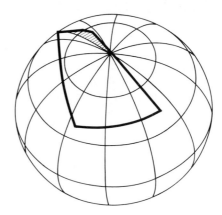

212

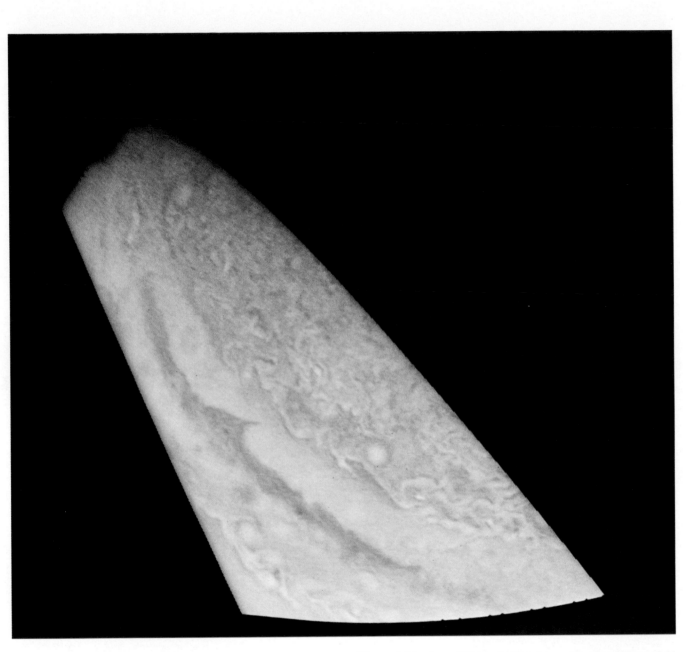

Figure 9-13. Area slightly farther from pole than Figure 9-11.

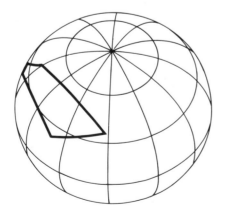

Image no.	Mid time DOY:hr:min	Range 10^5 km	10^5 mi.	Phase angle, deg
D2	337:10:10	4.35	2.70	59.8

This image (D2), taken 4 hr after periapsis, is farther from the pole than that in Figure 9-12, as shown in the inset line drawing. It would have been contiguous with that in Figure 9-12 except that the imaging photopolarimeter instrument was reconfigured to guard against radiation effects.

213

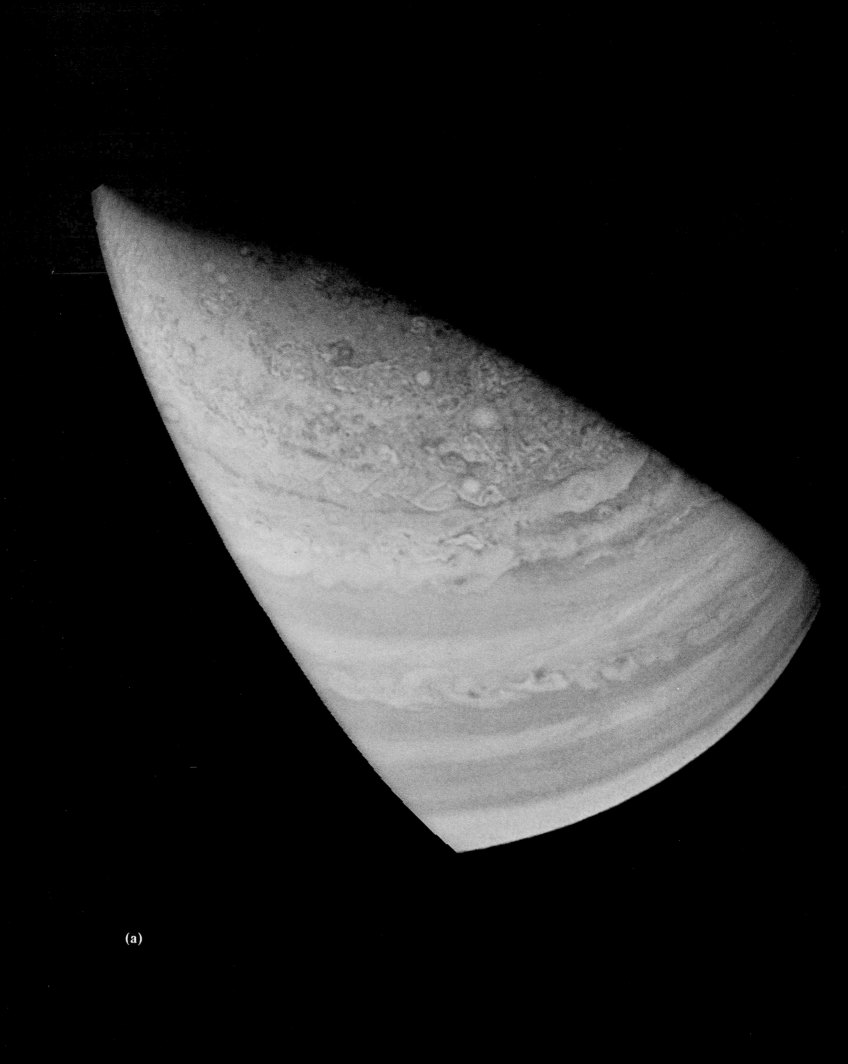

(a)

(b)

(c)

Figure 9-14. Important Pioneer 11 image showing stretch from north polar regions to equatorial regions. (a) Color composite, (b) blue-channel image, (c) red-channel image, and (d) location chart.

Image no.	Mid time DOY:hr:min	Range 10^5 km	10^5 mi.	Phase angle, deg
D4	337:12:27	6.10	3.79	51.7

This image (D4) was perhaps the most scientifically important image of Jupiter obtained by Pioneer 11. It covers an area of the planet from the equator to the north polar regions as shown on the line drawing, and shows details of the cloud features ranging from bands to polar cells. Figure 9-14(a) is the computer-processed color image. But the colors are probably less authentic than those images obtained before periapsis because of an apparent change in the instrument after Pioneer 11 passed through the intense radiation belts. Figures 9-14(b) and 9-14(c) show smaller versions of the blue- and red-channel images, respectively. The large uniform area on the red-channel image was caused by detector saturation which resulted in a loss of information — the gain had been deliberately set at a high level so that the darker regions near the north pole could be imaged well. Since the corresponding area in the colored image also lacks this information, the color balance is affected.

(d)

215

Figure 9-15

The series of images (D8, D10, D11, D12, D14, and D15) in Figures 9-15 through 9-20 show Jupiter as Pioneer 11 receded from the giant planet and rose high above the ecliptic plane on its way to Saturn. Because of an anomaly that affected the rate at which the telescope of the imaging photopolarimeter swept across the planet, the command sequence to obtain these pictures had to be changed day by day. Nevertheless, no images were lost, despite the fact that there was no time to verify the command sequence by computer simulation before the commands were implemented.

Image no.	Mid time DOY:hr:min	Range 10^5 km	10^5 mi.	Phase angle, deg
D8	337:19:31	10.79	6.71	42.4

Figure 9-16

Figure 9-16	Image no.	Mid time DOY:hr:min	Range		Phase angle, deg	Image no.	Mid time DOY:hr:min	Range		Phase angle, deg	
			10^5 km	10^5 mi.				10^5 km	10^5 mi.		
	D10	337:23:25	13.10	8.14	40.1	D11	338:08:29	15.39	9.56	38.5	Figure 9-17

Figure 9-17

Figure 9-18

Image no.	Mid time DOY:hr:min	Range 10^5 km	10^5 mi.	Phase angle, deg
D12	338:04:21	15.86	9.85	38.2

Figure	Image no.	Mid time DOY:hr:min	Range 10^5 km	10^5 mi.	Phase angle, deg
9-19	D14	338:07:57	17.77	11.04	37.3

Figure	Image no.	Mid time DOY:hr:min	Range 10^5 km	10^5 mi.	Phase angle, deg
9-20	D15	338:09:16	18.47	11.48	37.0

218

Figure 9-19

Figure 9-20

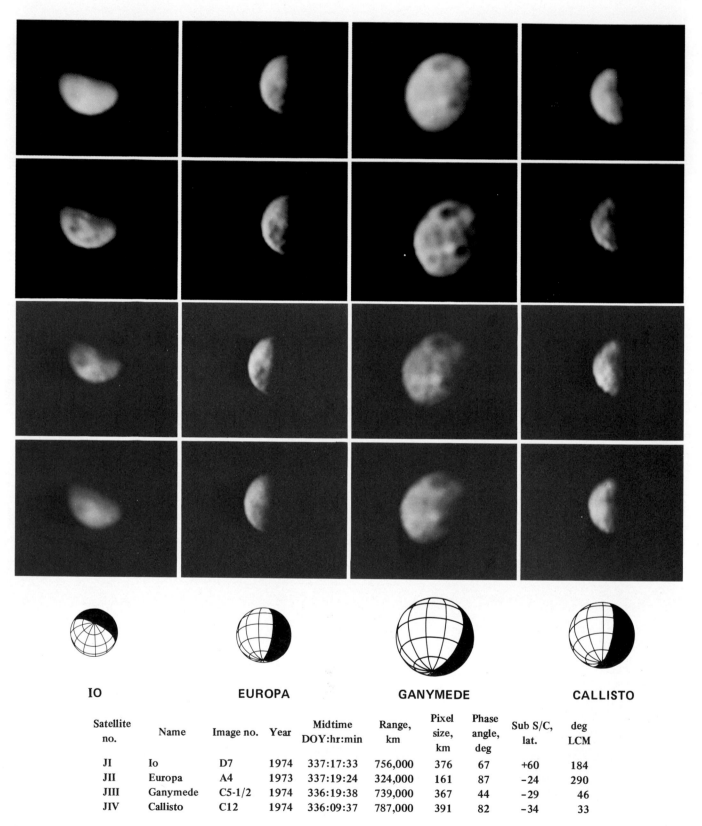

	IO	EUROPA	GANYMEDE	CALLISTO

Satellite no.	Name	Image no.	Year	Midtime DOY:hr:min	Range, km	Pixel size, km	Phase angle, deg	Sub S/C, lat.	deg LCM
JI	Io	D7	1974	337:17:33	756,000	376	67	+60	184
JII	Europa	A4	1973	337:19:24	324,000	161	87	−24	290
JIII	Ganymede	C5-1/2	1974	336:19:38	739,000	367	44	−29	46
JIV	Callisto	C12	1974	336:09:37	787,000	391	82	−34	33

Figure 9-21. Best images of the four Galilean satellites obtained by
   Pioneers 10 and 11.

220

With telescopes on Earth, astronomers are afforded only the barest hints of the markings on the Galilean satellites. Pioneers 10 and 11 recorded images of all four of these satellites, which provided a much better idea of the albedo and color variations across their disks before larger spacecraft that followed the trail-blazing Pioneers through the Jovian system later produced detailed pictures of their surfaces. Although all colors could not be represented properly since only red and blue data were recorded, it was certain that the yellow-orange regions were redder than white regions.

Only one good image of Io was obtained — D7 from Pioneer 11. Pioneer 10 did not obtain an image of Io because of the radiation environment of Jupiter. The Pioneer 11 image was a view from over the north pole of Io. From Earth, previous observations had suggested that the polar regions of Io are reddish colored. On this Pioneer image, there is orange coloration at the polar region, as contrasted with the whitish equatorial region of the satellite. Io is strongly affected by the Jovian radiation environment since its orbit is well within the radiation belts and the satellite sweeps up energetic particles from these belts. Also, its presence in the radiation belts affects the decametric radio emission of Jupiter. Although there was no indication of it in this Pioneer image, Io is the only Galilean satellite known to have an atmosphere, although it is much less dense than those of Earth and Mars.

The single image of Europa recorded by Pioneer 10 (A4) has little color variation, but there is a broad dark region with some gross detail. Europa is one of the most reflective satellites and is thought to have a crust of mainly water ice.

Two excellent images of Ganymede were recorded by the Pioneer spacecraft. These images show very little color variation, but there are substantial albedo differences over the disk of this largest Galilean satellite. Ganymede's low density may result from the presence of a high percentage of ices with some silicates from primordial material and from material impacting from space.

Several good images of Callisto showed only small color differences and small albedo variations. The darkest of the Galilean satellites, Callisto, has a low density that requires a high percentage of ices in its bulk structure. Two different views — one a half-moon shape (reproduced in Figure 9-21) and the other a gibbous shape — show the same prominent light region near the terminator.

Figure 9-21 shows the best images of the four Galilean satellites obtained by Pioneers 10 and 11. Each column is for an individual satellite. The top image in each column is the color composite: the next image shows this same color image further enhanced by computer processing. Below this is the blue-channel image followed by the red-channel image. Finally, at the bottom of each column, a line drawing identifies the viewing aspect of each satellite.

10
Saturn Encounter

The encounter of Pioneer 11 with Saturn produced unusual views of this ringed planet, views that cannot be obtained from Earth. As it approached Saturn, Pioneer 11 obtained full-disk images of the planet and its rings somewhat like those obtained by Earth-based instruments but with the rings presenting their shadowed face toward the spacecraft. On August 30, 1979, when Pioneer 11 was approximately 2 million kilometers (1.3 million miles) from Saturn, the field of view of the instrument was no longer sufficient to obtain images of the planet and the rings together.

Two hours before closest approach to Saturn, the imaging photopolarimeter on Pioneer 11 obtained its most detailed pictures, with resolved cloud features of 80-100 km (50-60 miles). When beneath the rings, Pioneer 11 was moving too fast and was too close to the rings and the planet to obtain high-resolution images. A low-resolution image was, however, obtained from polarization data. On the outward leg of its trajectory, the spacecraft's view of Saturn was of a partially illuminated disk, about 1/2 to 1/3 of which was sunlit. Again, the unilluminated face of the rings was presented to Pioneer 11.

On September 2, 1979, Pioneer 11 made its closest approach to the large satellite Titan and obtained several images. But Pioneer 11 was too far away and the resolution was insufficient to reveal any details in Titan's clouds and hazes, if there were any. The image coverages and presentations of the planet and ring system during the encounter sequence are shown in Figure 10-1.

As Pioneer 11 approached Saturn on August 26, 1979, details of the planet's belts and its rings became visible. The resolution began to approach that achieved with the best Earth-based telescopes. Figures 10-2 through 10-4 show a sequence of increasing resolution in color with black/white renditions of the blue and red channels. The range is almost 5.5 million kilometers (3.4 million miles) and the Encke gap is clearly apparent in the outer ring. The belted structure of the planet is beginning to emerge.

Subsequent images showed only parts of the planet and its ring system as Pioneer 11 hurtled toward its closest encounter. Figure 10-5 is a high-resolution image of Saturn and its ring system, showing the major features of the rings and planetary cloud belts in great detail. In Figure 10-6, the southern hemisphere of Saturn, although similar to the northern hemisphere, shows subtle differences in belt structure and color. The darker belt near the south pole separates the temperate region from the pole which has been in darkness for a decade (tilted away from our Sun). The irregular edges of the rings and of their shadows result from uneven stepping of the imaging photopolarimeter and by the size of its aperture.

Figure 10-7 is the "discovery" picture that revealed the F ring and a new satellite of Saturn. The F ring and the satellite have been enhanced in this picture to improve the reproduction in this book. Satellite 1979 S1, another possible discovery by Pioneer 11, appears in the lower right of the picture. The bright satellite above the ring is

Tethys. Remarkable detail in ring A and in the Cassini division is shown.

Taken at 850,000 km (528,000 miles), the image in Figure 10-8 shows part of the Saturnian disk. Figure 10-9, taken September 1 at 672,000 km (417,500 miles), is a close-up view of the southern hemisphere showing the remarkable

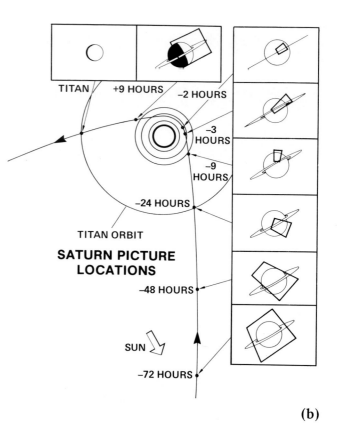

(b)

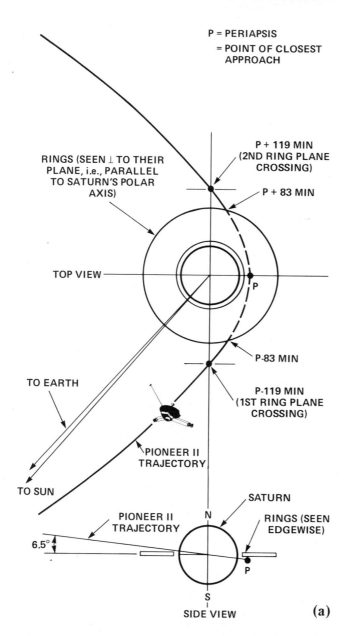

Figure 10-1. The trajectory of Pioneer 11 past Saturn (a) from above the north pole of the planet and in a side view. (b) Position of Pioneer 11 from 72 hr before periapsis to just beyond Titan's orbit, with views of Saturn from the spacecraft at various times.

regularity of the belt system of Saturn, which suggests a highly stable and uniform system of atmospheric dynamics. Unlike Jovian cloud systems, most structure in Saturn's atmosphere is linear, with few plumes or spots. There is little detail because the atmosphere is covered by a deep haze layer.

Silhouetted against the planet, the rings in Figure 10-10 appear jet black, except where light from the planet passes through the ring divisions. The Encke gap is barely visible. The Cassini division extends out from the globe of the planet. Subtle differences in color and form are apparent in the northern and southern cloud structures. The bright spot near the left limb of the planet — the satellite Mimas — casts its shadow near the right edge of the image.

Taken at only 395,000 km (245,500 miles), a close-up view of the north equatorial region of Saturn is reproduced in Figure 10-11. The delicate linear cloud structure and a few irregular cloud features suggest minor local instabilities. Remarkable detail in the C ring is revealed, and the division between rings B and C is quite prominent against the background of Saturn.

The high-resolution image (Figure 10-12) covers the northern equatorial and temperate regions of Saturn, from latitude 31° north (upper left) to the equator (bottom). Numerous low-contrast cloud features are revealed.

Figure 10-13 is the highest resolution pre-periapsis image of the Saturn encounter. The aperture size projected onto the planet (Figure 10-13(d)) is about 250 km. The remarkable lack of detail at this resolution demonstrates the dramatic difference between the atmospheric dynamics of Jupiter and Saturn. The mottled structure of the image results from noise in the data at the high-gain setting used.

After periapsis, the images of Saturn presented another new view. On the outward leg of its flight, Pioneer 11 obtained the first view ever of Saturn in the crescent phase (Figure 10-14). There is no belt structure because of the forward scattering of sunlight by a very thin, high-level haze. The ring system crosses the top of the image; the Encke gap and the Cassini division appear as two parallel lines near the top of the image. Since the data were taken by exposing four separate and partial images, it took the imaging photopolarimeter about 30 min to scan them. These partial images were combined to make the single image shown here. The irregularity of the left edge of the image is a result of the data being acquired in groups.

As the phase angle decreased because of Pioneer's motion along its outbound trajectory, the belt structure of Saturn became more apparent (Figures 10-15 and 10-16). At a phase angle of 114°, the belts became marginally visible. The Encke gap and Cassini division in the rings appear against the background of the planet. The decreasing width of the ring shadow on Saturn results from a change in scale as Pioneer 11 moved away from the planet. Contrast these pictures with the crescent images of Jupiter shown in Figure 8-13. On the crescent images of Jupiter the contrast in belt structure was also much reduced.

As Pioneer moved farther away from Saturn, the cloud features became less visible. In Figure 10-17, gain changes were not corrected to improve the visibility of the rings. To obtain the best image data to overcome the effect of low-data transmission rate (necessitated by the Sun's direction and the spacecraft's antenna axis being essentially coincident), the sampling rate was halved by recording every other sector. This caused the ropelike appearance of Saturn's rings and their shadows and the "blocky" edge of the planet. A scattered light image is visible on either side of the planet, which may be an optical effect within the imaging photopolarimeter.

Leaving Saturn behind, Pioneer 11 passed Titan and obtained five images from which the one shown in Figure 10-18(a) was constructed — the best rendition of Titan. Since Titan has never before been seen from this aspect and range, there is no standard by which to judge its color. The image was color-processed using the color appearance of Saturn as a guide. The polar orientation is shown in the accompanying line drawing (Figure 10-18(b)). No surface details are apparent because of the distance of the spacecraft from Saturn. Titan appears to be covered by clouds of which no specific structure or patterns are visible.

Data from two images taken by the imaging photopolarimeter on September 1, 1979, were used to show the transmission of red light through the rings. A radial intensity profile was made consisting of five-pixel azimuthal averages for each point plotted (see Figure 6-37(c)). This intensity profile was then swept over a photographic film in an arc to produce the synthetic image of the ring system shown in Figure 10-19(a). Naturally, no azimuthal variation that may have been present can be shown on this synthetic figure. However, it does show clearly the various rings, divisions, and gaps identified in Figure 10-19(b).

The image shown in Figure 10-20(a) was received on September 1 as mode 3 (polarization) data when the range was decreasing through 148,000 km (91,970 miles), at the midtime, to the radial distance of the A ring, when the image ended. The latitude was slightly southerly, –0.7 to 1.5° south, so the sunlit side of the rings progressively veiled Saturn as the data were obtained at fixed viewing (from left to right). The rapidly passing rings were distorted in this view, which approximately rectifies the limb of Saturn. The ring features are identified in the line diagram in Figure 10-20(b). This unique view of Saturn through the veiling rings can be rectified for either background and foreground, but not for both simultaneously. This view rectifies Saturn's limb, but the ring features remain distorted, as though they were not in orbit about Saturn.

Figure 10-2.

Image no.	Mid time DOY:hr:min	Range 10^5 km	10^5 mi.	Phase angle, deg
F-33E	242:05:43	25.8	16.0	14.9

Figure 10-3. Satellite Rhea appears at 4 o'clock relative to Saturn. This image is enhanced to show cloud belts on the planet and to improve the visibility of the rings. (a) Color. (b) Blue channel. (c) Red channel.

Image no.	Mid time DOY:hr:min	Range 10^5 km	10^5 mi.	Phase angle, deg
F-81E	238:09:22	57.0	35.4	18.5

226

Image no.	Mid time DOY:hr:min	Range		Phase angle, deg
		10^5 km	10^5 mi.	
F-19.5	243:09:21	15.8	9.8	12.1

Figure 10-4. A computer-generated mosaic of two separate images. It provides the highest resolution global view of Saturn during encounter. Near the center, the isolated white spot with a dark halo around it is a convection feature. The irregular edge of the the ring in front of the planet is caused by stepping anomalies of the imaging photopolarimeter that could not be fully compensated. (a) Color. (b) Blue channel. (c) Red channel.

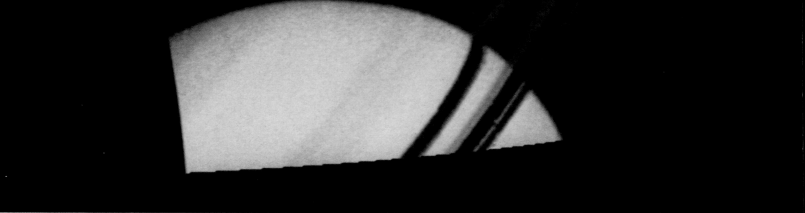

Figure 10-5. (a) Color.

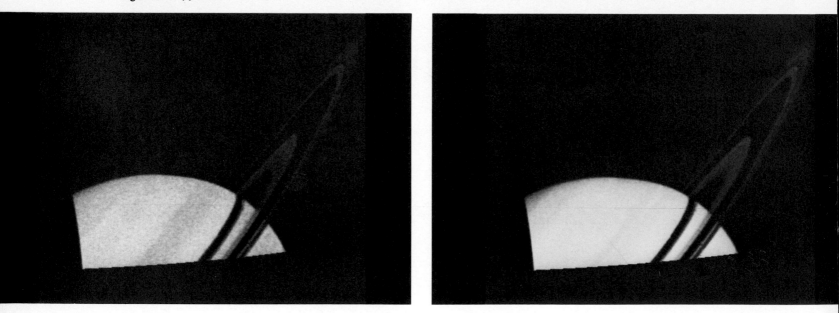

(b) Blue channel.

(c) Red channel.

Image no.	Mid time DOY:hr:min	Range 10^5 km	10^5 mi.	Phase angle, deg
F-16	243:16:57	12.5	7.8	10.5

228

Figure 10-6.

Image no.	Mid time DOY:hr:min	Range		Phase angle, deg
		10^5 km	10^5 mi.	
F-13	243:23:00	10.04	6.24	8.8

Figure 10-7.

Image no.	Mid time DOY:hr:min	Range 10⁵ km	10⁵ mi.	Phase angle, deg
F-12E	244:00:29	9.41	5.85	8.4

230

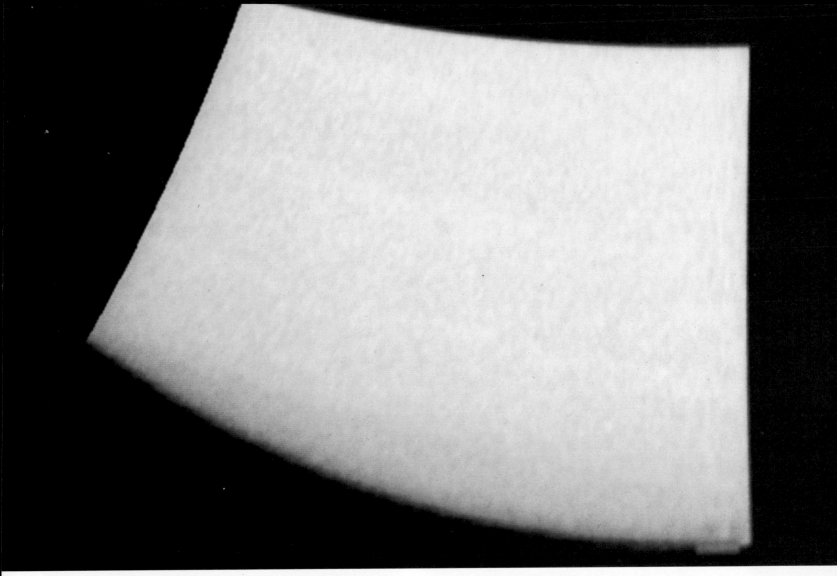

Figure 10-8. (a) Color.

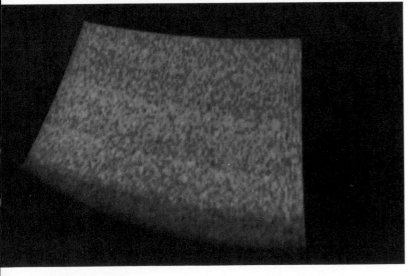

(b) Blue channel.

(c) Red channel.

Image no.	Mid time DOY:hr:min	Range		Phase angle, deg
		10^5 km	10^5 mi.	
F-11	244:02:49	8.39	5.21	7.8

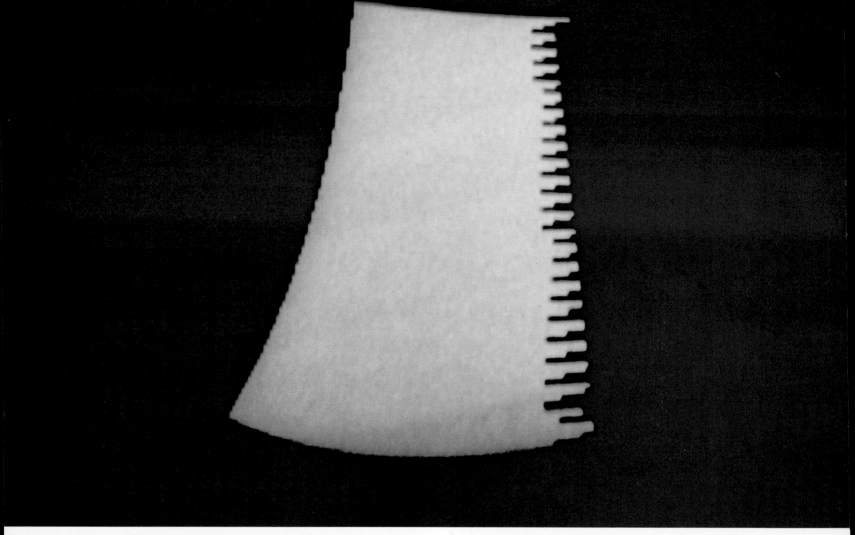

Figure 10-9. (a) Color.

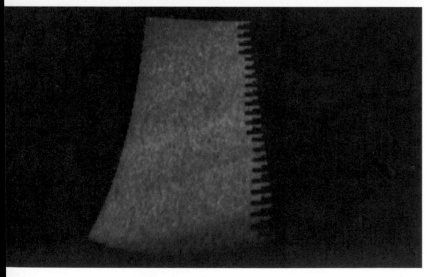

(b) Blue channel.

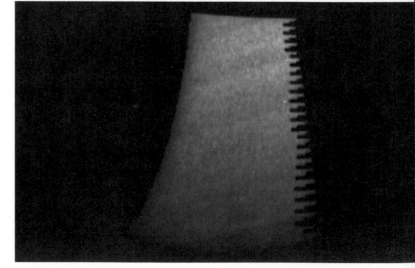

(c) Red channel.

Image no.	Mid time DOY:hr:min	Range 10^5 km	10^5 mi.	Phase angle, deg
F-9	244:06:21	6.78	4.21	7.4

Figure 10-10.

Image no.	Mid time DOY:hr:min	Range 10^5 km	10^5 mi.	Phase angle, deg
F-7	244:09:58	5.05	3.14	9.7

233

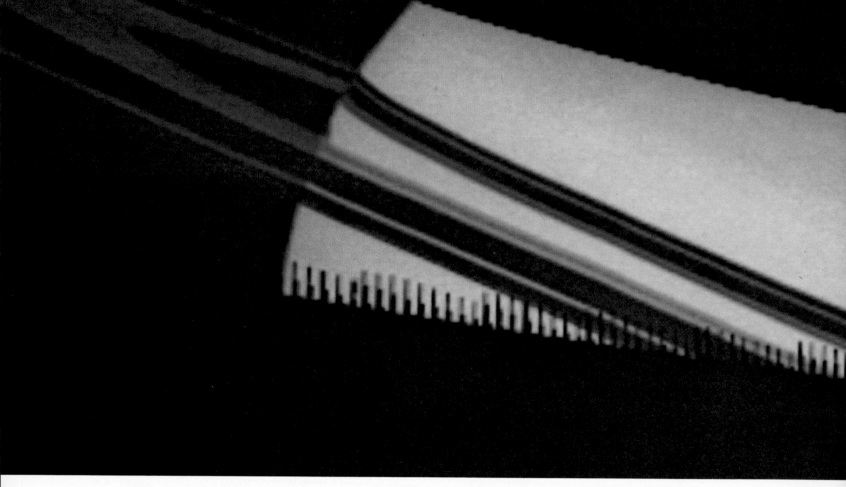

Figure 10-11. (a) Color.

Image no.	Mid time DOY:hr:min	Range 10^5 km	10^5 mi.	Phase angle, deg
F-6E	244:12:02	3.98	2.47	13.8

234

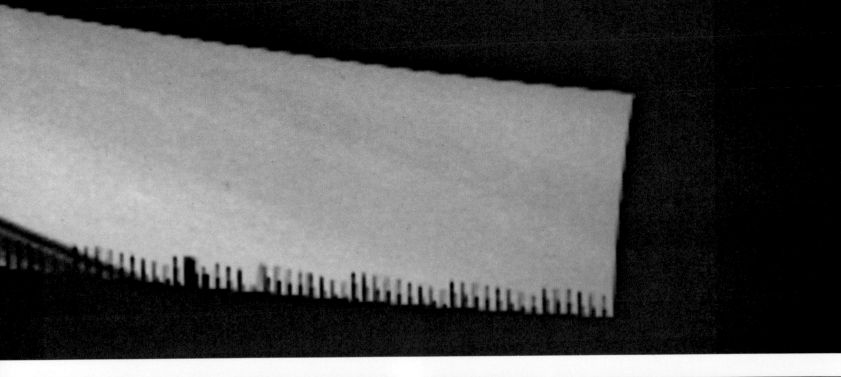

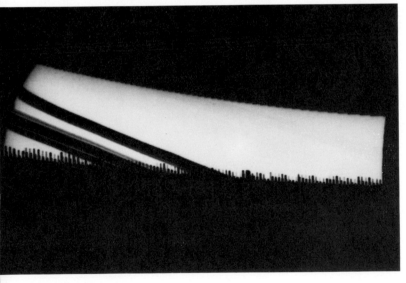

(b) Blue channel.

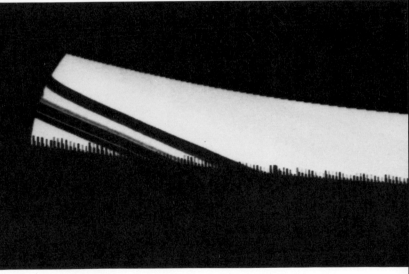

(c) Red channel.

235

Figure 10-12. (a) Color.

(b) Blue channel.

(c) Red channel.

Image no.	Mid time DOY:hr:min	Range 10^5 km	10^5 mi.	Phase angle, deg
F-5	244:13:35	3.13	1.94	19.7

236

Figure 10-13. (a) Color.   (b) Blue channel.   (c) Red channel.

Image no.	Mid time DOY:hr:min	Range 10^5 km	10^5 mi.	Phase angle, deg
F-4	244:14:40	2.51	1.56	26.5

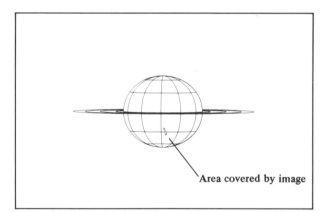

Area covered by image

237

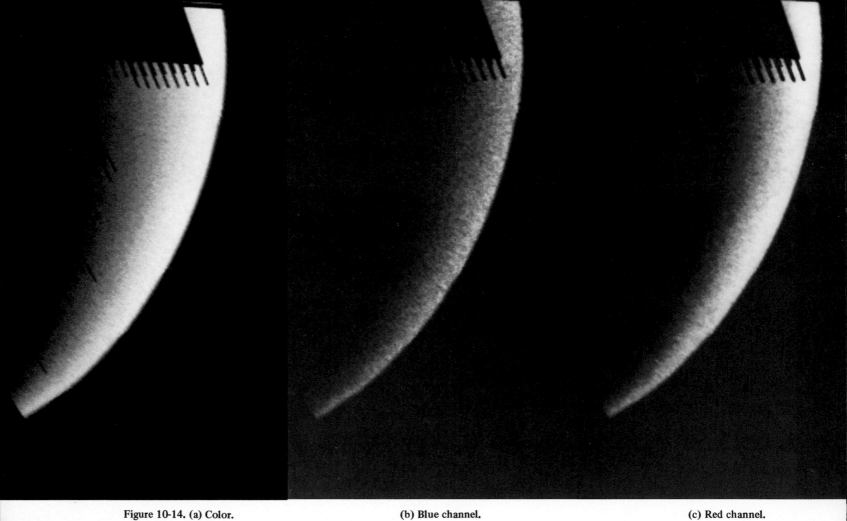

Figure 10-14. (a) Color.   (b) Blue channel.   (c) Red channel.

Image no.	Mid time DOY:hr:min	Range 10^5 km	10^5 mi.	Phase angle, deg
G-3	244:20:07	1.83	1.14	135.1

238

Figure 10-15. (a) Color.

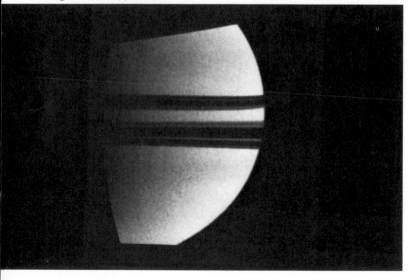

(b) Blue channel.

(c) Red channel.

Image no.	Mid time DOY:hr:min	Range 10^5 km	10^5 mi.	Phase angle, deg
G-4	244:22:43	3.35	2.08	113.2

239

Figure 10-16. (a) Color.

(b) Blue channel.

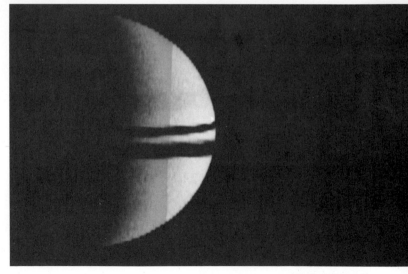

(c) Red channel.

Image no.	Mid time DOY:hr:min	Range 10⁵ km	10⁵ mi.	Phase angle, deg
G-8	245:09:31	8.58	5.33	94.2

Figure 10-17. (a) Color.

(b) Blue channel.

(c) Red channel.

Image no.	Mid time DOY:hr:min	Range 10^5 km	10^5 mi.	Phase angle, deg
G-21	246:18:19	21.47	13.34	85.3

241

(a) Color.

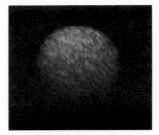

(b) Blue channel.

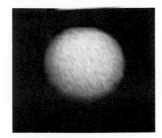

(c) Red channel.

Figure 10-18. Best image of Titan.

Image no.	Mid time DOY:hr:min	Range 10⁵ km	10⁵ mi.	Phase angle, deg
G-14	245:18:48	3.6	2.24	23.0

Figure 10-19. An intensity synthesis of two images, F-6 and F-12, as viewed from above the north pole of Saturn on September 1, 1979.

242

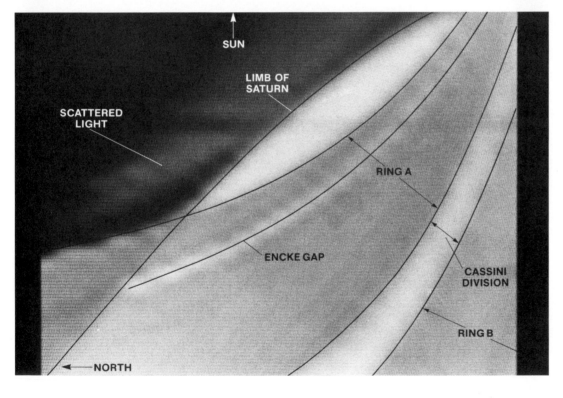

Figure 10-20. The only image showing the bright side of the rings near periapsis. However, it was made from polarization data, which accounts for the low resolution.

Image no.	Mid time DOY:hr:min	Range 10^5 km	10^5 mi.	Phase angle, deg
R-2	244:16:14	1.48	0.92	70

243

Its mission to Saturn a success, Pioneer 11 completed the first phase of mankind's exploration of the Solar System, investigating at close hand all the planets known to the ancients. Beyond Saturn, the planets discovered in relatively modern times are still waiting to be explored. In giving us the first close view of the spectacular ringed planet Saturn and its system of satellites, Pioneer 11 is helping to unravel some of the mystery that has surrounded Saturn since Galileo first saw its strange appendages in 1610.

- Pioneer discovered that Saturn has a magnetic field, trapped radiation belts, and a complex magnetosphere.

- Pioneer discovered that several of the Saturnian satellites absorb particles from the radiation belts. A previously unknown satellite was discovered through this absorption effect.

- Pioneer discovered that the rings also absorb particles to produce a nearly radiation-free environment close to the planet. A cloud of hydrogen around the rings was found.

- A new ring of Saturn was discovered beyond the A ring.

- The temperatures of Saturn's atmosphere, rings, and its largest satellite, Titan, were measured.

- Pioneer confirmed that Saturn emits more energy than it absorbs from the Sun.

- The equatorial yellow band on Saturn was found to be colder than other parts of the planet, implying that, like the zones of Jupiter, it is probably a region of high clouds.

- An extensive ionosphere of Saturn was discovered.

As Pioneer 11 left Saturn behind, it joined Pioneer 10 in exploring interplanetary space toward the outermost reaches of our Solar System.

Epilog
Beyond the Outer Giants

At the National Air and Space Museum of the Smithsonian Institution in Washington, D.C., a Pioneer spacecraft hangs between the Wright Brothers' airplane and Lindbergh's Spirit of St. Louis. This spacecraft was the third built for the Jupiter/Saturn mission. Identical to Pioneers 10 and 11, it was never flown but served as a backup. As Pioneers 10 and 11 move into interstellar space, this third Pioneer spacecraft is a perpetual reminder of the first pioneering missions to the giant outer planets of the Solar System. Beyond Jupiter and Saturn, the two active spacecraft continue on their extended missions, gathering important data about the outer reaches of the Solar System to and beyond the orbits of Pluto and Neptune.

The spacecraft continue to function and have reserve power to last for many years. Throughout the Pioneer missions, the capabilities of the ground receiving system have been improved faster than the strength of signals from the Pioneer spacecraft has decreased as they move away from Earth. The Pioneers can be commanded to tremendous distances, and by use of the large, 1000-ft-diameter radio telescope at Arecibo, Puerto Rico, data could be received from the spacecraft up to a distance of at least 88 times Earth's distance from the Sun — 13.2 billion kilometers (8.2 billion miles).

Traveling at about 440 million kilometers (275 million miles) per year, the spacecraft will search for the boundary between the interstellar medium and solar system space within which the solar wind modulates incoming galactic cosmic rays (as discussed in chapter 6). They will also look for evidence of a heliopause where the solar wind effectively stops and where there is perhaps a shock wave between the heliosphere and the interstellar medium.

The spacecraft may be able to detect any large planets beyond Neptune and search for evidence of gravity waves. The gravity wave radiation may be detected when the spacecraft are at opposition relative to the Sun. Then the "noise" on the Doppler signals will be at a minimum. Also, non-symmetrical events such as the collapse of very massive stellar objects, occurring perhaps about once per week, might be detected by the Pioneer spacecraft. Because they are leaving our Solar System in opposite directions, the Pioneers can sensitively search for the gravitational effects of previously unknown outer planets. If such bodies exist, they cannot be detected from Earth with present observational techniques. But in the outer reaches of the Solar System, where the spacecraft are relatively free of gravitational perturbations from the inner planets and far from the known outer planets, minute changes in gravitational fields might be detected as changes to the motion of the spacecraft. The precision with which such changes can be detected by analysis of the radio signals from the spacecraft has increased dramatically in recent years.

The imaging photopolarimeter can be used to record the light from the galaxy free from the scattering of particles in the inner Solar System.

Galactic cosmic rays with energies less than several hundred million electron volts per nucleon reveal significant information on their acceleration, injection, and propagation through interstellar space. For example, ionization energy losses in the interstellar medium should produce systematic changes in the low-energy spectra of various nuclear species. Also, it is in this energy range that isotopes can be resolved observationally, thus allowing the lifetimes of cosmic-ray particles to be determined from measurements of isotopes such as beryllium-10 and aluminum-26. The isotopic composition of cosmic rays should also provide information on how atomic nucleii are synthesized in the regions of space where the particles originate. An appreciable fraction of the total cosmic-ray energy could be contained in the low-energy component.

This energy region, which contains such a wealth of cosmic-ray information, is also the region most severely affected by solar modulation (as discussed in chapter 6). As cosmic rays penetrate the heliosphere, they encounter magnetic irregularities moving outward in the solar wind. The resulting processes of particle diffusion, convection, and adiabatic energy loss in the expanding solar wind result in significant modulation of cosmic rays with energies below 500 MeV per nucleon.

The only feasible direct approach to the study of low-energy cosmic rays is to make measurements at great distances from the Sun where residual modulation effects may be small. The Pioneer 10 and 11 missions provide the first opportunity for such a study. At the time of writing, data were available from Pioneer 10 out to 20 times Earth's distance from the Sun, while Pioneer 11 at half that distance provided an intermediate observation point. The Pioneer spacecraft will continue out to much larger radial distances. As the two Pioneers move out of our Solar System in opposite directions, they will continue with this important work of gaining a better understanding of the galactic cosmic rays.

The extended mission provides scientists with an opportunity to continue to explore the outer Solar System, with particular emphasis on two major solar effects: the interaction of the solar wind with the interstellar medium and the influence of changing solar activity on the structure and dynamics of the interplanetary medium.

With increasing distance from the Sun, the solar wind is probably affected by inward pressure exerted by the interstellar plasma and magnetic fields. The solar wind is expected to undergo a deceleration, heating, and deviation from a mainly radial outflow so that it can turn and slide along a boundary — the heliopause — that separates the solar wind from interstellar plasmas and fields. There are major uncertainties in the size and shape of the heliosphere, the volume occupied by the solar wind plasma, as well as in the distance at which heating and deflection of the solar wind occur. Some scientists have speculated that the properties of the solar wind will change abruptly at a thin shock surface within the heliosphere. One objective of the extended missions of Pioneers 10 and 11 is to seek evidence of such a shock or, alternatively, a thick transition region caused by the interstellar interaction. If such a change occurs, it should be readily observable in the data returned from the magnetic field and plasma instruments onboard the spacecraft.

It is also possible that, before a terminal shock or transition region is reached, other effects of the interstellar gas will be detected. As the neutral interstellar gas enters the Solar System and becomes ionized, it will probably exert a drag force on the solar wind which will lead to significant heating and presumably to the production of waves and other irregularities in the interplanetary field. If the heliopause is at great distances from the Sun, such drag effects may be the first indication of the heliopause observed by the Pioneer spacecraft.

The interplanetary structure was observed by the two Pioneers under circumstances especially favorable for effects associated with corotating solar features such as the equatorial current sheet and the interaction regions between fast and slow streams of the solar wind. The observations were made during the recent minimum in solar activity when the Sun was dominated by coronal holes and other structures that evolve slowly. However, during the extended mission, solar conditions will change drastically to those associated with maximum solar activity.

Several aspects of this enhanced solar activity are expected to affect the structures of the interplanetary field at great distances from the Sun. Solar features will most probably evolve more rapidly and the interplanetary structure throughout the heliosphere will be dominated by transient, rather than corotating, phenomena. For example, solar flares can be expected to give rise to numerous plasma outbursts, accompanied by shocks, which will propagate into the outer Solar System. Since propagation delays are long for flare-generated plasma to reach the outer Solar System, the structure of the distant field and solar wind may be very different from that observed during the earlier parts of the mission. In this regard it will be very helpful to be able to compare the results from the two Pioneer spacecraft in the outer Solar System with those from ISEE-3 and Pioneer Venus Orbiter, in the inner Solar System, and the two Voyagers that are following the Pioneers.

It will also be important to study the changes that take place in the interplanetary current sheet during and after the maximum in solar activity. The fields above and below the current sheet appear to be intimately related to the fields observed in the polar cap of the Sun. These are known to reverse polarity a year or two after solar maximum; when this reversal occurs, there should be a restructuring of the heliospheric field on a grand scale. The interplanetary current sheet also must reverse its polarity. One way it might do this is by the sheet rotating through 180° over the poles of the Sun. Another way might be by the current sheet becoming fragmented or filamentary and then reestablishing itself with opposite polarity. The extended mission should provide data to show which of these or other processes actually takes place.

During the mission beyond Jupiter and Saturn, the ultraviolet photometers onboard the spacecraft will provide a relatively complete sky survey of ultraviolet emissions from B-type or earlier stars, yielding data on both the observed stars and the interstellar extinction coefficient. Also, these instruments can measure the physical parameters of the interplanetary hydrogen and helium gases, such as their density and temperature, at large solar distances. Heliosphere boundary data, including observations of ultraviolet emissions from neutral hydrogen and helium and emissions from the hot plasma at the heliosphere boundary can be used to determine the physical conditions at the boundary.

The correlation of results to establish the shape of the heliosphere is greatly enhanced by combining the results of different spacecraft that are following quite different trajectories out of the Solar System. The Pioneer 10 spacecraft leaves the Solar System in the downwind direction while both Pioneer 11 and Voyager will leave in the upwind direction. Thus, the combined ultraviolet observations on the shape and extent of the heliosphere will provide significant results on the galactic pressure (magnetic and particle). Since all spacecraft occasionally view the same ultraviolet stars, a cross-calibration is available to assure the reliability of the data. This same ability to view ultraviolet stars will also provide continuing roll attitude data for Pioneer 10 which the spacecraft system cannot provide much beyond 22 AU.

Continued Pioneer 10 and 11 photometer observations at great distances will allow scientists to determine the radial dependence of the "fast" hydrogen density and hence to locate the heliosphere boundary, the depth and location of the transition region, and the plasma densities outside the heliosphere.

When signals from the two Pioneers can no longer be received at Earth, they will have another mission as they continue into interstellar space. This final mission began when, in a high vacuum, Pioneer 10 gleamed under the harsh lights of an artificial sun in the space simulator at TRW Systems, California. The final test was underway before the spacecraft was to be shipped to Kennedy Space Center. A group of science correspondents from the national press were at TRW Systems for a briefing on Pioneer and had been invited to see the spacecraft under test.

Looking at Pioneer through the portholes of the simulator, one of the correspondents, Eric Burgess, then with *The Christian Science Monitor*, visualized Pioneer 10 as mankind's first emissary beyond our Solar System. This spacecraft should carry a special message from mankind, he thought, a message that would tell any finder of the spacecraft a million or even a billion years hence that planet Earth had evolved an intelligent species that could think beyond its own time and beyond its own Solar System.

He mentioned this idea to Richard Hoagland, a freelance writer, and to Don Bane, then with the *Los Angeles Herald-Examiner*, and they enthusiastically agreed. The result was that Burgess and Hoagland approached Dr. Carl Sagan, Director of the Laboratory of Planetary Studies, Cornell University, who was then visiting the Jet Propulsion Laboratory, Pasadena, in connection with Mariner 9's mission to Mars. A short while earlier, Dr. Sagan had been involved in a conference in the Crimea devoted to the problems of communicating with extraterrestrial intelligences and, together with Dr. Frank Drake, Director of the National Astronomy and Ionosphere Center, Cornell University, had designed one type of message that might be used to communicate with an alien intelligence.

Dr. Sagan was enthusiastic about the idea of a message on the Pioneer spacecraft. He and Dr. Drake designed a plaque, and Linda Salzman Sagan prepared the artwork. The design was presented to the National Aeronautics and Space Administration; they accepted it for this first Pioneer from our Solar System into the Galaxy.

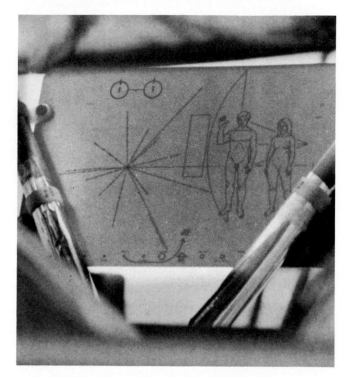

Figure Ep-1. Plaque mounted on the Pioneer spacecraft.

The plaque design was etched into a gold-anodized aluminum plate 15.25 by 22.8 cm (6 by 9 in.) and 0.127 cm (0.05 in.) thick. This plate was attached to the antenna support struts of the spacecraft in a position where it would be shielded from erosion by interstellar dust (Figure Ep-1).

When Pioneer 10 flew by Jupiter, the spacecraft acquired sufficient kinetic energy to carry it completely out of our Solar System. In about 100,000 years, it will have coasted to the distance of the nearest star, in the direction of the constellation Taurus. Sometime, perhaps many billions of years from now, it may pass through the planetary system of a remote stellar neighbor, one of whose planets may have evolved intelligent life.

If that life possesses sufficient capability to detect the Pioneer spacecraft — needing a higher technology than mankind possesses today — it may also have the curiosity and the technical ability to pick up the spacecraft and take it into a laboratory to inspect it. Then the plaque with its message from Earth should be found and possibly deciphered.

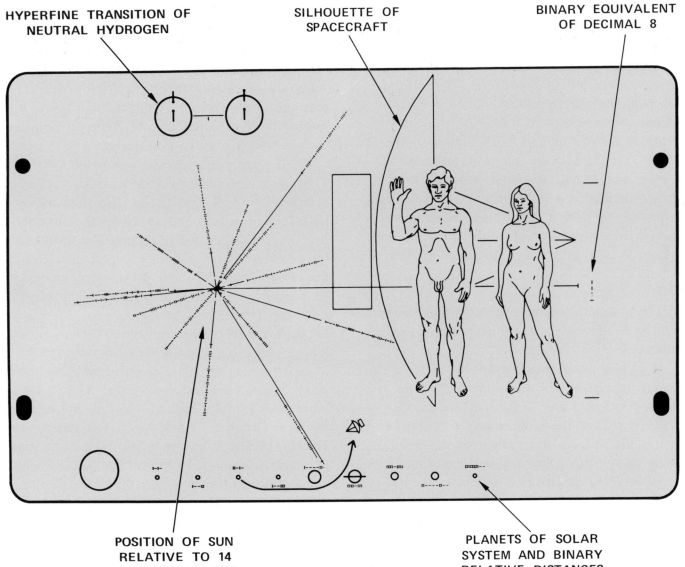

HYPERFINE TRANSITION OF
NEUTRAL HYDROGEN

SILHOUETTE OF
SPACECRAFT

BINARY EQUIVALENT
OF DECIMAL 8

POSITION OF SUN
RELATIVE TO 14
PULSARS AND THE
CENTER OF THE GALAXY

PLANETS OF SOLAR
SYSTEM AND BINARY
RELATIVE DISTANCES

Figure Ep-2. Line drawing of the plaque (meanings of the etchings
are described in the text).

Pioneer 11 carried an identical plaque. After that spacecraft's encounter with Saturn, it, too, possessed sufficient velocity to escape from our Solar System, but in almost the opposite direction to Pioneer 10. Pioneer 11 headed out of our Solar System in the general direction our Solar System is moving through space.

The plaques on the two spacecraft tell of Man, where and when the species lived, and its biological form. At top left of the plaque (Figure Ep-2), a schematic of the hyperfine transition of neutral atomic hydrogen — a universal "yardstick" — provides a basic unit of both time and physical length throughout the physical universe. As a further size check, the binary equivalent of the decimal number 8 is shown between the tote marks indicating the height of the two human figures to be compared with the scale of the spacecraft itself, which is also shown in line silhouette on the plaque.

The hydrogen wavelength — 21.11 cm (8.3 in.) — multiplied by the binary number representing 8 alongside the woman, gives her height, namely, 169 cm (66 in.).

The radial pattern to the left of center of the plaque represents the position of our Sun relative to 14 pulsars and to the center of our Galaxy. The latter direction is indicated by the long horizontal line with no binary digits on it. The binary digits on the other lines denote time. This can be deduced because they represent precision to 10 decimal digits, which is unlikely for distances to stellar objects but quite feasible for measurements of time. And from the unit of time established from the hydrogen atom, the extraterrestrial intelligence should be able to deduce that all the times are about 0.1 sec — the typical period of pulsars.

Since the periods of pulsars run down at well-established rates, they act as galactic clocks. An advanced civilization would be able to search its galactic records and identify the star system from which the Pioneer spacecraft originated, even if each spacecraft is not intercepted for several billions of years.

Below the orientation diagram, as a further aid to identification of the spacecraft's origin should it be intercepted while our Solar System is still in the galactic records, another diagram shows the relative distances of the solar planets and identifies the bright-ringed planet Saturn and the planet from which the spacecraft originated. After accelerating past the largest planet as shown by a track, the spacecraft is depicted with its antenna pointing back to its origin on the third planet.

Finally, the plaque depicts a man and a woman. The man is depicted in what to humans is a characteristic gesture of friendliness, also showing how limbs can be moved and displaying the important four fingers and opposing thumb. The figures and physiognomy were carefully chosen and drawn for ethnic neutrality, and no attempt was made to explain to an alien intelligence what may to such an intelligence be mysterious differences between the two physical types shown on the plaque — man and woman.

As an epilog to the Pioneer mission to these giant planets of our Solar System, the plaque is more than a cold message to an alien life form in the most distant future. It signifies an attribute of mankind that, in an era when troubles of war, pollution, clashing ideologies, and serious social and supply problems plague them, mankind can still think beyond themselves and have the vision to send a message through space and time to contact intelligence in a star system that perhaps has not yet condensed from a galactic nebula.

The plaque represents at least one intellectual cave painting, a mark of Man, that might survive not only all the caves of Earth, but also the Solar System itself. It is an interstellar stela that shows mankind possesses a spiritual insight that transcends the material problems of the age of human emergence into space.

Appendix
Technical Det[...]

The tables on the following pages li[...]
tant parameters regarding the significa[...]
images taken by Pioneers 10 and 11 [...]
encounters with the giant planets [...]
Saturn.

The first column in each table gives [...]
of the images, or image number, num[...]
to periapsis and up afterward (e.g., [...]
table for the Pioneer 10 encounter v[...]
"A" images are before periapsis, "B" [...]
after periapsis). Missing numbers (e. [...]
A24) refer to images of satellites n[...]
this table. The mid time is the tin[...]
the data forming the central line of [...]
was received on Earth (expressed in [...]
(DOY), hours and minutes of Univ[...]
(UT)). The other columns refer to t[...]
of the spacecraft when the data v[...]
Range, measured from the spacecr[...]
center of the planet, and pixel size a[...]
km). The pixel size can be used to [...]
resolution limit of an image. The ph[...]
the angle between the direction from [...]

Appendix 1
The Imaging Photopolarimeter

The entire complex of scientific instruments carried onboard each Pioneer spacecraft was needed to provide the first close-up investigations of Jupiter and Saturn and their environments. The imaging photopolarimeter (IPP) returned the data from which the colored images of the cloud covers of Jupiter and Saturn and of the magnificent rings of Saturn were constructed to reveal details never before seen. This appendix provides further technical details of this instrument.

The IPP consisted basically of a positionable optics-detector assembly and an electronic equipment housing, supported on a central mounting frame. Special optical materials were selected to retain their transparency even after being subjected to radiation effects from trapped energetic protons and electrons in the radiation belts of Jupiter and Saturn.

The optical system shown diagrammatically in Figure A-1 consisted of a 2.54-cm (1-in.) diameter Maksutov-type telescope, a calcite Wollaston prism polarization analyzer, multilayer filters to separate red and blue components of the reflected light from Jupiter and Saturn, relay optics, and two dual-channel multiplier detectors, each designed to sense two polarization components in one of two colors (a total of four channels). The field of view of the instrument could be varied by use of three apertures on a carrier that also carried polarization processing elements (depolarizer and half-wave retardation plate) and an internal calibration lamp.

Analog signals from the detectors were digitized, buffered in the spacecraft's data storage unit, and transmitted together with instrument status information in either of two telemetry formats.

After a command into the data-taking mode had been received, the electronic logic processor automatically provided all internal commands required to sequence a complete measurement operation with the IPP and then return the instrument to standby. Additional commands were available to adjust power supply voltages, thereby controlling the gain of the instrument, to alter

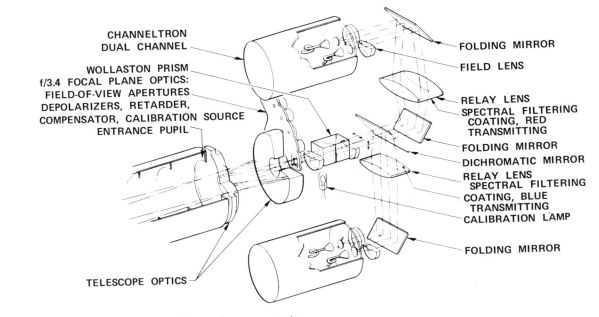

Figure A-1. The IPP optical system and its major components.

sampling rates, to in
the direction in whi
and so on.

The field of view
employed in the imag
field of view was move
of the spacecraft, unl
Step direction could b
six-bit telemetry form
gray for imaging. In t
four detector channels
was depolarized before
place on the dark sky
was used to compensa
background caused by
ment. Detector output
colors, each 0.015° o
if the low sampling rate
spacecraft buffer store
over 14° of each roll c
rate.

The manner in whicl
duce an image is show
ure A-2. Scan lines, an

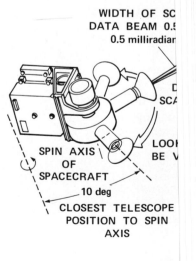

WIDTH OF SC
DATA BEAM 0.!
0.5 milliradiar

D
SCA

LOO
BE V

SPIN AXIS
OF
SPACECRAFT
10 deg
CLOSEST TELESCOPE
POSITION TO SPIN
AXIS

Figure A-2. How the IPP imaging
duce an image.

Appendix 3
Pioneer Team

PIONEER PROJECT MANAGEMENT

NASA Headquarters
  Office of Space Science
  Office of Tracking and Data Acquisition

Jet Propulsion Laboratory, Pasadena, California

Ames Research Center, NASA, Moffett Field, California
  Pioneer Project Staff

Lewis Research Center, NASA, Cleveland, Ohio

Kennedy Space Center, NASA, Florida

AEC Space Nuclear Systems Division

TRW Systems Group

EXPERIMENTS AND INVESTIGATORS

Magnetic Fields Experiment

Principal Investigator .... Edward J. Smith
Jet Propulsion Laboratory, Pasadena, California

Coinvestigators .... Palmer Dyal
Davis S. Colburn
Ames Research Center, NASA, Moffett Field, California

Charles P. Sonett
University of Arizona

Douglas E. Jones
Brigham Young University, Provo, Utah

Paul J. Coleman, Jr.
University of California at Los Angeles

Leverett Davis, Jr.
California Institute of Technology, Pasadena

S-Band Occultation Experiment

Principal Investigator . . . . Arvydas J. Kliore
Jet Propulsion Laboratory

Coinvestigators . . . . Dan L. Cain
Gunnar Fjeldbo Lindal
Boris L. Seidel
Jet Propulsion Laboratory

S. Ichtiaque Rasool
NASA Headquarters, Washington, D.C.

PIONEER CONTRACTORS

Contractor	Item
Allen Design Burbank, Calif.	Propellant Valves
Amelco Semiconductor Mountain View, Calif.	Integrated Circuits
Analog Technology Corporation Pasadena, Calif.	Ultraviolet Photometry
Bendix Corporation Columbia, Md.	Mission Operations and Software
Bendix Mosaic Fabrication Division Sturbridge, Mass.	Fiber Optics
Computer Communications Inc. Inglewood, Calif.	Communication Stations
Data Products Corp. Woodland Hills, Calif.	ADP Line Printer
Edcliff Instrument Division Systron Donner Monrovia, Calif.	Despin Sensor Assembly
Electra Midland Corp. Cermatrik Division San Diego, Calif.	Current Limiters

Electronic Memories Division of Electronic Memories and Magnetics Corp. Hawthorne, Calif.	Memory Storage Units
EMR Telemetry Division Weston Instruments Inc. Sarasota, Fla.	Telemetry Decommutation Display Equipment
Frequency Electronics Inc. New Hyde Park, N.Y.	Oscillator (TCXO)
General Dynamics Convair Division San Diego, Calif.	Launch Vehicle — First and Second States
General Electric Company Philadelphia, Pa.	Asteroid/Meteoroid Detector
Holex Inc. Hollister, Calif.	Explosive Cartridge
Honeywell, Inc. Radiation Center Lexington, Mass.	Sun Sensor Assemblies
Jet Propulsion Laboratory Pasadena, Calif.	Helium Vector Magnetometer
Los Alamos Scientific Laboratory Los Alamos, N.M.	RTG Fuel Discs
McDonnell-Douglas Corp. Astronautics Company Huntington Beach, Calif.	Launch Vehicle — Third Stage Motor
Mound Laboratories Miamisburg, Ohio	Radioisotope Heater Unit Capsules RTG Fuel and Capsules
Pratt and Whitney Aircraft Co. East Hartford, Conn.	Launch Vehicle — Second Stage Motor
Pressure Systems Inc. Los Angeles, Calif.	Propellant Tanks
Rockwell International Rocketdyne Division Canoga Park, Calif.	Launch Vehicle — First Stage Motor

Santa Barbara Research Center Santa Barbara, Calif.	Imaging Photopolarimeter and Infrared Radiometer
Siliconix Inc. Santa Clara, Calif.	Integrated Circuits
Teledyne Isotopes Germantown, Md.	Radioisotope Thermoelectric Generators (RTGs)
Teledyne Microwave Sunnyvale, Calif.	RF Transfer Switch
Texas Instruments Dallas, Texas	Integrated Circuits
Thiokol Chemical Company Elkton, Md.	Launch Vehicle — Third Stage Motor
Time Zero Corporation Torrance, Calif.	Plasma Analyzer and Magnetometer Electronics
TRW Systems Group TRW Inc. Redondo Beach, Calif.	Spacecraft
United Detector Technology Inc. Santa Monica, Calif.	Silicon Photo Detectors
University of California at San Diego San Diego, Calif.	Trapped Radiation Detector
University of Chicago Chicago, Ill.	Charged Particle Instrument
University of Iowa Iowa City, Ia.	Geiger Tube Telescope
Watkins-Johnson Co. Palo Alto, Calif.	Traveling Wave Tube Amplifier
Wavecom Inc. Chatsworth, Calif.	Diplexer Assemblies
Xerox Data Systems El Segundo, Calif.	Computer Systems
Yardney Electric Corp. Pawcatuck, Conn.	Silver-Cadmium Battery Cells

Appendix 4
Pioneer Award Recipients

DISTINGUISHED SERVICE MEDAL

Charles F. Hall

EXCEPTIONAL SERVICE MEDALS

Jupiter Encounter:

Richard O. Fimmel
John V. Foster
Robert U. Hofstetter
Ralph W. Holtzclaw
Harold Jaffe
James W. Johnson
Eldon W. Kaiser
William E. Kirhofer
Fred D. Kochendorfer
Joseph E. Lepetich
Norman J. Martin
Edwin T. Muckley
Robert R. Nunamaker
Alfred J. Siegmeth
Arthur C. Wilbur

Saturn Encounter:

Arthur C. Bouck
John W. Dyer
Robert P. Hogan
Robert E. Ryan

EXCEPTIONAL SCIENTIFIC ACHIEVEMENT MEDALS

John D. Anderson
R. Walker Filius
Tom Gehrels
Darrell L. Judge
William H. Kinard
Guido Münch
James H. Trainor
James A. Van Allen

PUBLIC SERVICE AWARD

William J. Dixon
Herbert A. Lassen
Walter L. Natzic
Bernard J. O'Brien
William F. Sheehan
Louis A. Watts

PUBLIC SERVICE MEDALS (Saturn Encounter)

L. Ralph Baker
Charles Blenman, Jr.
Lyn R. Doose
Martin C. Tomasko

PUBLIC SERVICE GROUP ACHIEVEMENT AWARDS

Pioneer 10 Team, TRW System Group
Pioneer 10 Radioisotope Thermoelectric Generator Contractor Team
Pioneer 10 Team, Bendix Field Engineering Corporation
Pioneer 10 Scientific Instrument Team
Pioneer Saturn Mission Operations Support Team
Bendix Field Engineering Corporation

GROUP ACHIEVEMENT AWARDS

Ames Pioneer 10 Scientific Instruments Team
Ames Pioneer 10 Spacecraft Team
Ames Pioneer 10 Mission Analysis and Launch Operations Team
Ames Pioneer 10 Mission Operations Team
Ames Pioneer 10 Project Management Team
Ames Pioneer 10 Contracts Team
Ames Research Center Support Groups
Pioneer 10 Mission Analysis Team, Jet Propulsion Laboratory
Pioneer 10 Ground Data System Team, Jet Propulsion Laboratory
Pioneer 10 RTG Team, Atomic Energy Commission
Pioneer 10 Radio Science Team
Pioneer 10 Headquarters Staff Support Group
Pioneer Saturn Mission Navigation Team, Jet Propulsion Laboratory
Pioneer Saturn Deep Space Network Team, Jet Propulsion Laboratory

Arvydas J. Kliore, Edward J. Smith, and John H. Wolfe were also nominated for the Exceptional Scientific Achievement Award. However, since NASA makes only one such award to an individual, these principal investigators did not receive the award again for their work on Pioneer 10. John A. Simpson was nominated for his work in connection with both Pioneer 10 and Mariner 10 and elected to accept the award for Mariner.

Index

A ring, 2,15,107,108,147,149,150, 152,153,177,224
absorption by atmosphere, 21,64
acceleration processes, interplanetary, 115
Acuna, Mario H., 55,266
Advanced Research Projects Agency, 25
aerosols, 134,149,150
Aldebaran, 103
alpha particles, 114,115
aluminum-26, 246
Alverez, José M., 63,268
Amalthea, 96,99,130,132
Ames Research Center (see NASA)
American Astronautical Society, 27
ammonia, 17,19,20,106,133,134, 140,156
Ananke (Andrastea), 96
Anderson, John D., 65,268,273
Andrastea, 96
angle, phase, 149,150,179,225
anomalies, 84,98,103,175
antenna, ground, 31,37,38,39
spacecraft, 39,43,46,49,73
apparitions of planets, 9
Arecibo radio telescope, 245
argon, 63
asteroid, 28,32,33
Apollo, 33
belt, vii,viii,24,28,50,51,75,76, 78,91,117,118
Hidalgo, 33
Hygiea, 33
Nike, 75
sizes of, 32,34
asteroid-meteoroid detector, 61,62, 73,91,99,118,271
astronomical unit, 113
Atlas-Centaur launch vehicle, 26, 28,43,72,73
atmosphere, Io, 53,121
Jupiter, 11,99,133-143
planetary, 17,53,66
Saturn, 156-157
Titan, 150
Atomic Energy Commission (AEC), 27,48,69,265
attitude control, 44,46,73

AU, 113
aurora, 53,56,64,157
awards, EMMY, 84,85
Pioneer, 273,274
axis, magnetic, 125,144
spacecraft, 46,47,49
azimuth, other Pioneers, 77

B ring, 15,105,149,150,152,153
Baker, Daniel N., 60,267
Baker, L. Ralph, 83,274
Bane, Don, 248
bar, 120
Barclay, Patrick J., 27
Barnard, E. E., 8
Barnes, Aaron, 57,266
belts, Jupiter, 11,12,138-141,183, 192,
Saturn, 15,106,156,223,224
Bendix Field Engineering Corporation, 27,274
beryllium, 58,246
Beshore, E., xi
Beta Scorpii, 135
bit rate, 39,40,98,101,106,108, 109,252
bits and pixels, 159
blackout, radio, 84,98,108
Blenman, Clarles Jr., xi,68,268,269, 274
blue festoons, 183
Bode, Johann Elert, 32
Bond, G. P., 8,152
boron, 58
Bouck, Arthur C., 273
bow shock, heliosphere, 113
Jupiter, 80,82,96,122-129
Saturn, 106,109,143-145
brightness, zodiacal light, 117
Burgess, Eric, 248,285
Burke, James J., xi,68,269

C ring, 14,105,152,153,224
Cain, Dan L., 66,270
Callisto, 6,7,65,96,99,119-121,220, 221
Canopus, 46
Carame (Pan), 96
carbon, 58,116,140,150
Carlson, Robert W., 63,268

Cassini division, 15,105,150,224, 225
celestial mechanics experiment, 65, 119,133,152,245
cells, detector, 63,91
Cerenkov counter, 60
Ceres, 32
Chase, Stillman, C., 64,269
charged particle experiment, 51,53, 56,58,59,60,61,73,272,246
Christian Science Monitor, The, 248
Clements, Arthur, 68,268
clouds, Jupiter's, 11,99,140,141
Saturn's, 156,157
Coffeen, David L., 68,269
Colburn, David S., 55,265
Coleman, Paul J., Jr., 55,265
Collard, H., 57,266
color, Jupiter, 11,140
satellites, 221,225
Saturn, 14,156
synthesis, 83,85,104,172
comets, 5
composition, charged particles, 58
Jupiter, 134
Saturn, 155
computer image processing, 177
command and control, 34,40,88, 245
commanding IPP, 164,251
command, 39,40,79,83,97,109
contingency, 36,83,97
distribution unit, 40
photopolarimeter, 163,164
spurious, 36,84,99
rate, 40
communications, 23,34,37,40,47, 56,70,98,110,245
delay, 2,23,34,36,74,76,110
distances, 110,113,245
frequencies, 47
Conical Scan (CONSCAN), 49
conjunctions, planetary, 9,101
constellation, Taurus, 103,248
contractors, Pioneer, 270-272
control, mission (see Operations)
Copernican model, 80
core, Earth, 154

Jupiter, 10,16,17,126,133
  Saturn, 13,16,17,144,155
correction, images, 166-178
Cortright, Edgar M., 25
cosmetic enhancement, 168
cosmic rays, 26,45,50,51,58,59,
      112,113,116,147,245,246
  experiment, 58,59,245,246
  intensity gradient, 113
  modulation of, 114,245
counterglow, 74,117,118
crepe ring (see C ring)
crossings, ring plane, 107,108,
  142,143
current sheet, 124,129,145,247

D' ring (see E ring)
DaCosta, B., xi
data formats, 48
  for images, 253-263
  handling, 39,47
  rates, 40,252 (see also bit rate)
  storage, 40
dates, arrival, 31
Davis, Leverett, 55,265
Day of Year (DOY) (see Time)
Deep Space Network (DSN), 29,
  31,37,38-41,47,98,101,104,108,
  110,113
DeFrance, Smith J., 25
Demeter, 96
density, Galilean satellites, 119,120
detector, infrared, 65
  particle, 56-63
  ultraviolet, 63,64,247
deuterium, 58
DIAL, 174
diameter, Jupiter, 10,120
  satellites, 119,147,149,150
  Saturn, 13,153
  rings system, 153
  Titan, 109
Dione, 109,145
direct ascent, 28
"discovery" picture, 223
direction, counterglow, 117,230
distance, Earth to Sun, 113
distortion, image, 162,166,174
  "rubber sheet," 167
Dixon, William T., 27,274
Dodeck, H. H., 79
Dollfus division, 152,153

Doose, Lyn R., xii,68,84,97,269,
  274
Doppler shift, 49
  residual, 28,49
  tracking data, 28,49,65
dosage, radiation, 32,132,146
downlink, 47
DOY, 180
Drake, Frank, 248
Dunn Instruments, 104
dust, interplanetary, 51,63,118
Dyal, Palmer, 55,265
Dyer, John W., xi, 27, 273
dynamics, atmospheric, 138,139,
  156
  Jovian magnetosphere, 130

E ring, 15,105,145,151-153
Earth, 2,5,8-10,16,17,19,21,25,31,
  34,36,48-50,55,56,74,82,101,
  117,118,120,122,130,139,143,
  144,146
Earth's Moon, 3,4,7,18,25,35,73,
  119,120,122,130
Elara (Hera), 96
electrical power, 24,34,45,48,69,70
electrons, 12,23,53,59,98,116,
  124-132,145-148,157
ecliptic, 9,37,51
  plane, 9,37,51,69,91,111,116,
  118,119
EMMY award, 84,85
Enceladus, 145,148
Encke gap, 15,153,223
encoder, convolutional, 47
encounter, trajectory, 31,32,92,93,
  102,119,142,143,224
  effects, 40,90,93,107-109,171,
  174
  phases, 96
energy received, 39,40
energy spectra, cosmic rays, 59
ephemerides, 32,53
ethane, 95
Europa, 6,7,65,96,119-121,130,
  132,149,220,221
evolution, planets, 17,21
experiments, interplanetary, 28,50,
  51,53-68,245-247
  Jovian system, 28,53-68
  Saturnian system, 53-68
  selection, 53

F ring, 108,149,152,153,223
features, Galilean satellites, 120
Feibelman, W. A., 151
Feldman, William C., 57,266
Fillius, R. Walker, 61,267,273
Fimmel, Richard O., 27,90,273,284
first by Pioneer, 1,79
Fletcher, James C., 81
flux-gate magnetometer, 53,55,56
flux tube, 131,132
Foster, John V., 207,273
Fountain, John W., x
Frank, Joseph L., 106
Frank, Louis A., 57,266
free radicals, 140
French division, 152
frequencies, communications, 47

G ring, 149
galactic cosmic rays, 58,113,245,
  246
Galactic Jupiter probe, 26
Galaxy, 50,58,64,113,117,128,248
Galilean satellites, 6,7,53,70,96,
  119-121,126,220,221
  (see also names of satellites)

Galileo, 5,6,80,82,150
Galileo Project, vii,129,142
Galle, 8
Ganymede, 6,7,65,96,119-121,130,
  132,164,220,221
Gauss, Frederich, 32
Gegenschein (see counterglow)
Gehrels, Tom, 67,268,273
Geiger tube telescope, 59
Geiger-Muller tubes, 59
General Electric Company, 63,267
general structure, Pioneer space-
  craft, 46
Goddard, Robert H., 1
Goddard Memorial Symposium, 26
Goertz, Christopher K., 60,267
Gotobed, Joseph S., xi
Goves, Thomas S., 27
gravity assist, 22,26,32,91,92,131,
  132
  waves, 245
Great Red Spot (see Spot, Great
  Red)
Ground Data System, 41
Guerin, P., 152

Hades, 79
Hale Observatories, 140 (see also Palomar)
Hall, Charles F., 25,27,70,72,74,75, 80,82,109,273
Hameen-Anttila, Jyrki, 68,268
Hanner, Martha, 68,269
Harding, Karl Ludwig, 32
hazards, 22,23,32,118
heat flux, planetary, 5,65,136,141, 142,156
Helin, Eleanor, 33
Helios, 79
heliopause, 54,69,110,113,245,246
heliosphere, 51,56,64,110,113-116, 245-247
helium, 17,56,58,63,114-116,134, 155,247
helium/hydrogen ratio, 64,67,134, 156,157
helium vector magnetometer, 55, 271
Hera, 96
Herschel, William, 8,32
Hestia, 96
Himalia (Hestia), 96
Hoagland, R., 248
Hofstetter, Robert U., 27,106,273
Hogan, Robert P., 27,273
Holtzclaw, Ralph W., 27,70,74, 106,273
Hooke, Robert, 11
"hooks," 192
Hubbard, William B., 65,268
Humes, Donald H., 63,268
Hummer, Robert F., 68, 269
Huygens, 8,150
hydrazine, 47
hydrogen, 10,14,18,51,58,59,63, 64,67,69,116,134,144,150, 153,155,247
    clouds, 17,63,121,150
    metallic, 17,126,134,144,155
    wavelength, 250
hydrogen/helium ratio, 64,67,134, 156,157
Hygiea, 33

Iapetus, 53,149
image codes, 180,202,253
    converter system, 83,84,86,87, 94-96,104
    correction, 166-175
    quality, 168
    rectification, 175
    synthetic, 225,241
images, quick look, 84,86,87,94,95
    technical data, 253-263
imaging (see photopolarimeter)
    photopolarimetry experiment, 6,162
information transfer, 39 (see also bit rate)
infrared radiometer, 64,65,76,98, 101,132,135,140,142,157,272
Ingersoll, Andrew P., 64,269
inner planets, 17,18
instrument turn-on, 73
insulation, spacecraft, 48
integrated starlight, 68,117,245
intensity gradients, cosmic rays, 113
interior planets, 16,17,133,154
International Planetary Patrol, 13
interplanetary acceleration process, 115
    experiments, 51,63,245-247
    medium, 63,111,245-247
    particle experiment, 51,58,92, 118,119
    shock waves, 114,115,247
interstellar material, 51,58,116
    medium, 54,63,64,113,114,245
    message, 250
    wind, 113,116,246
Intriligator, Devrie, 57,266
investigators, Pioneer science, 55, 57-68,265-270
Io, 6,7,12,53,65,66,67,70,75,79, 83,96,119-121,125,130-132, 149,182,220,221
ionosphere, 66,67,121,131,142
ISEE-3, 247
isotope source, 49

Jackson, Robert W., 27
Jaffe, Harold, 27,273
James, George C., 106
Janus, 148
Jet Propulsion Laboratory (JPL), 27,35,36,64-66,248,265,268, 270
Johnson, J. W., 27,273
Jones, Douglas E., 55,265
Judge, Darrell, L., 63,268,273
Juno, 32

Jupiter, 3,5-8,10,11,12,13,16,17, 19,22,26-28,31-33,39-41, 48-50,53-55,58,59,64,66-70, 73,74,83-99,113,117,118, 122-144,146,147,164,174, 179-219
    atmosphere, 11,133-142
    belts and zones, 12,138-141
    current sheet, 124
    density, 5,120
    diameter, 10,120
    dust concentration, 118
    encounter, 84,91,98,119,179, 201
    ephemeris, 32
    environment, 32,122-132
    heat flux, 65,141,142
    infrared, 140-142
    interior, 133
    ionosphere, 142
    magnetic field, 13,53,82,125, 126,134
    magnetosphere, 124,129,130
    mass, 10,65,119
    phases, 179,201
    poles, 138,201,212,215
    radiation belts, 13,22,32,34,58, 61,125-130
    rotation period, 10
    satellites, 6,7,8,28,50,92, 119-121,130,181,220,221 (see also by individual name)
    system, 7,122-142
    temperatures, 133-135
    volume, 10

Kaiser, Eldon W., 273
KenKnight, Charles E., xi,68,268, 269
Kennedy, John F., Space Center (see NASA)
Kliore, Arvydas J., 66,270,274
Kinard, William H., 62,268,273
Kingston, Robert, xi
Korhofer, William E., 273
Kochendorfer, F. D., 27,273
Kowal, Charles, 92
Kraemer, Robert, 84,90
Kuiper, G. P., 151

Laplace, 8
Lassen, Herbert A., 274

launch, accuracy, 73
  dates, 69
  delay, 72,78
  speed, 73,79
  vehicle, 26,28,43,72,73,271
  window, 31,72,78
Lepetich, Joseph E., 27,273
Lewis Research Center (see NASA)
life, possibilities on Jupiter, 19
  on Titan, 149
limb, darkening, 140
  flattening, 170
Lindal, Gunnar Fjeldbo, 66,270
Lindbergh's Spirit of St. Louis, 245
Lippershey, Hans, 5
lithium, 58
longitude systems, 253
look angle, 162
loop at opposition, 10
Los Alamos Scientific Laboratory, 57,266
Los Angeles Herald-Examiner, 248
Lust, Reimar, 57,266
Lysithia (Demeter), 96

McCracken, Kenneth G., 59,267
McDonald, Frank B., 59,267
McIlwain, Carl E., 61,267
McKibben, R. Bruce, 58,266
McKibbin, D. D., 57,266
magnetic field,
  Earth, 55,125,126,144
  experiment, 54
  interplanetary, 50,51,113,116, 128,247
  Jupiter, 53,82,83,125-127,134
  Saturn, 1,53,108,143
  solar, 101,102,116
  solar wind, 113
magnetic scattering region, 112,113
magnetometer, 46,54,55,73
magnetopause, 82,143
magnetosheath, 122
magnetosphere, 53,82,96,106,109, 122-132,143-147
Man, mark of, 250
maneuvers, 47
Mariner 10, 31
Marius, Simon, 5-7
Mark, Hans, 79,81
Mars, 3,4,17,18,21,24,26,28,33,51, 54,56,74,75,79,111,118,120, 161,248

Martin, Norman J., 27,106,273
mass, Jupiter, 10,119
  Moon, 119
  rings, 152
  Saturn, 13
  satellites, 99,120
Matthews, H. F., 27
Maxwell, James Clerke, 8
medium, interstellar, 54,63,64,246, 247
MEGATEK, 177
memory, command, 40
Mercury, 3,4,5,18,21,108,119,125, 144
Meteor Crater, 18
meteoroids, 28,118
meteorite-asteroid detector, 61,62, 73,91,99,118
methane, 17,19,20
Michener, J., viii
Mihalov, John, 57,266
Miller, Richard B., 27
Mimas, 146-149,224
Minerals Research Laboratory, 59, 267
mission, hazards, 22,23,32
  extended, 109,110,245-247
  objectives, 21,28
  operations (see Operations)
  overview, 28,157
modes, IPP, 68,164,252
modulation, 10-hr, 109,111
moments, magnetic field, 106,125, 144
Moon, 3,4,5,7,16,18,21,25,35,73, 119,120,122,130,179
Morse code, 39,161
motion, retrograde, 10
Muckley, Edwin T., 273
Munch, Guido, 64,269,273

NASCOM (see NASA Communications Network)
National Aeronautics and Space Administration (NASA), 1,24, 25-27,53,66,84,102,104,142, 248,265,270
  Ames Research Center, 25, 26-28,35,36,55,57,69,80, 96,174,177,265,266
  Communications Network (NASCOM), 37,177,178

Goddard Institute for Space Studies, 68,269
Goddard Spaceflight Center, 27, 37,55,59,266,267
Johnson Space Center, 62,267
Kennedy Space Center, 26,27, 35,72,78,247,265
Langley Research Center, 62, 63,268
Lewis Research Center, 27,35, 265
Lunar and Planetary Missions Board, 26
Pioneer Mission Operations Center (PMOC), 35,36,41, 74,85
Scientific Technical and Information Facility, x
National Academy of Sciences, 26
National Air and Space Museum, 245
National Oceanic and Atmospheric Administration (NOAA), 161
National Astronomy and Ionosphere Center, 248
Natzic, Walter L., 27,274

navigation, 32,44,49,108
neon, 59
Neptune, 17,23,37,245
Ness, Norman F., 55,266
Neugebauer, Gerry, 64,269
Nimbus-3, 49
nitrogen, 58,63,115,116
NOVA, 177
Nunamaker, Robert R., x,27,273
Null, George W., 65,268

O'Brien, B. J., 27,90,92,93,274
observation charts, 165
occultation experiment, 31,66,70, 120,132,134,135,156
offset, magnetic field, 125
O'Gallagher, Joseph J., 58,266
Olbers, Heinrich, 32
O'Neal, Robert L., 63,268
operations, mission, 27,34,40,41, 270
oppositions, 9
optical system, photopolarimeter, 187
optional targeting, 31,69,70,100, 101

orbits, 5,7-9,23,31,33
orientation spacecraft, 46,73
Orton, Glenn S., 64,269
Outer Planets Panel, 26
"Over-the-hill-gang," 106
overview, mission, 28
oxygen, 58,115,116,121,148

Pallas, 32
Palomar, 33,92
Pan, 96
parameters, Jovian images, 189
particle detector, 56-63,
   propagation, 116
Particles, cloud, 140
   from Jupiter, 125-128
   interstellar, 116
   recirculation, 129
paths in space, 31
patterns, circulation, 133,138-140
payload, scientific, 50,51-68
periapsis, 84,91,98,100,108,119,143
periodicity, 10-hr, 128-130,132
Pesses, Mark E., 60,267
phase angle, 149,150,179,225
phases, encounter, 96
   Jupiter, 31,179,201
   mission, 35,36
Phoebe, 104
phosphorus, 136,140
photometry, ultraviolet, 63
photopolarimeter, imaging (IPP),
   36,50,67,73,74,83,84,97,101,
   109,117,148,149,159-166,223,
   251,252,272
Piazzi, Giuseppe, 32
PICS, 83,84,94-96,104,174
Pictorial Output Device (POD), 177
Pioneer, 8,15,21,25,30,33
   Pioneer 1, 25
   Pioneer F (see also Pioneer 10),
     24,27
   Pioneer G (see also Pioneer 11),
     24,27
   Pioneer 6, 26,28,77
   Pioneer 7, 26,28,77
   Pioneer 8, 26,28,77
   Pioneer 9, 26,28,77
   Pioneer 10, 28,29,30,35,43-52,
     54,56,59,63,66,70,73-75,78,
     79,82-84,90-93,103,110,111,
     113,116-118,122,125,126,
     130,135,142,174,179,248

Pioneer 11, 1,2,15,28-30,36,38,
   43-52,54,56,59,63,70,76,78,
   91-93,96-98,101,105,106,
   110,111,113,116,118,
   124-126,130,132,135,142,
   201,223-225,248
Pioneer awards, 273,274
   contractors, 270-272
   Encounter Planning Team, 41
   gap, 153
   Interplanetary, 25
   —Jupiter (see Pioneer 10
     and 11)
   Mission Operations Center (see
     NASA)
   mission hazards, 22,23,32
   mission objectives, 21,28,69
   mission overview, vi,vii,28
   mission phases, 35,36
   mission planning, 27,34,69
   plaque, 248-250
   records, viii,ix,79
   —Saturn, 99 (see Pioneer 11)
   —Venus, 247

pixel, 159,175
plane of ecliptic (see ecliptic plane)
planetary evolution, 17
   interiors, 16,17,133,154,155
planets, 3,9 (see also individual
   listings)

   trans-Neptunian, 245
plaque, interstellar, 248-250
plasma analyzer, 57,73,99,104,145,
   272
plume, Jupiter, 120,148,188,196,
   198
Pluto, 2,3,91,103,111,245
polar flattening, 10,13,65,120,153,
   177
plutonium-238, 48,49
polarimetry, 68
polynomial transformations, 175
power amplifier, 47
   output, RTG, 49,113
   radiated, 39
pressures, Jovian, 134
primordial gas, 17
propulsion, spacecraft, 44,46
protons, 53,56,58,59,98,115,116,
   145-147
pulsars, 250

quality of images, 168
quiet time electron events, 125

Radioisotope Thermoelectric
   Generators (RTGs), 26,27,34,
   46,48,49,69,70,72,73,78,110,
   113,271,272
radiation, 32
   balance, 53,65,141,156
   belts, planetary, 13,22,32,61,92,
     125,126,130,146,147
   decametric, 12,53,125,131
   decimetric, 12,53,58
   effects, 171
   gravitational, 51
   thermal, 12,13,53,65,141
radicals, free, 140
radiometry, infrared, 64,65,141
radio noise, 12,40
   causes of, 12-14
   telescope, Arecibo, 245
radio occultation, 66
Randall, Bruce A., 60,267
Randall, Roger F., 60,267
Rasool, S. Ichtiaque, 66,270
received energy, 39,40
receiver, 47
rectification, geometric, 130
red spots (see also spots), 115,
   116,150,167,171
redundancy, 39,47
regions, magnetospheres, 124,145
Reiff, Glenn A., 27,70
reliability, 34,39,41
residual, Doppler, 28,49,245
retrograde motion, 10
Rhea, 53,149,226
ring, Jupiter, 2,132
rings, Saturn, 2,8,15,53,56,68,104,
   105,107,147,149-153,223-243
   absorption of energetic particles,
     106,147
   dimensions, 15,153
   divisions and gaps, 15,105,
     149-153
   hydrogen glow, 153
   mass, 152
   particles, 15,107,152
   Pioneer gap, 149
   synthetic image of, 225,242
   temperature, 152
Rock, B., 27

rocket thrusters, 46,47,78,103,104
Roche, Edward, 8
Roelof, Edmond C., 59,266
Roemer, Ole, 6,7
rotation, Jupiter, 10
    Saturn, 13
Ryan, Robert E., 273

Sagan, Carl, 248
Sagan, Linda Salzman, 248
San Francisco Bay, 160
Santa Barbara Research Center, 64,68,269
satellites (see individual names)
    Jupiter's, discovery of, 6,7,92
    Jupiter's, Pioneer pictures of, 220
    Saturn's (see also Titan), 7,8, 109,142
    sweeping effects, 130,147,148
    S1/S2, 1979, 2,147,223,230

Saturn, 1,2,3,7,8,13-17,19,20, 22,23,27,28,31-33,37,39-41, 48,50,53-55,58,59,64,67,68, 70,79,91,92,100,101, 103-109,113,119,125, 142-157,164,174,223-243, 252
    atmosphere, 156
    belts and zones, 15,156,224,225
    density, 5,14
    diameter, 13
    dust concentration, 119
    encounter, 40,100,108,119,142, 143,223-243
    heat flux, 65,156
    interior, 16,155
    ionosphere, 154
    magnetic field, 1,15,106,143, 144
    magnetopause, 144
    magnetosphere, 1,106,143-147
    radiation belts, 146,147
    ring system, 1,2,8,15,37,100, 104,105,107,142,143, 150-153,223-243
    rotation, 13
    satellites, 2,8,50,108,142,225, 242
    spots, 14,227
    temperature, 155-157

S-band, 47,50,53,66,67,157

scan imaging, 160
    maps, 161
    sequences, 160-165
scattering regions, 69,97
Schroeder, Gilbert A., 27
Schroter Observatory, 32
science commands, 40
Seidel, Boris L., 66,270
sensor, high-energy particles, 58
    starlight, 46,110
    sunlight, 46,110,271
Sentman, Davis D., 60,267
Sheehan, William F., 274
shocks, interplanetary, 114,115, 247
Shramo, D. J., 27
sidereal periods, 9
Siegmeth, A. J., 27,273
Simpson, John A., 58,266,274
Sinope (Hades), 79,96
size,
    antennas, 39,46
    asteroids, 33
    cores, 16,133,155
    Jupiter, 10,69,119,120
    ring particles, 15,152
    rings, 14,147,150,153
    satellites, 7,119,147
    Saturn, 13,153,154
    spacecraft, 46,250
    Titan, 150
slingshot technique, 22,31,32,132
"slot," 145
Smith, Edward J., 55,265,274
Smithsonian Institution, 245
SNAP-19, 27 (see radioisotope thermoelectric generators)
Soberman, Robert K., 62,267
sodium on Io, 121
software, image processing, 178
solar, corona, 111
    current sheet, 116
    flares, 76,116,125,247
    magnetic field, 101,102,116, 246,247
    probe, 25,26
    radiation, 34,51,54
    storms, 76
    system, 2,3,12,17,21-24,26,37, 40,46,51,54,63,64,72,73,78, 80,91,101,110-113,116,118, 142,147,154

wind, 51-53,55-57,69,76,77,80, 82,109,111-114,116,122, 130,143,144,246
wind blasts, 114,247
wind experiment, 56
Sonett, Charles P., 55,265
Soviet satellite, 108
spacecraft, commands, 40
    contractor, 272
    designations, 27
    Pioneer 10 and 11, 39 (see also Pioneer)
    Voyager (see Voyager)
Space Flight Operations Facility, 35
Space Science Board, 26
Space Technology Laboratories, 25
Spahr, J. Richard, 106
speed, light, 7
    Pioneer 10 at Jupiter, 79
    Pioneer 11 at Jupiter, 93
    Pioneer 11 at Saturn, 143,174
    radio waves, 2
    solar wind, 82,112,144
spin rate, 46,47,78
spin-scan imaging, 50,53,67,132, 159-164,252 (see also photo-polarimeter)
"spoke" commands, 163,164,252
spots,
    Great Red, 11,12,14,53,96,99, 136-140,180,182,190,198, 202,211
    red, 136,190
    Saturn, 14,227
    white, 13,183
stabilization, spin, 46,47
stamp, commemorative, 109
starlight, integrated, 68,117,245
    sensor, 46
Starry Messenger, 6
stars, composition of, 113
    ultraviolet, 247
streams, corotating, 112,115
Strickland, Robin, xi
structure, spacecraft, 44,46
subsystems, spacecraft, 43,44
sulfur, 140
sulfur dioxide, 121
Sun, 1,3,5,8-10,12,17,23,31,34,46, 48,50,53,54,56-59,74-78,82, 101,111-113,117,122,129,133,141

sunrise on Jupiter, 85
Swindell, W., xi,68,268
Symposium, Goddard Memorial, 25
synodic periods, 9

targeting options, 31,70,100,101
Taurus, 248
Teegarden, Bonnard J., 59,267
Telecommunications, 39 (*see also* communications)
Teledyne Isotopes, 27
telescope
    Arecibo, 246
    cosmic ray, 58-60,73
    Geiger tube, 59,272
    infrared, 65
    invention of, 5
    Maksutov, 251
    particle, 58,62
    photopolarimeter, 67,68,162, 251
    ultraviolet, 63
temperature, control, 45,48
    Jupiter, 19,133-135
    Galilean satellites, 120
    rings, 152
    Saturn, 155-157
    solar wind, 82,111,122,144
    spacecraft, 48
    Titan, 149,223
Tethys, 109,145,148,149,224
thermal control, spacecraft, 45,48
thermal radio waves, 12,53
thickness, rings, 152
thorium, 59
Thomsen, Michelle F., 60,267
thruster, 45-47,78,92,103,104
thunderstorms, 19,136
tilt, magnetic dipole, 125,144
time
    arrival, 31
    command sequence, 40
    Day Of Year (DOY), 180
    to planets, 23,29,31
    Universal (UT), 140

Titan, 2,8,37,53,100,101,108,149, 150,223,225,242
    atmosphere, 149,150
    density, 149
    diameter, 109,150
    hydrogen cloud, 150
    temperature, 149
Tomasko, Martin C., 68,268,269, 274
tracking and data acquisition, 37
tradeoff, mission, 32
Trafton, Laurence M., 64,269
Trainor, James H., 59,267,273
trajectory, 31,32,50,100,179,201, 224
trapped particles (*see* radiation belts)
    radiation detector, 60,272
transmitter, 47,272
tropical convergence, 139,140
TRW Systems, 27,70,72,90,92,247, 248,265
Turner, Richard E., 63,268
turn on, instruments, 73
Tuzzolino, Anthony J., 58,266

ultraviolet photometer, 63,73,132, 150,247,270
universal "yardstick," 250
Universities
    Arizona, xi,55,65,67,68,83,84, 97,172,178,265,268
    Brigham Young, 55,265
    California Institute of Technology, 33,55,64,265,269
    California, Los Angeles, 55, 265,268
    California, San Diego, 61,267
    Chicago, 58,127,128,266
    Cornell, 248
    Drexel, 267
    Iowa, 26,57,60,266,267
    Maryland, 51,266
    Max Planck Institute fur Physik und Astrophysik, 57,266

New Hampshire, 59,267
New York, State, Albany, 68, 269
    Southern California, 57,63,266
    Texas, 64,269
uplink, 47
Uranus, 17,23,37,39,79,91,103,111
U.S. Postal Service, 109

Van Allen belts, 25,56
Van Allen, James A., 26,60,267, 273,284
velocity, light, 7
    Pioneer, 79,93,143,174
    Solar System, 64
    solar wind, 82,112,144
Venus, 3-5,17,122
verifying commands, 41
Vesta, 32
volcanoes, 121
von Kármán vortices, 119
Voyager, vii,79,84,92,100,121,132, 147,157,174,247

water, 133
    vapor, 134
Watts, Louis A., 274
Webber, William R., 59,266
Weinberg, Jerry, 68,269
Westphal, J. A., 141
Wilbur, Arthur C., 273
Wolfe, John H., x,27,56,77,82, 266,274
Worden, A., 96
Wright Brothers' airplane, 245

"yardstick," universal, 250
Young, A. Thomas, 108

zodiac, 9,75,117
zodiacal light, 26,68,74,75,116-118
zones
    of Jupiter, 11,12,138-141,183
    of Saturn, 15,156
Zook, Herbert A., 62,267